The Effects of

Atomic Weapons

THE CIVIL DEFENSE OFFICE, NATIONAL SECURITY
RESOURCES BOARD, COMMENDS THIS PUBLICATION
AS A SOURCE OF SCIENTIFIC INFORMATION FOR
TECHNICAL PERSONNEL ENGAGED IN CIVIL DE-
FENSE PLANNING ACTIVITIES. ITS DETAILED
DESCRIPTION OF THE PHYSICAL PHENOMENA AS-
SOCIATED WITH ATOMIC EXPLOSIONS PROVIDES
CERTAIN BASIC DATA HELPFUL IN THE PREPARA-
TION OF PRACTICAL PLANS FOR ATOMIC WARFARE
DEFENSES.

PAUL J. LARSEN,
Director
Civilian Mobilization Office

THE EFFECTS OF

atomic

BOARD OF EDITORS:

J. O. Hirschfelder, Chairman • David B. Parker • Arn

Kramish • Ralph Carlisle Smith • Samuel Glasston

Executive Editor

THE COMBAT FORCES PRES

PREPARED FOR AND IN COOPERATION WITH THE

UNITED STATES DEPARTMENT OF DEFENSE AND

THE UNITED STATES ATOMIC ENERGY COMMISSION

UNDER THE DIRECTION OF THE LOS ALAMOS

weapons

SCIENTIFIC LABORATORY, IT IS IDENTICAL

WITH THE EDITION OFFICIALLY PUBLISHED BY

THE GOVERNMENT OF THE UNITED STATES

WASHINGTON, D. C. AUGUST 1950

*The Los Alamos Scientific Labora-
tory, Norris E. Bradbury, Director,
is operated by the University of California for the United States Atomic
Energy Commission under Contract
W–7405–ENG–36.*

Published by The Combat Forces Press, 1115 17th Street N.W., Washington 6, D.C.
Manufactured in the United States of America

Contents

Foreword

It was recommended some time ago that the Los Alamos Scientific Laboratory be given the responsibility for preparing for publication a handbook on the effects of atomic weapons. The recommendation was made by the Weapons Effects Classification Board, a committee of military and civilian scientists serving as advisers to the Atomic Energy Commission. The Board's recommendation was approved by the Atomic Energy Commission late in 1948, and this volume is the result.

Its purpose is to present, as accurately as is possible in the light of present knowledge, a technical summary of the results to be expected from the detonation of atomic weapons. Of necessity, classified information vital to the national security has been omitted.

The need for such a book, and the difficulties encountered in its preparation, arise from a common origin: the tremendous energy release resulting from an atomic bomb explosion. The need is for a book that can promote intelligent understanding of the effects of this enormous energy release when used as a weapon in war. The difficulties stem from the fact that the energy is released on a scale never before used by man, so that previous experience with conventional high explosives provides an inadequate basis for scientific prediction of results. In addition, atomic explosion phenomena are so complex as to make precise quantitative evaluation of their results almost impossible.

With the concurrence of the Atomic Energy Commission a technical staff was appointed by the Los Alamos Scientific Laboratory to compile the material for the book. Members of this staff were: Dr. Joseph O. Hirschfelder, professor of chemistry at the University of Wisconsin; Lt. Col. David B. Parker, Office of Deputy Assistant Chief of Staff, G–3, for Atomic Energy, U. S. Army General Staff; Arnold Kramish, a physicist on the staff of the Atomic Energy Commission in Washington, D. C.; and Dr. Ralph Carlisle Smith, an assistant director of the Los Alamos Scientific Laboratory.

Because experts in all the many aspects of this problem could not be found solely at Los Alamos, distinguished scientists were called upon by the editors to prepare their views on the subjects in which they were specialists. The various chapters of this book represent the integration of their ideas with those of equally distinguished critics and consultants.

When the first compilation had been prepared, Dr. Samuel Glasstone, professor of physical chemistry and the author of well-known scientific treatises, including the Atomic Energy Commission Sourcebook on Atomic Energy, was requested by the editors to join them as Executive Editor in the final rewriting of the manuscript. Part of his work was to minimize as far as possible the repetition of subject matter and the inconsistencies resulting from the multiple sources and from the lack of accurate knowledge in this relatively new field.

While the predictions of this book cannot be guaranteed to be precise, nevertheless they probably represent the most nearly quantitative approach to atomic bomb phenomenology which can be published at this time.

NORRIS E. BRADBURY
Director
Los Alamos Scientific Laboratory

Acknowledgment

The Board of Editors wishes to acknowledge the generous cooperation of a number of experts who have either supplied material which has been used in this book or who have read the manuscript in its various stages and have offered constructive criticism.

The main contributors were as follows:

Shock Waves and Blast Damage

S. R. BRINKLEY, JR., U. S. Bureau of Mines
J. G. KIRKWOOD, California Institute of Technology
C. W. LAMPSON, Ordnance Department, Department of the Army
F. REINES, Los Alamos Scientific Laboratory
S. B. SMITH, Corps of Engineers, Department of the Army
W. E. STROPE, Naval Radiological Defense Laboratory

Thermal Radiation and Incendiary Effects

R. M. LANGER, Consulting Physicist, Washington, D. C.
F. REINES, Los Alamos Scientific Laboratory
B. R. SUYDAM, Los Alamos Scientific Laboratory

Nuclear Radiation and Instrumentation

S. T. COHEN, The RAND Corporation
E. S. GILFILLAN, Consultant, Department of the Army
J. H. HINDS, Brig. Gen., Department of the Army with the Military Liaison Committee
M. S. PLESSET, California Institute of Technology
F. REINES, Los Alamos Scientific Laboratory
C. R. SCHWOB, Naval Radiological Defense Laboratory
F. R. SHONKA, Argonne National Laboratory
W. H SULLIVAN, Naval Radiological Defense Laboratory
B. R. SUYDAM, Los Alamos Scientific Laboratory

Effects on Personnel

J. P. COONEY, Brig. Gen., Medical Corps, Department of the Army, attached to the U. S. Atomic Energy Commission
G. M. LYON, Veterans' Administration
SHIELDS WARREN, U. S. Atomic Energy Commission

Protection of Personnel

E. S. GILFILLAN, Consultant, Department of the Army
G. M. LYON, Veterans' Administration
S. B. SMITH, Corps of Engineers, Department of the Army
T. N. WHITE, Los Alamos Scientific Laboratory

Miscellaneous Material

In addition to those mentioned above, valuable miscellaneous material was also received from the following:

E. A. BEMIS, Los Alamos Scientific Laboratory
H. L. BOWMAN, Consultant, U. S. Atomic Energy Commission
R. I. CONDIT, Naval Radiological Defense Laboratory
L. R. DONALDSON, University of Washington
R. D. EVANS, Massachusetts Institute of Technology
A. C. FABERGÉ, University of Missouri
G. GAMOW, George Washington University and Los Alamos Scientific Laboratory
B. HOLZMAN, Col., U. S. Air Force
R. REVELLE, Scripps Institute of Oceanography
D. W. SWEENEY, Los Alamos Scientific Laboratory
L. S. TAYLOR, U. S. Bureau of Standards
J. H. WEBB, Eastman Kodak Company
W. L. WHITSON, Consultant, Department of the Army
H. L. WYCKOFF, U. S. Bureau of Standards

The manuscript was reviewed in whole or in part by the main contributors and also by:

L. W. ALVAREZ	J. H. HILDEBRAND	J. E. ROSE
H. A. BETHE	A. HOLLAENDER	B. B. ROSSI
H. BOND	J. W. HOWLAND	C. C. RUCHHOFT
B. BRIXNER	W. E. KELLEY	J. S. RUSSELL
A. M. BRUES	W. H. LANGHAM	F. J. SANBORN
R. C. BRYANT	E. O. LAWRENCE	R. A. SAWYER
K. T. COMPTON	J. H. LAWRENCE	A. J. STAMM
G. H. DAMON	D. MACRAE	N. SUGARMAN
F. DANIELS	K. Z. MORGAN	E. TELLER
F. de HOFFMANN	A. R. MORITZ	STAFFORD WARREN
E. I. EVANS	W. A. NOYES	R. J. WATTS
G. FAILLA	M. P. O'BRIEN	H. T. WENSEL
W. C. FERNELIUS	H. M. PARKER	H. O. WHIPPLE
P. C. FINE	W. S. PARSONS	J. E. WILLARD
J. G. HAMILTON	H. E. PEARSE	A. WOLMAN
G. K. HARTMANN	R. P. PETERSEN	S. WRIGHT

Special indebtedness must be acknowledged to J. L. Magee, of the University of Notre Dame, and H. Scoville, Jr., of the Armed Forces Special Weapons Project, who have acted as Technical Advisors to the Editors, for their continued assistance during the preparation of this book.

SAMUEL GLASSTONE
J. O. HIRSCHFELDER
ARNOLD KRAMISH
DAVID B. PARKER
RALPH CARLISLE SMITH

The Effects of
Atomic Weapons

PRINCIPLES OF AN ATOMIC EXPLOSION

A. INTRODUCTION

CHARACTERISTICS OF AN ATOMIC EXPLOSION

1.1   The atomic bomb is a new weapon of great destructive power. It resembles bombs of the more conventional type in so far as its explosive effect is the result of the very rapid liberation of a large quantity of energy in a relatively small space.   But it differs from other bombs in three important respects: first, the amount of energy released by an atomic bomb is a thousand or more times as great as that produced by the most powerful TNT bombs; second, the explosion of the bomb is accompanied by highly-penetrating, and deleterious, invisible rays, in addition to intense heat and light; and third, the substances which remain after the explosion are radioactive, emitting radiations capable of producing harmful consequences in living organisms.   It is on account of these differences that the effects of the atomic bomb require special consideration.

1.2   A knowledge and understanding of the mechanical and radiation phenomena associated with an atomic explosion are of vital importance.   The information may be utilized, on the one hand, by architects and engineers in the design of structures; while on the other hand, those responsible for civil defense, including treatment of the injured, can make preparations to deal with the emergencies that may arise from an atomic explosion.

1.3   During World War II many large cities in England, Germany, and Japan were subjected to terrific attacks by high-explosive and incendiary bombs.   Yet, when proper steps had been taken for the protection of the civilian population and for the restoration of services after the bombing, there was little, if any, evidence of panic.   It is the purpose of this book to state the facts concerning the atomic bomb, and to make an objective, scientific analysis of these facts. It is hoped that as a result, although it may not be feasible completely to allay fear, it will at least be possible to avoid panic.

---

[1] Material contributed by G. Gamow, S. Glasstone, J. O. Hirschfelder.

PRINCIPLES OF A CHEMICAL EXPLOSION

1.4   Before the discovery of how atomic energy could be released for destructive purposes, the explosive material in bombs of the type in general use, often referred to as conventional bombs, consisted largely of TNT (trinitrotoluene) or of a related chemical material. These explosive substances have the characteristic of being unstable in nature, their break-up being associated with the liberation of a relatively large amount of energy, mainly as heat.   Once the decomposition of a few molecules of TNT has been initiated, by means of a suitable detonator, the resulting shock causes more molecules to decompose.   As a result, the over-all rate at which TNT molecules break up is very high.   This type of behavior is characteristic of many explosions, the process being accompanied by the liberation of a large quantity of energy in a very short period of time.

1.5   The products of the decomposition of conventional military explosives are mainly gaseous nitrogen and oxides of nitrogen, oxides of carbon and water vapor, and some solids, notably carbon, which are readily dissipated in the air.   To all intents and purposes, therefore, the substances remaining after the explosion do no more harm than the poisonous carbon monoxide present in the exhaust gases from automobile and airplane engines in the open.

1.6   In a chemical molecule the various atoms are held together by certain forces, sometimes referred to as valence bonds; when the molecule suffers decomposition, there is a rearrangement of the atoms, and there is a change in the character of the valence bonds. As stated above, a chemical explosive is an unstable compound, and in it the valence forces are relatively weak.   In its decomposition products, however, the same atoms are bound more strongly.   It is a law of physics that the conversion of any system in which the constituents are held together by weak forces to one in which the forces are stronger must be accompanied by the release of energy.   Consequently, the decomposition of an unstable chemical explosive results in the liberation of energy.   The manner in which this energy is converted into a destructive force will be described in Chapter III.

B.   NUCLEAR FISSION AND THE ATOMIC BOMB

NUCLEAR STRUCTURE AND ISOTOPES

1.7   An atomic explosion differs from one of the conventional type in the respect that the reaction taking place is not merely the rearrangement of the atoms among themselves, but rather of the redistribution of the extremely small particles among the nuclei of the atoms.[2] All atomic nuclei contain a definite number of *protons*, each of which carries a unit positive charge, and of *neutrons*, which are electrically neutral particles. The masses of the neutron and of the proton are very nearly the same, being close to unity on the ordinary atomic-weight scale. Because they are the units of which atomic nuclei are composed, and for other reasons, protons and neutrons are often referred to by the general term *nucleon*.

1.8 An atomic explosion may be described as the result of a particular nuclear reaction associated with the rearrangement of the constituent nucleons of a suitable atomic nucleus. Not all nuclear reactions can lead to explosions, but there are special circumstances operative in the type of reaction employed in the atomic bomb which can lead to the very rapid liberation of enormous amounts of energy.

1.9 Since the mass of a nucleon is approximately unity, the total number of nucleons in an atomic nucleus is equal to the atomic weight or, more correctly, to the *mass number*, i. e., the integer nearest to the atomic weight, of the element. The number of protons present is equal to what is known as the *atomic number*.

1.10 It is the atomic number, i. e., the number of protons, and not the atomic weight, which determines the chemical properties of an element. Thus, atoms with nuclei containing the same number of protons, i. e., with the same atomic number, but different numbers of neutrons, and hence different mass numbers (atomic weights), are essentially identical from the chemical standpoint, although they frequently exhibit differences of nuclear stability. Such species, having the same atomic number but different atomic weights, are called *isotopes*. Most elements present in nature exist in two or more stable isotopic forms, which are virtually indistinguishable chemically, although their atomic weights (or mass numbers) are different. Thus hydrogen exists in two stable isotopic forms, mass numbers 1 and 2; oxygen has three stable isotopes, mass numbers 16, 17, and 18; and tin has as many as 10 stable isotopes.

RADIOACTIVE ISOTOPES

1.11 In addition to these stable isotopes and a few unstable ones referred to below (§ 1.16), which occur naturally, it has been found

---

[2] The reader of this book will be familiar with the fact that all atoms consist of positively charged nuclei surrounded, at a relatively large distance, by negatively charged electrons. The number of electrons is equal to the number of positive charges on the nucleus, so that the whole atom is electrically neutral. Several books are available which give further information on the subject of atomic structure and of the fundamentals of atomic energy, for example, S. Glasstone, "Sourcebook of Atomic Energy," U. S. Atomic Energy Commission.

in recent years that it is possible to produce, by various nuclear reactions, unstable radioactive isotopes of all the known elements. In fact, there are many more of these so-called artificial, radioactive isotopes, or radioisotopes, known at the present time than there are stable species. About 280 of the latter exist in nature, but something like 800 radioisotopes have been made in various ways, and the number is still increasing.

1.12 If a particular atomic species is to be stable, the ratio of neutrons to protons in the nucleus must lie within a certain limited range. This may be seen from Fig. 1.12, in which the number of neutrons (ordinates) is plotted against the number of protons (abscissas) present in each of the known stable atomic nuclei. It is evident that the points lie within a relatively narrow band, corresponding to a restricted stability range for the ratio of neutrons to protons.[3] When the numbers of neutrons and protons in a specific nucleus are such that the neutron-to-proton ratio lies outside the stability range for that mass number, the given isotope will be radioactive. The unstable nucleus will then undergo spontaneous change in an effort to attain stability.

1.13 Should the isotope contain more neutrons or, what is the same thing, fewer protons than required for stability, a (neutral) neutron will change into a (positive) proton, at the same time expelling a negative electron from the nucleus. The product, which has a different atomic number, and hence is actually a different element, will thus be more stable than its parent. If it is not entirely stable, however, it also will be radioactive. After one, two, or more stages, in each of which a neutron is replaced by a proton and a negative electron is emitted, a stable species is formed.

1.14 Similarly, when the number of neutrons in the nucleus is too small, or the number of protons too large, for the neutron-to-proton ratio to be within the stability range, the particular isotope will be unstable. However, a proton will now tend to change into a neutron, and at the same time a positive electron is ejected from the nucleus of the radioactive isotope. As in the case considered above, a stable nucleus is formed after one or more stages of radioactivity.

1.15 The two types of radioactivity just considered are called *beta activity*. The term "beta particle" is really synonymous with "electron," but the former name is used when the electron originates in the atomic nucleus, as it does in the instances described above.

---

[3] The full line drawn across the figure represents a neutron-to-proton ratio of unity. It is seen that as the mass number, i. e., the sum of the neutrons and protons, is increased, the ratio increases steadily from about unity to nearly 1.6.

The emission of an ordinary, i. e., negative, electron may be referred to as negative beta activity, while the expression positive beta activity is used for the kind of radioactivity in which a positive electron (or positron) is expelled from the nucleus.

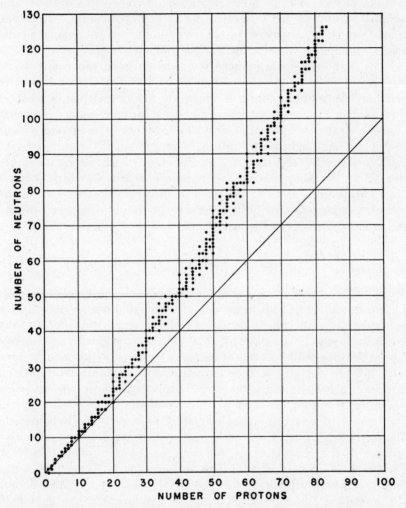

Figure 1.12.   Numbers of neutrons and protons in stable nuclei.

1.16   In the foregoing discussion it has been tacitly assumed that the radioactive species are isotopes of stable elements.   But not all unstable nuclei fall into this category.   The first radioactive substances to be discovered were in fact isotopes of the heaviest elements, that is, those of highest atomic weight, occurring in nature, which do not have any stable isotopic forms. Examples are uranium, thorium, and radium. About 30 radioactive isotopes of such elements occur naturally. There do exist in nature about 20 radioactive isotopes of certain elements which are also known in stable isotopic forms. Examples are bismuth, lead, and potassium. However, apart from their occurrence or otherwise in nature, there is no fundamental difference between the various radioactive species.

1.17 Although cases of negative beta emission are common, no instance of radioactivity accompanied by the emission of a positive beta particle has been observed among the heaviest elements, whether they exist in nature or have been obtained in other ways. For such of these elements, and for a very few isotopes of moderate atomic weight, as have neutron-to-proton ratios too small for stability, the condition can be adjusted in the direction of stability in another manner.[4] This is by the ejection of an *alpha particle*, which is made up of two protons and two neutrons in close combination. An alpha particle carries two unit positive charges, because of its two protons, and is more than seven thousand times as heavy as an electron.

RADIOACTIVE DECAY: HALF LIFE

1.18 The spontaneous change taking place in an unstable atomic nucleus is known as *radioactive decay;* each radioisotope decays at a characteristic rate, which cannot be changed, at least not by any available means. The rate of decay for any particular radioactive species is expressed by means of its *half life;* this is defined as the time taken for the activity of a given quantity of a radioactive material to decay to half its initial value. Because radioactive decay is exponential in nature, the half life has a definite value irrespective of the amount of active material originally present. The half life is a characteristic property of each radioisotope; different radioactive isotopes of the same element, for example, have different half lives. The known values, of which a few are recorded in Table 1.18, range from less than a millionth of a second for polonium 212, the isotope of the element polonium of mass number 212, to more than ten billion years for thorium 232, the most abundant isotope (mass number 232) of thorium.

---

[4] A further possibility, which needs only brief mention here, is for a proton in the nucleus to capture an external (orbital) electron of the atom, thus being converted into a neutron. This process is known as orbital-electron capture.

TABLE 1.18

HALF LIVES OF SOME RADIOISOTOPES

Isotope	Activity	Half Life	Isotope	Activity	Half Life
Sodium 24	β^-	14.8 hr.	Cesium 137	β^-	37 yr.
Potassium 40	β^-	1.5×10^9 yr.	Polonium 212	α	3×10^{-7} sec.
Selenium 81	β^-	17 min.	Radium 226	α	1,590 yr.
Bromine 87	β^-	55.6 sec.	Thorium 232	α	1.39×10^{10} yr.
Strontium 90	β^-	25 yr.	Uranium 233	α	1.65×10^5 yr.
Krypton 92	β^-	3 sec.	Uranium 235	α	7.07×10^8 yr.
Yttrium 93	β^-	10 hr.	Uranium 238	α	4.51×10^9 yr.
Molybdenum 93	β^+	6.7 hr.	Uranium 239	β^-	23 min.
Technetium 99	β^-	9.4×10^5 yr.	Neptunium 239	β^-	2.3 days
Iodine 131	β^-	8.0 days	Plutonium 239	α	2.41×10^4 yr.

1.19   It is because of the very long half lives of uranium 238, uranium 235, and thorium 232 that radioactive species of high atomic weight occur in nature, in spite of their instability.   Of the 42 such known isotopes, 39 are formed in various stages of decay of these three parents, or precursors, of three radioactive decay series.   The familiar element radium, for example, is a member of the series of which uranium 238 is the parent.   In nature the several products decay at various rates, but they are replaced virtually as fast as they decay, so that the amounts remain essentially unchanged.   In the course of millions of years, however, a slight decrease would become apparent, because of the slow decay of the parent element.   The final or end products of the three decay series are stable isotopes of lead, and so the quantity of this element in nature is increasing very slowly at the expense of the uranium and thorium.

1.20   Since the activity of a particular radioactive product is reduced to one-half in the half-life period, represented by the symbol T, it is evident that the amount remaining after n such intervals, i. e., after time nT, will be $(\frac{1}{2})^n$.   Thus, after five times the half life, the activity has fallen to $(\frac{1}{2})^5$, which is about 0.03, or 3 percent, of the original amount.   After 10 times the half-life period, the activity is reduced to only 0.1 percent of the initial value.   Hence, after the lapse of sufficient time decay may be regarded as virtually complete.

1.21   Except where the rate of decay is extremely rapid, the half lives of most of the known radioisotopes have been measured, usually by means of instruments of the type described in Chapter IX, and the results have been tabulated.   It is thus often a simple matter to identify a particular radioisotope if its rate of decay has been determined, and its half life calculated.

IDENTIFICATION OF RADIOISOTOPES

1.22   It was stated earlier that isotopes of a given element have the same chemical properties; this is true whether the isotopes are stable or unstable.   The chemistry of a radioactive species is thus indistinguishable from that of a stable isotope of the same element. Consequently the stable and unstable isotopes are chemically inseparable, for all practical purposes.   These facts have many important and interesting applications.   Because of the electrically charged alpha and beta particles they emit, radioactive substances can be detected in extremely minute amounts, much smaller than can be identified in any other way.   Quantities of radioactive material, less than a billionth of a gram in weight, which are too small to be visible in any optical microscope, can readily be detected by a Geiger counter or similar instrument (Chapter IX).   Nevertheless, in spite of the infinitesimal amounts which may be present, the chemistry of a radioactive species will be completely known, since it is the same as that of a familiar element with which it is isotopic.

GAMMA RAYS

1.23   Radioactive changes are frequently accompanied by the emission of penetrating radiations called *gamma rays*.   These are electromagnetic radiations, related to light rays and X-rays, but of shorter wave length, that is, in other words, of higher energy.   Actually, the longer gamma rays are identical with the shorter X-rays, so that the radiations are indistinguishable.   The term gamma rays is nevertheless used to describe the radiations of short wave length which have their origin in atomic nuclei.   Not all such gamma rays arise from radioactive changes, however, for they are often associated with other nuclear reactions.   In fact, the emission of gamma rays represents an important way in which a nucleus in a state of high (internal) energy, often referred to as an *excited nuclear state*, can rid itself of the excess energy.

NUCLEAR REACTIONS

1.24   In addition to radioactive decay, which is a type of spontaneous nuclear reaction that cannot be influenced in any practical manner, there are many other kinds of nuclear reactions brought about deliberately.   Some of these involve the bombardment of atomic nuclei by electrically charged particles, such as protons and alpha particles, which have been accelerated to high speeds, that is, given high energies, by means of certain devices, of which the cyclotron is perhaps the best known. But the most interesting nuclear processes, especially in connection with the problems associated with the atomic bomb, are those in which the electrically uncharged neutrons are employed to interact with atomic nuclei.

1.25 As already seen, neutrons are one of the two types of nuclear constituents or nucleons (§ 1.7); but free neutrons can be obtained as streams or rays which can be made to impinge on matter. Because they carry no electrical charge, they are not repelled by atomic nuclei, as are protons and alpha particles and, consequently, even neutrons of low energy, referred to as slow neutrons, can enter atomic nuclei. In fact, for reasons which need not be considered here, slow neutrons of low energy have a much greater probability of being captured by an atomic nucleus than fast neutrons of high energy. When such a neutron capture occurs, the resulting *compound nucleus*, as it is called, is in an excited state and, as indicated above, in the great majority of cases the excess energy is radiated as gamma rays. For obvious reasons, processes of this type are referred to as *radiative capture* reactions. Nearly all the known stable isotopic species, as well as probably many unstable ones, exhibit radiative capture of neutrons; that is to say, the neutron enters the atomic nucleus and at the same time—actually within an infinitesimal fraction of a second—gamma rays are emitted.

1.26 When a neutron is captured by a nucleus, the number of neutrons in the latter is obviously increased by unity, but the number of protons remains unchanged. The emission of the excess energy as gamma radiation does not affect the number of either kind of nucleon, and so the product of radiative capture of a neutron is a nucleus with the same number of protons, i. e., the same atomic number, as the original nucleus, but with one more neutron. The result is consequently an isotope of the original element, but with a higher atomic weight (mass number), due to the additional neutron. The radiative capture reaction, for example, between sodium 23 (Na^{23}) and a neutron (n^1) is represented by

$$Na^{23} + n^1 \rightarrow Na^{24} + \gamma,$$

so that the product is sodium 24. Because of the increased neutron-to-proton ratio, the residual nucleus is frequently radioactive, decaying by the emission of a negative beta particle (§ 1.13), perhaps accompanied by gamma rays. Such is actually the case for sodium 24 mentioned above.   In other words, the product of the radiative capture of neutrons may well be a radioactive isotope of the element which captured the neutrons.

NUCLEAR FISSION

1.27   The great majority of nuclear reactions, whether spontaneous or the result of bombardment of atomic nuclei by neutrons or by charged particles, are accompanied either by the emission of gamma rays or by the expulsion of a relatively small particle, such as an alpha particle, a proton, a neutron or an electron (beta particle). The product nucleus is then still close, both in atomic number and mass number, to the original nucleus.   With elements of high atomic number, that is, with the heavy elements lying toward the end of the periodic system, an entirely different type of nuclear reaction, known as *fission*, becomes possible.   The reacting nucleus then splits up into two, more or less equal, parts, both of which differ considerably in atomic number and mass number from the original nucleus.   Nuclear fission can be brought about in various ways, but by far the most important, especially for present purposes, is that in which neutrons are employed.   It is, in fact, the fission of certain atomic nuclei by neutrons which is the fundamental reaction in the atomic bomb.

1.28   Uranium, the element of highest atomic number existing in nature, occurs naturally as a mixture of three isotopic forms, with mass numbers 234, 235, and 238, respectively.   The uranium 238 isotope is present to the extent of 99.282 percent, while uranium 235 constitutes 0.712 percent; the very small remainder, which may be ignored here, consists of uranium 234 (Table 1.28).   It has been found that the more abundant uranium 238 undergoes fission when subjected to fast (high-energy) neutrons, but either fast·or slow neutrons will induce fission·of the less common uranium 235 isotope.

TABLE 1.28

ISOTOPIC COMPOSITION OF NATURAL URANIUM

Mass Number	Percent	Half Life
238	99. 282	4. 51×10^9 yr.
235	0. 712	7. 07×10^8
234	0. 006	2. 35×10^5

1.29   The fission of uranium 238 by fast neutrons competes, to some extent, with a radiative capture reaction, and for neutrons of lower speed, the latter process takes place exclusively. The result of the radiative capture is an isotope of uranium, mass number 239, formed by the reaction

$$U^{238} + n^1 \rightarrow U^{239} + \gamma.$$

The uranium 239 decays by the emission of a negative beta particle, with a half life of 23 minutes (Table 1.18), thus

$$U^{239} \rightarrow \beta + Np^{239},$$

the product being neptunium 239, an isotope of which only the merest traces, if any, exist in nature. This substance also exhibits negative beta activity, its half life being 2.3 days, thus

$$Np^{239} \rightarrow \beta + Pu^{239},$$

forming plutonium 239. This isotope, like its parent, i. e., neptunium 239, is extremely scarce in nature.

1.30 Plutonium 239 is a substance of special interest. Like uranium 235, it will undergo fission as a result of the action of either slow or fast neutrons. It has a relatively long half life, about 24,000 years, so that it decays very slowly, accompanied by the emission of alpha particles. The decay product of plutonium 239 is the long-lived uranium 235, so that the fission properties would remain essentially unchanged for millions of years. The fission of uranium 235 or of plutonium 239 can be utilized in atomic bombs.

ENERGY RELEASE IN FISSION

1.31 One of the notable characteristics of the fission reaction is that it is associated with the release of a large amount of energy, about ten times as great as for any previously known nuclear process. The reason for the large energy release is due to circumstances which are essentially the same as those responsible for the energy liberated in the decomposition of TNT or other chemical explosive. In the case of nuclear fission, the binding forces between the nucleons, i. e., the protons and neutrons, in the uranium or other nucleus undergoing fission is less than they are in the nuclei formed as a consequence of fission. As seen in § 1.6, this state of affairs must lead to a liberation of energy, as is actually observed.

1.32 It is of interest to consider briefly why the binding forces are greater in the lighter fission-product nuclei than they are in the heavier uranium or plutonium nuclei undergoing the fission reaction. It has been established that within the nucleus very strong forces of attraction exist between neutrons and protons and also between neutrons themselves. But the protons, being positively charged, repel one another and so introduce a force of repulsion, which is approximately proportional to the square of the number of protons present. The stability of a given nucleus is determined by the balance between these forces of attraction and repulsion.

1.33 With increasing atomic number, the number of protons in the nucleus, and hence the magnitude of the force of repulsion, increases rapidly, and relative stability can be attained only as a result of increasing the number of neutrons. The increased attractive force then counteracts, to some extent, the force of repulsion. The ratio of neutrons to protons is thus higher among elements of high atomic (or mass) number than among those of lower atomic (or mass) number (see Fig. 1.12). For example, the nucleus of uranium 238 contains 146 neutrons and 92 protons, so that the neutron-to-proton ratio is nearly 1.6. On the other hand, in the nucleus of tin 119, with half the mass number, there are 69 neutrons and 50 protons, so that the ratio is close to 1.4. In spite of the increased number of neutrons, which serve to provide some degree of stability, in the nuclei of high mass number, it is not surprising to find that the mean resultant binding force between the nucleons is smaller than it is for nuclei of lower mass number. Support for this statement is found in the fact, mentioned in § 1.16 that no stable isotopes of the heaviest elements are known, for they are all radioactive, thus indicating their relative instability.

1.34 Because the binding forces between nucleons in a nucleus are very much greater than those operative between the atoms in a molecule of a chemical compound, the amounts of energy released in nuclear reactions, particularly in fission, are considerably larger than those liberated in chemical processes. A convenient way of calculating the energy change is to utilize the fact that the forces in atomic nuclei manifest themselves in the respective nuclear masses. According to the theory of relativity there is an equivalence of mass and energy, which can be represented in the form of the Einstein equation

$$E \doteq mc^2, \tag{1.34.1}$$

where E is the energy equivalent of the mass m, and c is the velocity of light. If m is expressed in grams, and c is taken as 3×10^{10} centimeters per second, then the energy E will be in ergs; thus

$$E \text{ (ergs)} = 9 \times 10^{20} m \text{ (grams).} \qquad \cdot \tag{1.34.2}$$

In order to obtain the energy in calories, this result is divided by 4.2×10^7. The energy change in any nuclear reaction can then be obtained from this equation by inserting for m the difference in mass between the interacting nuclei and other particles, on the one hand, and the products of the nuclear reaction, on the other hand.

1.35 The total mass of a uranium 235 nucleus and a neutron, is known to be greater than the sum of the masses of the immediate products formed as a result of fission. This difference in mass is the equivalent of the energy released in the process. When 1 kilogram, i. e, 1,000 grams, of uranium 235 undergoes fission the decrease of mass is just less than 1 gram and, by equation (1.34.2), this is equivalent to somewhat below 9×10^{20} ergs, or 2.1×10^{13} calories.

1.36 In order to provide a definite basis for discussion, the present book will consider, primarily, the effects of a *nominal atomic bomb*, similar to those used at Hiroshima and Nagasaki. The energy release of such a bomb is approximately equivalent to that of 20 kilotons, i. e., 20,000 tons, of TNT, and since the energy equivalent of a ton of TNT is taken to be 10^9 calories, the energy release of the nominal atomic bomb is 2×10^{13} calories. Comparing this result with that given above for the energy produced in the fission of uranium 235, it is seen that in the complete fission of 1 kilogram, i. e., 2.2 pounds, of uranium 235 the energy released is essentially equivalent to that of 20 kilotons of TNT. Consequently, the fission of uranium 235 would liberate nearly 20 million times as much energy as the explosion of an equivalent weight of TNT. The same general ratio applies also to plutonium 239.

1.37 The amount of energy produced in the fission of 1 kilogram of uranium 235 or plutonium is expressed in various units in Table 1.37. It is of interest to add that it is also equivalent to about

TABLE 1.37

ENERGY EQUIVALENT OF FISSION OF 1 KILOGRAM OF URANIUM 235

20,000 tons of TNT
2×10^{13} calories
8.4×10^{20} ergs
6.2×10^{13} foot-pounds
2.3×10^7 kilowatt hours

7,000 tons of coal and to the daily output of Hoover Dam. Although the energy released in fission is very impressive, it is relatively small compared with the energies involved in the forces of nature. For example, it is about the same as the energy of the sun's rays falling on 2 square miles of ground during an average day, or to that released in a moderate rainstorm producing a quarter of an inch of precipitation over Washington, D. C. A strong earthquake involves almost as much energy as would be supplied by a million atomic bombs of the type under consideration.

1.38   When uranium 235 or plutonium undergoes fission, not all of the energy is released promptly; about 89 percent is liberated within the first second, while the remaining 11 percent appears later, as will be explained below (§ 1.55). Since the latter is not available to contribute either to the blast or to other immediate primary effects of an atomic bomb, it is not included in the energy values given above. The fission of a single atom of uranium or plutonium releases 6.7×10^{-12} calories, and hence, in order to produce 2×10^{13} calories, it is necessary for about 3×10^{24} atoms to suffer fission to release the energy equivalent to 20 kilotons of TNT. This number of atoms is, of course, approximately the total number present in 1 kilogram of uranium 235 or plutonium.

FISSION CHAIN REACTION

1.39   In spite of the enormous energy liberation in nuclear fission, this alone would not have made the atomic bomb possible. The important point, in addition, is that the fission process, initiated by neutrons, is accompanied by the almost instantaneous emission of more than one neutron for each nucleus undergoing fission. When it is recalled, as indicated above, that the proportion of neutrons to protons in the fissionable nucleus is normally much greater than in the lighter nuclei which result, it is not surprising that some neutrons are set free in the actual fission process. The neutrons liberated in this manner are able to induce fission of other nuclei, each such process resulting in the emission of more neutrons which produce further fission, and so on. Thus, in principle, a single neutron could start off a chain of fissions, the number of nuclei involved increasing at a tremendous rate.

1.40   Suppose, for simplicity, that for each uranium or plutonium nucleus suffering fission two neutrons are liberated; if each of these causes fission, with the release of two neutrons in each case, there will be four neutrons available. These could induce fission of four more nuclei, accompanied by the emission of eight neutrons, the chain continuing, in theory, until no more fissionable material remains. A single neutron might thus cause the fission of a large quantity of uranium 235, just as the detonation of a few molecules of TNT might bring about the explosion of a considerable charge.

1.41   If, as just suggested, the number of neutrons, and hence of nuclei undergoing fission, is doubled in each generation, then starting with a single neutron the numbers would increase steadily, thus, 1, 2, 4, 8, 16, 32, 64, ...   In about 80 generations enough neutrons would have been produced to cause the fission of every nucleus in 1 kilogram of uranium, resulting in the liberation of 2×10^{13} calories of energy.   The time required for the actual fission process is very small, and most of the resulting neutrons are emitted promptly.   Consequently, the interval between successive generations is determined by the average time required for a free neutron to be captured by a fissionable nucleus.   Supposing this to be about 10^{-8} second, then the eightieth generation would be attained in less than a millionth of a second.   The release of the enormous amount of energy in such a short interval of time would provide the conditions for a tremendous explosion.   It is seen, therefore, that because the fission process is accompanied by the instantaneous liberation of neutrons, as well as of large quantities of energy, it is possible, in principle, to produce a self-sustaining, chain reaction capable of being utilized in an extremely powerful bomb.   This is the atomic bomb, so called because it makes use of the energy of the fissionable atoms or, more correctly, of the nuclei of such atoms.

1.42   It may be pointed out that the foregoing calculations have been based on the postulate that every neutron liberated in the fission of each uranium nucleus goes on to produce fission in other nuclei. In actual practice this is not the case.   A proportion of the neutrons are always absorbed as a result of competing capture processes, while others escape from the system altogether.   If the rate at which the neutrons are lost in these ways exceeds the rate at which they are formed by the fission of nuclei, the fission reaction would soon come to a stop.   The escape of neutrons occurs at the exterior of the fissionable material, and this depends on the surface area, whereas the fission process, which results in the formation of more neutrons, takes place in the interior, so that it is proportional to the volume.   Hence, the relative rate of loss of neutrons by escape can be minimized by increasing the size of the system, for in this manner the ratio of area to volume is decreased.

CRITICAL SIZE OF ATOMIC BOMB

1.43   If the quantity of material is too small, that is to say, if the ratio of the surface area to volume is too large, the loss of neutrons

will be so great that the propagation of the fission chain reaction, and
hence the production of an explosion, will not be possible.   But as
the size of the system undergoing fission is increased, and the relative
loss of neutrons by escape is decreased, as is shown diagrammatically
in Fig. 1.43, a point is reached at which the reaction becomes self-

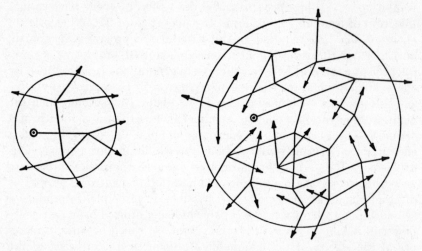

Figure 1.43.   Diagrammatic representation of effect of size of fissionable material
on relative loss of neutrons by escape.

sustaining, once it has been initiated.   This is referred to as the *critical
size* of the chain-reacting system.   An atomic bomb, to be effective,
must thus contain a sufficient amount of fissionable material to exceed
the critical size.[5]   The critical size depends, among other things, on
the isotopic composition of the fissionable material and on the presence
of substances which capture neutrons.   By surrounding the system
with a suitable neutron reflector, the loss of neutrons by escape can
be reduced, and hence the critical size diminished to some extent.

1.44   Because of the presence of stray neutrons in the atmosphere,
a quantity of fissionable material exceeding the critical dimensions
would be liable to explode.   Therefore, it is necessary that before
detonation the bomb should consist of two or more separate parts,
each of which is less than the critical size.   To cause an explosion,
these parts must be brought together very rapidly.   Extreme rapidity

---

[5] The atomic bomb differs from conventional bombs in the respect that the former must contain more
than a critical quantity of fissionable (explosive) material, while the latter can contain any desired quantity
of explosive from a pound or so up to several tons.   Consequently, conventional bombs may have large or
small energy releases, but a "small" effective atomic bomb cannot be made.

is necessary, because if the chain reaction were to be initiated by stray neutrons before the parts had reached their closest position, a relatively weak explosion would occur which would cause the bomb to break apart without releasing any appreciable amount of its energy. A bomb exploding in this manner would be called a "fizzle." The possibility that such "fizzles" might be encountered in an atomic attack must be borne in mind.[6]

1.45 In order to produce an atomic explosion it is necessary to induce fission by means of fast (high-energy) neutrons, for if slow neutrons were used the rate of energy liberation would be too slow to cause an effective explosion.[7] It might be supposed, therefore, that uranium 238, the most abundant isotope of this element, which undergoes fission with fast neutrons, could act as the fissionable material in an atomic bomb. However, this is not so, because uranium 238 captures neutrons to an appreciable extent in a nonfission reaction, as stated in § 1.29. This competes with fission to such a degree that the propagation of a chain reaction is not possible.

PRODUCTION OF FISSIONABLE MATERIAL

1.46 Uranium 235 is a rare isotope, constituting a little over 0.7 percent, i. e., about 1 part in 140, of naturally occurring uranium (Table 1.28), while plutonium 239 does not exist at all on the earth, except perhaps in extremely minute traces. It is obvious, therefore, that the production of fissionable material for atomic bombs is a slow and difficult process. Uranium 235 is separated from the more abundant uranium 238 by making use of the fact that the lighter isotope, in the form of its hexafluoride compound, diffuses through a porous diaphragm slightly more rapidly than does the heavier isotope.

1.47 Plutonium, on the other hand, is made artificially by nuclear processes taking place in a chain-reacting *pile* or *nuclear reactor*. Cylinders of pure uranium, containing the 235 and 238 isotopes, are inserted in a lattice of graphite; and fission of the uranium 235 is caused by neutrons which are slowed down by the graphite. Some of the neutrons produced in the fission process induce further fission of the uranium 235, while others, especially after being slowed down, are taken up by the uranium 238, in the radiative capture reaction described in § 1.29, to form uranium 239. After two stages of beta

---

[6] The term "fizzle" should not be confused with "dud" which is used to define a bomb that fails to explode at all.

[7] The neutrons emitted in the fission process are initially fast (high-energy) neutrons. They are slowed down by collisions with atomic nuclei, especially those of low atomic weight.

decay the relatively long-lived plutonium 239 is formed, and it is separated from the unchanged uranium cylinders by chemical processes. These are carried out by remote control behind thick walls of concrete, because of the intense radioactivity of the material removed from the pile.

FISSION PRODUCTS

1.48 So far little has been said concerning the nature of the products formed when a uranium or plutonium nucleus undergoes fission after taking up a neutron. It might be thought that the compound nucleus (§ 1.25) would split in an approximately symmetrical manner, but such is not the case. Actually, the uranium 235 nucleus splits up in from 30 to 40 different ways, for more than 60 primary products have been detected. The range of mass numbers is from 72, probably an isotope of zinc (atomic number 30), to 158, believed to be an isotope of europium (atomic number 63). About 97 percent of the uranium 235 nuclei undergoing fission yield products which fall into two groups, a "light" group with mass numbers from 85 to 104, and a "heavy" group, with mass numbers from 130 to 149, as shown in Fig. 1.48. This curve, for the fission of uranium 235 by slow neutrons, represents the fission yield, i. e., the percentage of fissions resulting in the formation of products with a given mass number, as a function of mass number. It should be mentioned that since each nucleus undergoing fission yields two product nuclei, the total fission yield, for all the mass numbers, adds up to 200 percent.

1.49 The most probable type of fission, representing about 6.4 percent of the total, is seen to give products with mass numbers 95 and 139. It is apparent from these results, that fission of uranium 235 is far from symmetrical. If the compound nucleus split into two equal fragments, the mass of each would be 117 or 118; actually, only 0.01 percent of the uranium nuclei suffering fission break up in this manner. In the fission of plutonium 239 the results are much the same, although there are slight differences from the numbers quoted above for uranium 235.[8]

1.50 It was seen in § 1.33 that the ratio of neutrons to protons in uranium 238 is nearly 1.6, and the values for uranium 235 and plutonium 239 are not very different. If these nuclei are split into two smaller nuclei, the neutron-to-proton ratio in the fragments will still be close to 1.6, assuming that the division of neutrons and protons occurred in much the same proportion. It is true that about one to

---

[8] The data given here refer to fission by slow neutrons. In the atomic bomb the fission is due mainly to fast neutrons, and the products may be formed in somewhat different proportions.

three neutrons are lost in the fission process; nevertheless, the neutron-to-proton ratio in the instantaneous products of fission will be much greater than the stable value, which is about 1.4, or less, for the same mass numbers.   In other words, the lighter nuclei formed at the

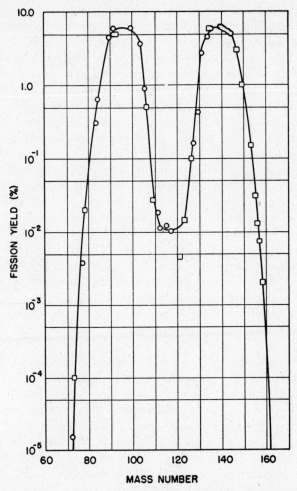

Figure 1.48.   Fission yield as function of mass number in the slow neutron fission of uranium 235.

instant of fission contain too many neutrons for stability and hence, in accordance with the statements in § 1.13, they will exhibit negative beta activity.

1.51   Suppose, in order to simplify the argument, that a uranium 235 nucleus, upon fission by a neutron, splits up into two nuclei of mass numbers 95 and 139, these being the ones formed in largest amount (Fig. 1.48). It will be assumed, further, that the neutrons (n) and protons (p) divide in the same proportion, i. e., 57 $n + 38$ p, giving mass number 95 in one nucleus, and 85 $n + 54$ p, giving mass number 139 in the other nucleus. These would correspond to the isotopes strontium 95 and xenon 139, respectively. The heaviest stable isotopes of these elements are strontium 88, i. e., 50 $n + 38$ p, and xenon 136, i. e., 82 $n + 54$ p, respectively, so that the fission products obviously contain neutrons in excess of the number permissible for stability for the respective mass numbers. The stable species of the same mass numbers nearest to the postulated fission products are molybdenum 95 and lanthanum 139, and these could be formed from strontium 95 and xenon 139 by three and four stages, respectively, of beta decay.

1.52   Each direct fission product nucleus contains, on the average, three neutrons too many for stability; hence, it undergoes this same number of stages of beta decay before being converted into a stable isotope. Since the direct products, sometimes called *fission fragments*, start to decay immediately they are formed, their decay products begin to accumulate and decay in turn. The result is that within a very short 'time nearly two hundred different radioactive species, including fission fragments and their decay products, as well as a number of stable isotopes, are present. It is easy to understand, therefore, why the substances remaining after the explosion of an atomic bomb will be highly radioactive, emitting both beta and gamma rays.

1.53   The half lives of the fission products, that is, of the direct fragments and their decay products, range from a small fraction of a second to many years.[9] It would thus take a considerable time for the activity to decay to virtual completion. Taking the activity after 5 minutes from the atomic bomb explosion as a point of reference, the radioactivity, in terms of the rate of emission of particles, will be reduced to about 5 percent of this value at the end of an hour, and to 0.1 percent within a day. Nevertheless, activity will be detectable after the lapse of a year.

ENERGY DISTRIBUTION IN NUCLEAR FISSION

1.54   In the decomposition of a chemical explosive virtually all of the energy liberated appears as kinetic energy of the products; in

---

[9] See "Nuclei Formed in Fission: Decay Characteristics, Fission Yields and Chain Relationships," *J. Amer. Chem. Soc.*, *68*, 2411 (1946); *Rev. Mod. Phys.*, *18*, 513 (1946).

other words, nearly the whole of the energy appears instantaneously as heat. In the case of an atomic explosion due to a fission-chain reaction, most of the energy evolved at the instant of fission is heat energy; some is also emitted in the form of gamma rays and as energy of the neutrons which are expelled within a very short time. In addition there is the radioactive energy of the fission products. These latter forms of energy ultimately appear as heat, but they make only a minor contribution to the force of the explosion.

1.55 In the fission of uranium 235 by slow neutrons, about 83 percent of the total energy liberated is converted into kinetic energy of the fission fragments, 3 percent is energy of the instantaneous gamma radiation, and another 3 percent of the energy is carried off by the neutrons, thus making a total of 89 percent of the fission energy, which is released promptly (§ 1.38). The remaining 11 percent is set free in the course of time as energy of the beta and gamma rays produced by the radioactive decay of the fission products. When uranium 235 or plutonium 239 suffers fission by fast neutrons, as in the atomic bomb, the energy distribution is somewhat different, but the general principles are the same.

C. CONSEQUENCES OF AN EXPLOSION

Shock Waves

1.56 When a large amount of energy is released explosively in a bomb, there is a considerable rise in temperature which results in the almost complete vaporization, or gasification, of the products of the explosion (or fission), and also of the container. The very hot gases so produced in a restricted space are at a very high pressure, and immediately following the explosion they start to move outward, that is, toward the external atmosphere where the pressure is lower. The great expansion which occurs then pushes away the surrounding medium, e. g., air, water or earth, with considerable force, and thus initiates a complex series of effects (see Chapters III and IV), which are responsible for the damage caused to structures and personnel. Although differing somewhat in detail, according as the explosion occurs at a high or low altitude in the air, or at shallow or deep levels under water, or at various distances underground, the fundamental phenomena are the same.

1.57 One of the important aspects of the air blast is the formation of a *shock wave*, capable of producing severe destructive effects; it is formed in somewhat the following manner. Almost immediately after an explosion, expansion of the hot gases initiates a pressure wave in the surrounding medium as represented very roughly by the curve in Fig. 1.57a; this shows the general nature of the variation of pressure with the distance from the explosion at a given instant. As the wave is propagated away from the center of the explosion, the following (or inner) part moves through a region which has been already compressed and heated by the leading (or outer) parts of the wave. The disturbance moves with the velocity of sound characteristic of the medium, and since this velocity increases with temperature and pressure the. former part of the wave moves more rapidly and catches up on the latter, as shown in Fig. 1.57b. The wave front thus gets steeper and steeper, and within a very short period it becomes mathematically abrupt, as indicated in Fig. 1.57c. This represents the

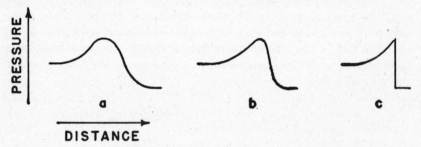

Figure 1.57. Simplified representation of development of shock wave.

destructive shock wave which continues to move forward through the medium for some time, essentially unchanged in form, but with gradually decreasing intensity. It can be seen that at the advancing front of the wave, called the *shock front*, there is a very sudden drop of pressure, to that of the surrounding atmosphere. The shock front thus behaves like a moving wall of highly compressed air or water.

1.58   When the shock wave strikes a resistant surface, such as the earth, it is reflected back; this reflected wave is also capable of causing material damage. Under certain conditions the incident and reflected shock waves fuse for a limited distance, so that the air blast in this range is much greater than that due to the incident shock (see Chapter III).

Emission of Radiation in Atomic Explosion

1.59   Apart from the mechanical or blast damage, which is characteristic of all bombs, the atomic bomb produces additional effects due to the radiation emitted at the time of the explosion. For convenience this almost instantaneous radiation may be divided into two main categories, namely, *thermal radiation*, or heat rays, and *nuclear radiation*, consisting of gamma rays and neutrons.[10] Because of the very high temperatures attained in the explosion of an atomic bomb, initially approaching that of the sun's interior, there is a large amount of thermal radiation. This is capable of causing physiological damage, due to burns, in human beings and animals, as well as fires in combustible structures directly exposed to the heat rays (Chapter VI). The nuclear radiations can also produce harmful effects depending upon the quantity of radiation absorbed, determined largely by the distance from the explosion. If the amount absorbed is large, the consequences will probably be fatal; however, if it is not very great, there may be various unpleasant symptoms, but apparently complete recovery takes place within six months (Chapter XI).

1.60 It may be noted that the effects of thermal radiation referred to above will result only if there is direct exposure when the atomic explosion occurs. Buildings and clothing will provide some shielding from thermal radiation; shielding from the penetrating, instantaneous (or initial) nuclear radiation is more difficult and will be discussed later (Chapter VII).

1.61 In addition to the instantaneous radiation mentioned above, consideration must be given to the residual radiations, that is, the beta particles and gamma radiation emitted by the fission products for some time after the atomic explosion. If an atomic bomb burst takes place some distance above the surface of the earth or water, most of the fission products would be dissipated, and hence should bring about little or no deleterious effects. However, circumstances might arise, especially in the case of an underwater explosion (§ 2.45 *et seq*.), in which the radioactive products of fission were spread over a limited region. Because of their beta and gamma activity, these would be a source of considerable danger to human life, and adequate steps would have to be taken to minimize the hazard.

1.62 In this chapter there has been given an elementary outline of the fundamental principles of the atomic bomb, and a brief introduction to its physical and biological effects. These latter aspects of an atomic explosion, and methods of protection, will be treated in greater detail in the succeeding chapters of this book.

[10] Beta particles, i. e., electrons, and some alpha particles are liberated as part of the instantaneous nuclear radiation. The penetrating power of these particles is low, and since they are completely stopped by a relatively small thickness of air, they are not considered here. They are important, however, in connection with the residual radiation mentioned below (§ 1.61).

DESCRIPTION OF AN ATOMIC EXPLOSION

A. INTRODUCTION

THE NOMINAL ATOMIC BOMB

2.1   In the treatment which follows, and in fact throughout the whole of this book, it will be assumed that the effective energy released in the atomic bomb within a short time is roughly equivalent to that produced by the explosion of 20,000 tons, i. e., 20 kilotons, of TNT, namely, about 2×10^{13} calories (§ 1.36).   This corresponds approximately to the energy of the atomic bombs dropped over Japan.   As stated in Chapter I such a hypothetical weapon will be referred to as a *nominal atomic bomb*.   Since there is a possibility that atomic bombs with different energy equivalents may be developed, scaling laws will be given wherever feasible, so that the effects of any bomb of known energy can be calculated from those given for the nominal, i. e., 20 kilotons TNT energy equivalent, atomic bomb.

2.2   As seen in § 1.36, the fission of 1 kilogram of uranium 235 or of plutonium should liberate the same amount of energy as the nominal atomic bomb.   Consequently, if all the atoms present suffered fission, 1 kilogram of material would be sufficient to produce the specified energy.   However, the efficiency in a bomb will be less than 100 percent, so that some fissionable material, i. e., uranium 235 or plutonium 239, will remain after the explosion.

2.3   An atomic explosion is associated with a number of characteristic phenomena, some of which produce visible effects while others are not directly apparent.   Certain aspects of these phenomena will depend on various circumstances, such as whether the atomic bomb is exploded in the air, under water, or on the ground.   In addition, meteorological conditions, such as temperature, humidity, wind, and atmospheric pressure will influence some of the observed effects.

2.4   The description of an atomic explosion given in this chapter will refer in particular to the immediate visible effects of the detonation.   Actually no complete observations of all the phenomena have been made, and the effects described are based partly on experiment and partly on theoretical calculations.

[1] Material contributed by R. I. Condit, J. O. Hirschfelder, B. Holzman, F. Reines, B. R. Suydam.

2.5   It will be supposed, in the first place, that the explosion takes place in the air, i. e., an air burst, at a distance of about 2,000 feet above the earth's surface.   Some of the special phenomena associated with an underwater burst will be considered later in this chapter.

2.6   It was stated in Chapter I that the fission of the uranium or plutonium in an atomic bomb leads to the liberation of a large amount of energy in a very small period of time within a limited space.   The resulting extremely high energy density causes the fission products to be raised to a temperature of more than a 1,000,000° C.[2]   Since this material, at the instant of explosion, is restricted to the region occupied by the original constituents of the bomb, the pressure will also be very considerable, of the order of hundreds of thousands of atmospheres.

B.   ATOMIC EXPLOSION PHENOMENA: AIR BURST

The Ball of Fire

2.7   Because of the extremely high temperature, there is an emission of energy by electromagnetic radiations, covering a wide range of wave lengths, from infrared (thermal) through the visible to the ultraviolet and beyond.[3]   Much of this radiation is absorbed by the air immediately surrounding the bomb, with the result that the air itself becomes heated to incandescence.   In this condition the detonated bomb begins to appear, after a few millionths of a second, as a luminous sphere called the *ball of fire* (Fig. 2.7).   As the energy is radiated into a greater region, raising the temperature of the air through which it passes, the ball of fire increases in size, but the temperature, pressure, and luminosity decrease correspondingly.   After about 0.1 millisecond[4] has elapsed, the radius of the ball of fire is some 45 feet, and the temperature is then in the vicinity of 300,000° C. At this instant, the luminosity, as observed at a distance of 10,000 yards (5.7 miles), is approximately 100 times that of the sun as seen at the earth's surface.

2.8   Under the conditions just described, the temperature throughout the ball of fire is almost uniform; since energy, as radiation, can travel rapidly between any two points within the sphere, there are no

---

[2] This figure may be compared with a maximum temperature of about 5,000° C. in a conventional high explosive bomb.

[3] The effect of the nuclear radiations, particularly gamma rays and neutrons, which are produced in the fission process (§ 1.59) will not be considered in this chapter.

[4] A millisecond, abbreviated to ms., is 0.001 sec., i. e., a one-thousandth part of a second.

appreciable temperature gradients.   Because of the uniform temperature the system is referred to as an *isothermal sphere*[b] which, at this
stage, is identical with the ball of fire.

Figure 2.7.   Test "Able" at Bikini, showing ball of fire and its reflection, the shock
wave on the surface of the water, and the ring cloud due to the "cloud-chamber"
(§2.19) effect.

2.9   As the ball of fire grows, a shock wave (§ 1.57) develops in the
air, and at first the shock front coincides with the surface of the isothermal sphere and of the ball of fire.   Below a temperature of about
300,000° C., however, the shock wave advances more rapidly than
does the isothermal sphere.   In other words, transport of energy by
the shock wave is faster than by radiation.   Nevertheless, the luminous ball of fire still grows in size because the great compression of
the air due to the passage of the shock wave results in an increase of
temperature sufficient to render it incandescent.   The isothermal
sphere is now a region of high temperature lying inside the larger ball
of fire; and the shock front is coincident with the surface of the latter,
which consequently becomes sharply defined.   The surface of separation between the very hot inner core and the somewhat cooler,
shock-heated air is called the *radiation front*.

[b] Since isothermal implies *constant* temperature, this term is not really correct; a better expression would
be *homothermal sphere*, indicating a *uniform* temperature.

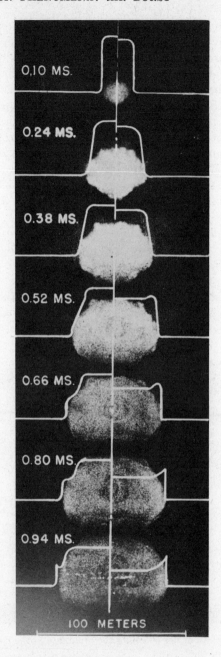

Figure 2.10. Qualitative representation of variation of temperature and pressure in ball of fire.

2.10   The phenomena described above are represented schematically in Fig. 2.10; qualitative temperature gradients are shown at the left, and pressure gradients at the right, of a series of photographs of the ball of fire taken at various intervals after detonation of an atomic bomb.   It can be seen that at first the temperature is uniform throughout the ball of fire, which is then an isothermal sphere.   Later, two distinct temperature levels are apparent, where the ball of fire has moved ahead of the isothermal sphere in the interior.   It may be noted that the luminosity of the outer region of the ball of fire prevents the isothermal sphere from being visible in the photograph.   At this time, the rise of the pressure to a peak, followed by a sharp drop at the surface of the fire ball, indicates that the latter is identical with the shock front.

2.11   The ball of fire continues to grow rapidly in size for about 15. milliseconds, by which time its radius has increased to approximately 300 feet; the surface temperature has then dropped to around 5,000° C., although the interior is very much hotter.   The temperature and pressure of the shock wave have also decreased to such an extent that the air through which it travels is no longer rendered luminous.   The faintly seen shock front moves ahead of the fireball (Fig. 2.11), and

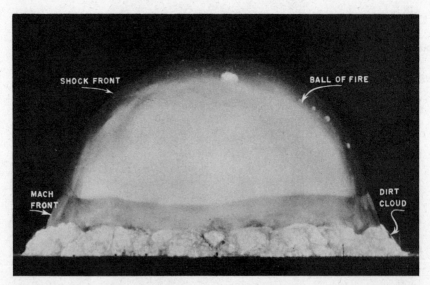

Figure 2.11.   The ball of fire touching the ground, and the shock front soon after the breakaway in the "Trinity" test at Alamogordo.   The Mach front (§3.53), due to reflection of the shock wave, and the dirt cloud (§2.24) are indicated.

the onset of this condition is referred to as the *breakaway*. The rate of propagation of the shock wave is then in the vicinity of 15,000 feet per second.

2.12 Although the rate of advance of the shock front decreases with time, it continues to move forward more rapidly than the ball of fire. After the lapse of one second, the ball of fire has essentially attained its maximum radius of 450 feet, and the shock front is then some 600 feet further ahead. After 10 seconds the ball of fire has risen about 1,500 feet, the shock wave has traveled about 12,000 feet and has passed the region of maximum damage.

2.13 An important feature of an atomic explosion in air, which will be considered more fully in Chapter VI, occurs at about the time of the breakaway of the shock front. The surface temperature falls to about 1,700° C. and then commences to rise again to a second maximum around 7000° C.[6] The minimum is reached approximately 15 milliseconds after the explosion, while the maximum is attained about 0.3 second later. Subsequently, the temperature of the ball of fire drops steadily due to expansion and loss of energy.

2.14 It is of interest to note that most of the energy radiated in an atomic explosion appears after the point of minimum luminosity of the ball of fire. Only about 1 percent of the total is lost before this time, in spite of the much higher surface temperature. The explanation of this result lies, of course, in the fact that the duration of the latter period, i. e., about 15 milliseconds, is very short compared with the several seconds during which radiation takes place after the minimum has been passed.

2.15 As stated above, the ball of fire expands very rapidly to its maximum radius of 450 feet within less than a second from the explosion. Consequently, if the bomb is detonated at a height of less than 450 feet, the ball of fire can actually touch the earth's surface,[7] as it did in the historic "Trinity" test at Alamogordo, New Mexico (see Fig. 2.11). Because of its low density, the ball of fire rises, like a gas balloon, starting at rest and accelerating within a few seconds to its maximum rate of ascent of 300 feet per second.

2.16 After about 10 seconds from detonation, when the luminosity of the ball of fire has almost died out and the excess pressure of the shock wave has decreased to virtually harmless proportions, the immediate effects of the bomb may be regarded as over.[8] The emission

---

[6] The first maximum is the high temperature, over a million degrees, attained almost at the instant of the detonation of the atomic bomb.

[7] For a bomb detonated over water, this would, of course, be the surface of the water.

[8] The nature of the shock waves produced by an atomic explosion will be considered in Chapters III and IV; the visible, destructive effects will be described in Chapters V and VI.

of gamma rays and neutrons accompanying fission will also have ceased by this time. It is true that the fission products present will still give off beta and gamma rays, but in general they will be far enough from the earth for these radiations to be absorbed by the air. They will, consequently, no longer be able to reach the earth's surface in sufficient intensity to constitute a serious hazard.

2.17   An interesting initial effect of an atomic explosion in air, although it persists for some time, may be mentioned here. Soon after the detonation, a violet-colored glow is observed, particularly at night or in dim daylight, at some distance from the ball of fire. This glow may persist for a considerable length of time, being distinctly visible in the column of cloud which forms after the ball of fire has disappeared (§ 2.21 *et seq.*). It is believed to be the ultimate result of a complex series of processes initiated by the action of gamma radiation on the nitrogen and oxygen of the air.[9]

2.18   The brownish or peachlike tint of the cloud which has been reported, particularly in the Bikini "Able" airburst, is apparently due to nitrogen dioxide. This is a brown gas formed by combination of atmospheric nitrogen and oxygen at high temperatures (§ 6.10).

Cloud-Chamber Effect

2.19   One of the earliest phenomena following an air burst is the *cloud-chamber effect*, analogous to that utilized by nuclear physicists in the Wilson cloud chamber. It will be seen in § 3.12 that after it has progressed for a short interval of time, a shock wave is, in certain circumstances, followed by a rarefaction or suction wave. During the compression or shock phase the temperature of the air rises (§ 3.12), and during the suction or decompression phase it will fall. For a moderately low value of the shock pressure the drop of temperature in cooling will be greater than the preceding rise; the temperature of the air will then fall below its original (preshock) value for a short period of time during the suction phase. If the air is saturated, or

---

[9] The intense gamma radiation accompanying the fission process, as well as that emitted by the fission products, causes ionization of the nitrogen and oxygen of the air (§ 7.18). After a short time, the positive and negative ions unite and in doing so release a large amount of energy. This energy is utilized for the breaking of chemical bonds in the air molecules, so that a mixture of nitrogen and oxygen atoms is formed. In addition, some atoms are produced by the direct action of the gamma radiation on the molecules. When these atoms recombine, the energy liberated is transferred to nitrogen or oxygen molecules, as energy of excitation. The excited molecules then return to their normal states by emitting energy in the form of visible radiation in the violet region of the spectrum. This constitutes the observed violet glow. These effects have long been known in connection with the study of the so-called "active nitrogen," and in the auroral glow due to excited oxygen molecules.

nearly saturated, with water vapor, condensation, accompanied by cloud formation, will occur in these circumstances (Fig. 2.19).

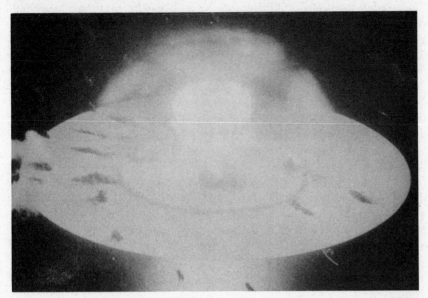

Figure 2.19.   The ball of fire visible within the "cloud-chamber" effect after the Bikini "Able" explosion.

2.20   The water-drop cloud actually forms at some distance from the ball of fire, because the shock wave has to travel a considerable distance before the pressure at the shock front has fallen sufficiently for the conditions necessary for condensation to be realized.   For example, air which is fully saturated with water vapor will form a cloud at a distance in the neighborhood of 2,500 feet from a bomb burst. Because of the necessity for relatively high humidity of the air, the cloud-chamber effect can be best observed in an atomic explosion occurring over or under water, for example, in the experimental bursts at Bikini.   Restoration of the air pressure causes the water droplets to vaporize and the cloud is dispelled, the whole effect being over in about a second or so.

ATOMIC CLOUD EFFECTS

2.21   There remain now to be considered what may be described as the residual effects of the atomic explosion, some of which, like the characteristic mushroom-shaped cloud, are merely spectacular, but others are a possible source of danger.   While the ball of fire is still luminous, the temperature, at least in the interior, is high enough to vaporize all the substances present, namely, fission products and unchanged uranium or plutonium, as well as the materials used for the casing of the bomb.

2.22   Because of its high temperature, and consequent low density, the ball of fire rises, as stated above, and as it rises it is cooled.   At temperatures down to about 1,500° C. the cooling is mainly due to loss of energy as thermal radiation; subsequently, the temperature is lowered as a result of adiabatic expansion of the gases and by mixing with the surrounding air through turbulent convection.   When the ball of fire is no longer luminous, it may be regarded as a large bubble of hot gases rising in the atmosphere, its temperature falling as it ascends.

2.23   As they cool, the constituents of the bubble condense, thus forming water droplets and a metallic oxide smoke made up of solid particles of varying sizes.   If the bomb is detonated at a low altitude, e. g., less than 500 feet, so that the ball of fire touches the ground, a considerable amount of dirt, steel or other material located in this area will be vaporized and taken into the ball of fire.[10]   Small solid particles of these materials will also separate out as the gas bubble cools.

2.24   Depending on the height of burst of the atomic bomb and on the nature of the terrain, high winds will occur in the immediate vicinity of the explosion.   These, together with the air blast due to the shock wave, will cause various amounts of dirt and other particles from the earth's surface to be sucked up.   In the event of a crater being formed, as it was in the Alamogordo ("Trinity") test, considerable quantities of dirt will be present (Fig. 2.11).   But it appears unlikely that there will be any appreciable crater formation for the explosion of a nominal atomic bomb at heights exceeding 250 feet.

2.25   At first the rising ball of fire carries the particles upward, but after a time they begin to fall under the influence of gravity at various rates dependent on their size.   Consequently, an ascending and expanding column of smoke is observed to form; it consists of water droplets, radioactive oxides of the fission products, and more or less debris, largely determined by the height of the explosion.   The rate of ascent depends on various meteorological conditions, as will be seen below, but the results in Table 2.25 may be taken as fairly typical.

---

[10] The energy required to heat up and vaporize sand, which may be taken to be representative of soil material, is 2,700 calories per gram.   Consequently, if 5 percent of the bomb's energy is used in vaporizing soil, about 360 tons of this material would be added to the gaseous constituents of the ball of fire.

TABLE 2.25

RATE OF RISE OF ATOMIC CLOUD

Height, feet	Time, minutes	Rate of rise, miles per hour
10, 000	0. 8	~200
15, 000	1. 5	~50
20, 000	2. 6	~33
25, 000	4. 6	~20
30, 000	8. 5	~12

2.26 The height to which an atomic cloud will rise depends on the thermal (heat) energy emitted by the bomb, the temperature of the surrounding air, and the density of the air. The greater the energy liberated as heat, the larger will be the buoyancy thrust on the rising cloud, and hence the greater will be the distance it ascends. It is believed that the maximum height attainable by an atomic cloud will be limited by the height of the base of the stratosphere. This is apparently in agreement with the observation on the "Trinity" test bomb at Alamogordo, New Mexico, for the cloud in this case rose to 40,000 feet.

2.27 If the radioactive cloud should pass through a temperature inversion layer [11] in the atmosphere, it will tend to "mushroom" out to a small extent. Because the air in the inversion layer is fairly stagnant, some of the particles in the cloud will tend to spread out horizontally instead of continuing to move vertically. Nevertheless, as a result of the enormous thermal energy of the hot gas bubble, most of the cloud will usually pass through an inversion layer.

2.28 Upon attaining a region where the density of the gas bubble is the same as that of the surrounding air, or upon reaching the base of the stratosphere, at about 40,000 to 60,000 feet, where the temperature of the atmosphere is almost constant and there is practically no motion due to convection, the radioactive column will spread out for a distance of several miles and form the characteristic mushroom shaped cloud (Fig. 2.28). The latter, having reached the final stage of its development, remains visible for an hour or more, until it is dispersed by the winds into the surrounding atmosphere.

THE FALL-OUT

2.29 When the radioactive, metallic oxide particles in the cloud collide with the particles of dirt, which are in general considerably

---

[11] At an inversion layer the temperature, which has been falling with increasing altitude, begins to increase.

Figure 2.28.   Mushroom cloud attaining a height of 5 miles after the "Able" test explosion.   The ice cap or scarf cloud at the top consists of myriads of small ice crystals; the gases above the mushroom expand and are consequently cooled, thus causing water vapor in the atmosphere to be converted into ice.

larger, they adhere. Consequently, the dirt particles in the cloud become contaminated with radioactivity. When the violence of the disturbance due to the bomb has subsided, the contaminated dirt particles gradually fall back to earth, giving rise to the phenomenon known as the *fall-out*. The extent and nature of this fall-out will be determined by the combination of circumstances associated with the height of the explosion, with the nature of the surface beneath, and with the meterorological conditions. It is possible that if the height of the bomb burst exceeds a certain value, there will be no detectable fall-out since no extraneous particles will be sucked into the cloud.

2.30 The importance of the fall-out in the present discussion lies in its radioactivity. It may be stated at the outset that only in exceptional circumstances would the intensity of the activity be great enough to constitute a hazard upon reaching the ground. The evidence from the Hiroshima and Nagasaki atomic bomb explosions, where the height of burst was about 2,000 feet, is that casualties ascribable to the radioactive fall-out were completely absent. However, if the bomb burst occurred relatively close to the ground, a situation which would be uneconomical from the standpoint of the destructive effect (§ 3.68), and considerable amounts of dirt and other debris were sucked into the radioactive cloud, the fall-out would have to be considered as a danger. The fall-out, consisting mostly of water drops, would also be important if the detonation took place at a low level above the surface of water; and the presence of salt in the water would enhance the hazard (§ 8.25).

Atomic Bombs and the Weather

2.31 There was at one time considerable speculation concerning the possible effects on the weather of an atomic burst, especially one over water. Forecasts of violent weather reactions were based primarily on two considerations. First, it was thought that large amounts of moisture in the air, such as is common in tropical areas, together with the water expected to be evaporated from the surface of the water, would be conducive to thunderstorm formation consequent upon the release of a large amount of energy by the explosion. Second, there was a possibility that the high concentration of ionized particles [12] resulting from the atomic explosion would serve as nuclei for condensation and thus promote the production of clouds and rainfall.

---

[12] The fission products are themselves ionized, i. e., electrically charged, and they, as well as the gamma rays, cause ionization of the air through which they pass.

2.32   Actually no such effects have been observed, and this is not surprising in view of the mechanism of the formation of a thunderstorm. Such storms require the transport aloft of moist masses of air by convection, or by mechanical lifting by fronts for a period of time, over relatively large areas, together with the existence of an appropriate vertical moisture structure. Convection caused by the warm land areas or the lifting of air masses by ascent over a high terrain or a front continues even after the storm has developed. An atomic explosion involves an almost instantaneous release of energy, and convection ceases as the hot gas bubble cools down on ascent and reaches its maximum altitude. An atomic bomb is therefore unable to produce convection of the sustained type necessary for thunderstorm formation. Even if the atmosphere is on the verge of instability, the sudden impulse of an atomic explosion cannot precipitate a thunderstorm because the energy release is so rapid that the atmosphere is unable to rearrange itself, within the limited time, so as to take advantage of the additional energy.

2.33   It is, of course, a well known fact that gaseous ions can act as nuclei for the condensation of water vapor, but quite a high degree of supersaturation is necessary before such condensation can occur. Actually the atmosphere always contains sufficient nuclei for condensation, and this is particularly so over the ocean where hygroscopic salt particles are present. Hence, the ions produced in the atomic explosion would not make any significant contribution to the condensation process.

2.34   The suggestion has been made that certain destructive, natural phenomena, such as hurricanes, tornadoes, or cold waves, could be dispelled by a sudden release of the large amounts of energy provided by an atomic bomb. But it is very doubtful if this could be done, because the amounts of energy that appear to be necessary are of a higher order of magnitude than those at present attainable.

2.35   Intermittent rain fell after the explosion of the atomic bomb over Hiroshima. This was due, indirectly, to the widespread fires which sustained convection for a considerable time after the explosion (§ 6.80). A similar phenomenon has been noted, under suitable air mass conditions, over large forest fires and over burning European cities during World War II.

2.36   Within 2 or 3 hours after the Bikini "Able" air burst, very small, light rain showers developed throughout the northern Marshall Islands. The rain falling in the path of the radioactive cloud was active, as might have been expected, but the amount of radioactivity was very small. Some attempt was made to relate the formation of the showers with the atomic cloud. But the showers were very widespread and were readily explained on the basis of the existing meteorological conditions. The radioactivity of the rain was the result of radioactive particles falling into the rain clouds, which were less than 6,000 feet high, or to the presence of such particles in the air which became attached to the drops of rain. The records of the Bikini "Able" test show that the only detectable changes which took place in the wind or atmosphere structure were the momentary effects of the blast and heat waves, and the violent changes occurring in a limited area in the vicinity of the burst. The main cloud pattern over the lagoon was unchanged, apart from the clouds directly associated with the explosion. A careful examination of all the available evidence would thus lead to the conclusion that an atomic bomb burst has a negligible effect on the weather.

C. ATOMIC EXPLOSION PHENOMENA: UNDERWATER BURST

SHALLOW UNDERWATER EXPLOSION

2.37 When an atomic bomb is detonated under water the phenomena observed differ, as might be anticipated, from those described above for an air burst. Although there are certain characteristic effects, the details would undoubtedly vary with the depth and area of the water and the distance below the surface at which detonation occurs. So far, only one underwater atomic burst, namely, the Bikini "Baker" test, has been reported. The burst was made well below the surface of the lagoon, which was about 200 feet deep. From the results of this test many of the effects of a deep underwater burst can be inferred.

2.38 In the underwater detonation, a ball of fire is undoubtedly formed, as in the case of an air burst. Observers of the "Baker" test at Bikini saw the water, in the vicinity of the explosion, lighted up by the luminosity of the ball of fire. The distortion due to the waves on the surface of the lagoon prevented any clear view of the ball, the general effect being described as having the appearance of light seen through a ground-glass screen. The luminosity remained for a few milliseconds, but it disappeared as soon as the bubble of hot gases constituting the ball of fire reached the water surface, for then the gases were expelled and cooled.

2.39 In the course of its rapid expansion the gas bubble, which now contains steam and its dissociation products, namely, atomic hydrogen and oxygen, in addition to the fission residue, initiates a shock wave. The trace of this wave, as it moves outward from the burst is evident, on a reasonably calm surface, as a rapidly advancing ring, apparently darker than the surrounding water. This ring, sometimes called the *slick* (Fig. 2.39), is visible in contrast to the undisturbed water because the ripples or small waves are partially

Figure 2.39. The "cloud-chamber" effect observed after the underwater ("Baker") explosion at Bikini. The slick, due to the shock wave, can be seen.

calmed by the reflection of the shock wave as a rarefaction (suction) wave at the surface of the water.

2.40   That part of the shock which passes into the air through the water surface causes a compression of the moist air; when this is followed by a rarefaction (suction) wave, the conditions may become favorable to the formation of the cloud-chamber effect (§ 2.19). This is illustrated by the dome-shaped cloud formed over Bikini lagoon almost immediately after the underwater ("Baker") burst (see Fig. 2.39).

2.41 Following the appearance of the slick, a mound or column of broken water and spray, called the *spray dome* (Fig. 2.41), is thrown up directly over the point of the burst by the reflection of the blast wave at the surface. The initial velocity of the water is proportional to the pressure of the incident shock wave, and so it is greatest di-

Figure 2.41.   The spray dome following the "Baker" explosion.

rectly over the explosion. Consequently, water thrown up over the center rises more rapidly and for a longer time than water farther away. As a result, the sides of the spray dome become steeper as the water rises. Its upward motion is terminated by the effects of gravity and the resistance of the air. The total time of rise and maximum height attained depend upon the energy of the explosion and upon its depth below the surface. For a very deep burst the spray dome may not be visible at all.

2.42 If the depth of detonation of the bomb is not too great, the bubble of hot gases will remain essentially intact until it rises to the surface of the water. At this point the gases, in the form of a jet, carrying some water by lateral entrainment, will be vented to the atmosphere. As the pressure of the bubble is released water rushes into the cavity, and the consequent complex phenomena cause the water to be thrown up as a hollow cylinder or chimney of spray known as the *plume* (Fig. 2.42). The radioactive contents of the gas bubble are vented through this hollow plume and form a mush-room-shaped cloud at the top.

Figure 2.42.   Formation of the plume (column) in the "Baker" test.

2.43   In the shallow underwater burst at Bikini the conical spray dome began to form at about 4 milliseconds after the explosion; its initial rate of rise was some 2,500 feet per second, but this was rapidly diminished by air resistance A few milliseconds later, the hot gas bubble reached the surface of the lagoon and the plume began to form, rapidly overtaking the spray dome at a height of a few thous-and feet. The maximum height attained by the hollow plume, through which the gases vented, could not be estimated exactly be-cause the upper part was surrounded by cloud. (Fig 2.43). It was probably some 8,000 feet, and the greatest diameter was about 2,000 feet. It is estimated that the maximum thickness of the walls of the plume was about 300 feet, and that approximately a million tons of water rose in the plume.

2.44   The cloud, which concealed a large part of the upper portion of the plume, resembled a cauliflower, rather than a mushroom, in shape. It contained some of the fission products and other bomb constituents, as well as water droplets. In addition, there is evidence that material sucked up from the bottom of the lagoon was also present, for calcareous sediment, which must have been part of the fall-out, was found on the decks of ships some distance from the burst.

Figure 2.43. The mushroom cloud and first stages of the base surge (§2.45) following the underwater ("Baker") explosion at Bikini. Water is beginning to fall back from the column into the lagoon.

The Base Surge

2.45 In the Bikini "Baker" test, it was observed that as the column of water and spray constituting the plume fell back into the lagoon, there developed, on the surface at the base of the column, a gigantic wave or cloud of mist, approximately 1,000 feet in height, completely surrounding the neck of the plume (Fig. 2.43). This wave began to form within about 10 seconds of detonation, and traveled rapidly outward, maintaining an ever-expanding doughnut-shaped form. The wave or wall of dense mist, much like the spray at the base of Niagara Falls or other waterfall of considerable height, represents the initiation of what is known as the *base surge*. It is, in effect, a dense cloud of liquid droplets which has the property of flowing almost as if it were a homogeneous fluid (Fig. 2.45).

Figure 2.45.   The base surge developing after the "Baker" test.

2.46   As the base surge at Bikini traveled outward at high speed, it gradually lifted from the surface of the lagoon and after about 5 minutes it had assumed the appearance of a mass of strato-cumulus cloud, which eventually reached a thickness of some thousands of feet (Fig. 2.46).   A moderate to heavy rainfall, moving with the wind and lasting for nearly an hour after the atomic bomb explosion, developed from this cloud mass.   In its early stages the rain was augmented by the small water droplets, equivalent, in a sense, to the fall-out of an air burst (§ 2.29), still descending from the cloud.

2.47   Were it not for the fact that the base surge is highly radioactive, due to the presence of fission products, it would represent merely a curious phenomenon.   Because of its radioactivity, however, which is augmented by that of the water droplets in the fall-out, it may represent a serious hazard, for a distance of several miles, especially in the downwind direction (Chapter VIII).

2.48   It is of interest to note that there are reasons for believing that the base surge can be produced only in fairly deep water.   It may be significant that, except for the Bikini test, base surges have not been definitely observed in connection with large explosions in water, such as that at Texas City in 1947. The conditions for the formation of a base surge, and the associated hazards will be considered more fully in later chapters.

2.49 In the event of a sufficiently deep underwater atomic burst, the hot gas bubble would lose its identity in a mass of turbulent water before reaching the surface and venting to the atmosphere. In this case, the spray dome would be relatively insignificant and no plume would be formed. Hence there would be no formation of a base surge and no appreciable fall-out. The disintegration of the gas bubble

Figure 2.46.   Later stage in the development of the base surge cloud at Bikini.

into a large number of very small bubbles, which are churned up with the water, would produce a radioactive foam or froth. When this reaches the surface, a small amount of radioactive mist would be emitted, but most of the activity would be retained in the sea water. The deposition of the highly active foam on a nearby shore might, however, represent a hazard.

2.50 It seems possible that a base surge, made up of small solid particles, rather than droplets of water, but still behaving like a fluid, might result from an atomic bomb burst below a soft terrain, consisting of sand or mud. The debris would, of course, be very radioactive.

2.51 In considering the phenomena associated with an atomic bomb explosion, as described in this chapter, no mention has been made of the destructive effects of the shock wave when it encounters structures on land or ships on the surface of the sea. Further, the harmful consequences of exposure to the radiations, both thermal and nuclear, emitted from the ball of fire, and the possible hazards due to fall-out and base surge have been no more than indicated. These subjects will, however, be treated in some detail in subsequent chapters of this book.

CHAPTER III[1]

SHOCK FROM AIR BURST [2]

A. INTRODUCTION ·

3.1 The shock wave produced by an air-burst atomic bomb is, from the point of view of weapon delivery and disruptive effect, the most important agent in producing destruction.   This implies that the other characteristics of an atomic bomb which can be employed in warfare, such as the presence of thermal and visible radiations, neutrons, gamma rays, and fission products, are, at present, not serious competitors in the production of damage by a bomb which is burst in the air.   There are of course other applications, such as the possible use of an atomic weapon as an instrument for radiological warfare by exploding it in a conveniently located body of water, so as to produce a base surge (§ 2.45), or in restricting the escape of the fission products by means of a subterranean explosion.   The bomb might also be employed to produce earth or water shock through a subsurface explosion.   Such uses, although potent, must, because of the restrictive conditions placed on the delivery problem and the target location and configuration, be regarded as special applications of the varied destructive characteristics of the atomic bomb.

3.2 A reason for the superiority of air blast as a producer of damage is found in the low air shock pressures (from 2 to 15 pounds per square inch overpressure) [3] required to damage the majority of man-made structures.   Judging from observations made during tests of atomic weapons, it is in fact not very difficult to design atom bomb-proof structures which will enable life to survive directly below an air burst bomb set to explode at that altitude, about 2,000 feet, which will generally suffice to cause maximum area damage.   It is, of course, another matter to redesign cities to withstand these blasts.   Because of its primary importance in atomic warfare, the subject of air blast has received more intensive investigation and, in consequence, is better understood than the other characteristics of a nuclear explosion.

---

[1] Material contributed by F. Reines.

[2] For a discussion of the theory of shock waves, see R. Courant and K. O. Friedrichs, "Supersonic Flow and Shock Waves," Interscience Publishers, Inc., N. Y., 1948.

[3] Ordinary atmospheric pressure at sea level is about 14.7 pounds per square inch (p. s. i.). The *overpressure* is the pressure in excess of that due to the atmosphere.

3.3 The formation of the shock wave in an atomic explosion and its propagation, at first coincident with and then in front of the ball of fire, was described briefly in Chapter II. It may be noted that the resulting air blast is still strong enough after 10 seconds, at about 12,000 feet from the explosion, to break windows, but after 30 seconds, at about 36,000 feet, almost all of its energy has been dissipated. The behavior of the shock wave on the ground, during the half minute of its existence and when it exerts its destructive effect, is of great importance for both offensive and defensive purposes. It is this aspect of the shock wave resulting from an air burst which will be considered in the present chapter. The nature and type of destruction that might be expected as a result of the accompanying blast will be described in Chapter V.

B. CHARACTERISTICS OF THE SHOCK WAVE IN AN INFINITE HOMOGENEOUS ATMOSPHERE

DEVELOPMENT OF SHOCK WAVE

3.4 No satisfactory detailed theory of the formation and evolution of the blast wave has been developed, although various approximations have been studied which, when coupled with experimental results, make up a reasonably complete description. The qualitative discussion which follows is intended to give a picture of the development of a blast wave from an atomic bomb which is exploded in an infinite homogeneous atmosphere. An examination of the effect of the proximity of the bomb to the ground will be reserved for a later section (§ 3.68).

3.5 Consider a small region in space which has been heated to a high temperature, say 100,000° C. At the boundary of this region is a shock wave which propagates outward as the region expands. The flow of material through the shock front is described by the Rankine-Hugoniot conditions which result from the conservation laws for energy, momentum, and mass.[4] These are important as boundary conditions in any analytical solution, and they also provide useful relationships between shock velocity, shock pressure, mass velocity, etc.

3.6 Initially, in the hot central region of the bomb the pressure exceeds atmospheric by perhaps a factor of many hundred thousand. As the shock front moves outward and the hot region grows in volume, it takes in air from outside of the shock front and drops in temperature

---

[4] See R. Courant and K. O. Friedrichs, *op. cit.*

and pressure. The pressure distribution behind the shock front in the very early stages is somewhat as illustrated in Fig. 3.6, which is a plot of the pressure against the distance from the center of the hot sphere at a given time. It shows the pressure at the shock front, indicated by p_s, dropping rapidly in a relatively small distance to a

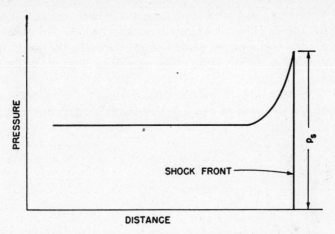

Figure 3.6.   Variation of pressure with distance in a shock wave at a given instant.

value about one-half the shock-front pressure. The ratio of the shock pressure to that in the interior then remains constant throughout the hot region.

3.7   Because of the Hugoniot conditions and the change in the equation of state of air as the shock pressure decreases, the pressure distribution in the region behind the shock front gradually changes as the expansion proceeds. The pressure ratio is no longer constant but drops off continuously as the center is approached. Eventually at large enough shock radii, the rarefaction which develops at the center causes a drop in pressure below the initial preshock value and a suction phase develops. The shock front weakens as it progresses outward and, as may be deduced from the Rankine-Hugoniot conditions, its velocity drops toward the velocity of sound in the initial cold air.[5] At the same time the areas of the positive (compression) and negative (rarefaction) phases become more nearly equal because of conservation requirements imposed on the net outward movement of the shocked air.

_____

[5] For the change of shock velocity with distance, see Fig. 3.13c.   In general the shock velocity exceeds that of sound in the shock front by an amount approaching the material velocity, i. e., of the air in the present case.

3.8   The net outward motion of the air comprising the shock can at most be equal to the thermal expansion suffered by the air because of the irreversible shock heating it has undergone.   As an example, the surface of a sphere of 1,000 yards radius, i. e., about 4×10^9 cubic yards in volume, heated uniformly by a nominal atomic bomb (§ 2.1), would move outward 20 yards.   This value for the net thermal expansion is to be compared with the maximum outward excursion of about 100 yards for shocked air originally at this radius.   In other words, the shock drives the parcel of air out 100 yards, in the positive phase, and it returns in the negative phase to within 20 yards of its original position.

3.9   The sequence of events just described for increasing times from t_1 to t_6 is depicted in Fig. 3.9; this shows the pressure distribution

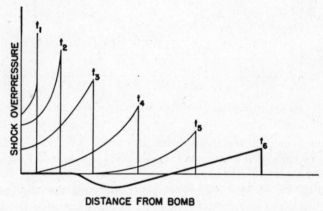

DISTANCE FROM BOMB

Figure 3.9.   Shock pressure-distance curves at successive times, increasing from t_1 to t_6.

in the shock as a function of the distance from the explosion at different stages in the expansion.   The absence of a negative phase out to a certain distance is apparent; however, it forms later and, as the shock weakens, approaches in area that of the positive phase.   At distances greater than 1,500 feet the negative pressure or the suction phase is well developed and the pressure distribution in the shock wave resembles the heavily-drawn curve in Fig. 3.9.

3.10   A more detailed description of the shock wave as it appears from this time on can be given in two different ways.   In Fig. 3.10, the heavy curve of Fig. 3.9, showing the variation of the shock overpressure with distance at a given time, is redrawn.   The arrows above the curve show the direction of the air-mass movement, that is, of the blast wind.   The spatial extension of the positive phase is indicated by L; the magnitude of this extension is important in considering the damage caused.   In general, the peak pressures reached in the positive phase, at the head of the blast wave, are higher than the pressures

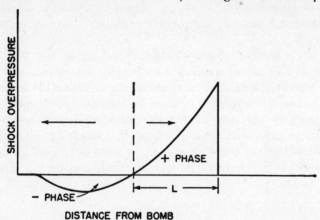

Figure 3.10.   Shock pressure-distance curve at a given instant, showing positive and negative phases.

reached anywhere during the negative phase.   Consequently, the blast wind is of higher velocity and shorter duration in the positive phase than in the negative or suction phase.

3.11   The same shock wave may be considered, alternatively, by plotting the variation of the overpressure with time, at a fixed location, as in Fig. 3.11.   The symbol τ represents the time taken for the shock wave to travel from the explosion to the chosen location, and t_+ is the duration of the positive phase.   Because the velocity of the shock is

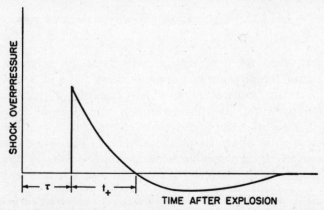

Figure. 3.11.   Shock pressure-time curve showing positive and negative phases.

related to the peak overpressure by the Rankine-Hugoniot conditions, the time of arrival τ may be derived from a curve which gives the variation of peak overpressure with distance. At the 10 pounds per square inch overpressure level the spatial extent of the positive phase is in the neighborhood of 1000 feet, and its duration is something of the order of 0.5 second; the negative phase, however, lasts a few seconds.[6]

3.12   Certain other characteristics, for example, the temperature variation of the air at a given location as the shock wave passes through (see Fig. 3.12), are also of interest. When the shock front strikes the air, its temperature rises practically discontinuously to a value related to the pressure by the Rankine-Hugoniot conditions. An adiabatic expansion occurs behind the shock front so that the temperature-time sequence at a fixed location is related to the pressure-time-distance characteristics. An examination of Fig. 3.12

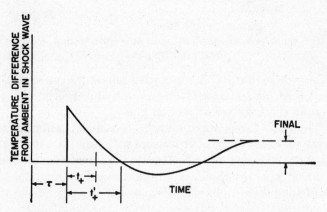

Figure 3.12.   Temperature-time curve in shock wave.

shows, first, that the temperature returns to its preshock value (time t'_+) after the pressure has done so (time t_+); and, second, that the minimum in temperature does not coincide in time with the minimum of pressure.   It will be seen, too, that after the shock wave has passed, i. e., after the pressure has returned to normal, the temperature is slightly above its preshock value.   The latter result is a consequence of the irreversible heating which occurs in the shock front.   Because of the decrease of temperature below ambient in the

---

[6] As in an underwater explosion, successive secondary shocks might be expected as the air mass oscillates (§ 4.22).   Such shocks should be much weaker and have in fact not yet been observed.

region of the minimum, the striking phenomenon of the condensation of water vapor in the air, known as the cloud-chamber effect, is observed, as described in § 2.19.

3.13 A complete summary of the variation with distance and time of the pressure due to a shock wave in an infinite homogeneous atmosphere, derived from experimental and theoretical sources, is given in Fig. 3.13a.[7] The change of peak pressure with distance

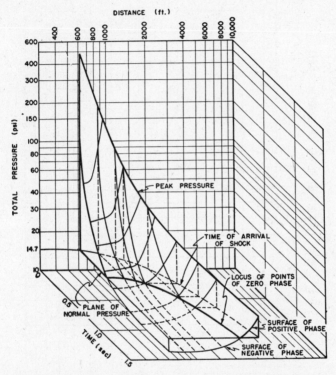

Figure 3.13a. Total pressure-time-distance diagram for shock wave in infinite homogeneous atmosphere.

from the bomb is depicted in Fig. 3.13b; this is of interest since, as will be seen later, the damage and peak pressure are very intimately related. In Fig. 3.13c the shock, sound and material velocities associated with the peak pressure in the shock front are shown as functions of distance from the explosion, and Fig. 3.13d gives the peak temperature

[7] Because the pressure scale is logarithmic, the total pressure rather than the overpressure is plotted, since the latter is negative in the rarefaction phase.

behind the shock front in terms of the same variable. In Fig. 3.13e is plotted the duration of the positive phase of the shock wave, also against the distance. Fig. 3.13f presents another special feature of

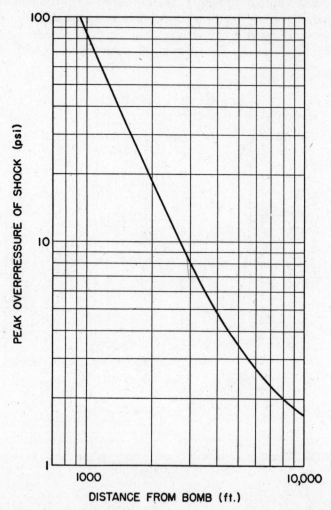

Figure 3.13b. Peak overpressure in shock wave as function of distance from atomic explosion in infinite homogeneous atmosphere.

Fig. 3.13a, namely, the time of arrival of the shock as a function of the distance from the source. It can be seen that, as expected, the slope of this curve approaches the velocity of sound as the shock weakens.

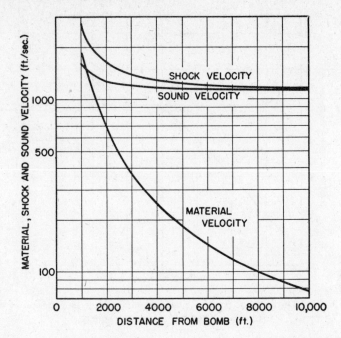

Figure 3.13c. Material, shock and sound velocities immediately behind shock front as functions of distance in infinite homogeneous atmosphere.

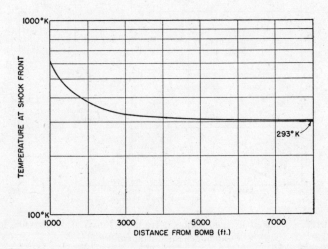

Figure 3.13d. Temperature at shock front as function of distance in infinite homogeneous atmosphere.

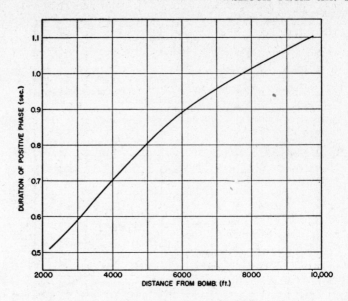

Figure 3.13e.   Duration of positive phase of shock wave as function of distance
in infinite homogeneous atmosphere.

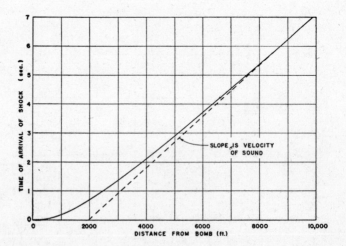

Figure 3.13f.   Time of arrival of shock front as function of distance in infinite
homogeneous atmosphere.

Scaling Laws[8]

3.14   Fortunately for the simplicity of the discussion, it is possible, given the above set of characteristics for the nominal atomic bomb explosion, to derive, by means of scaling laws, similar quantitative characteristics which apply to atomic explosions in general.   The existence of simple scaling laws depends on the hydrodynamical equations which apply to shock waves.   From these it is possible to show that two explosions, having the same initial conditions, differ only with respect to a scaling factor applied to both distance and time.[9]

3.15   It is, of course, necessary to prove, in addition, that two different atomic bombs, having different masses and constitutions, will in fact scale.   The success of scaling in the case of atomic bombs is due primarily to the high concentration of energy which they produce.   This means that although in the very early stages in which the bomb masses are comparable with the air, the two explosions are dissimilar, these masses soon become negligible with respect to the mass of air engulfed by the shock wave.   The two systems may then both be considered, with reasonable precision, to have originated from a point source or, more correctly, from small isothermal spheres which have been generated by the intense heating of the air by the bombs.   The validity of the scaling procedure has been studied theoretically and the solutions do, in fact, become more amenable to scaling as the shock fronts expand.

3.16   On the basis of the foregoing arguments, the state variables, i. e., pressure, temperature, and density, can be written as functions of radial distance (r) and time (t) for any atomic explosion, once they are given for a specific atomic explosion, by scaling all distances and times by the ratio of the energy yield or energy release (W) of the explosion under consideration to that of the reference explosion raised to the ⅓ power.   Thus,

$$\frac{r}{r_0} = \left(\frac{W}{W_0}\right)^{\frac{1}{3}}$$

(3.16.1)

---

[8] A discussion of the scaling laws for chemical explosives is given by R. H. Cole, "Underwater Explosions," Princeton University Press, Princeton, N. J., 1948.

[9] The behavior of atomic bombs as regards shock is compared with that of a conventional TNT bomb. This comparison is reasonable, since both produce blast, and the destructiveness of TNT bombs is well documented.   However, because of the enormously greater energy density present in an atomic explosion, the blast characteristics of the latter are somewhat different from those of a quantity of TNT with the same energy release.   In the first place it seems that, on the average, less energy goes into blast for an atomic explosion.   Further, if the peak pressure-distance curves for TNT and for an atomic bomb of the same energy release match at 10 pounds per square inch, the pressures at smaller distances are greater for the atomic weapon, while at larger distances they are greater for TNT.

and
$$\frac{t}{t_0} = \left(\frac{W}{W_0}\right)^{\frac{1}{3}},$$ (3.16.2)

where W_0, r_0, and t_0 apply to the reference explosion, which is the nominal atomic bomb in the present case.

3.17   A useful concept to introduce at this point is that of "similarity" or "corresponding states." Two explosions may be said to be in similarity or in corresponding states when the state variable contours are the same except for a radial scale factor. This means, for example, that the peak overpressure is a universal function of a variable equal to $(r/W^{\frac{1}{3}})$. It follows, therefore, that if a bomb with an energy release equivalent to 20 kilotons of TNT produces an overpressure of 10 pounds per square inch at a distance of 2,500 feet, a 30-kiloton equivalent bomb will produce the same overpressure at a distance of $2,500 \times (30/20)^{\frac{1}{3}} = 2,860$ feet.

3.18   The quantitative curves given in earlier sections have been derived partly from measurements and partly from theoretical calculations. Unfortunately, at present, neither theory nor experiment alone provides a complete and reliable picture. With respect to experiment, for example, free air measurements of the peak overpressure have not yet been made because of the difficulties attendant on the placing of detectors. Consequently, it has been necessary to deduce the curve for the variation of the free air pressure with distance from data obtained on the ground from an air burst. This procedure has the unsatisfactory feature that an assumption must be made as to the nature of the reflection. As will be seen shortly, this reflection is most complicated at distances from ground zero [10] which are comparable with the height of burst. Furthermore, the amount of energy absorbed by the ground is not particularly well known. Fortunately for both these considerations, the height of burst in the Bikini "Able" test was large enough to avoid significant loss of energy to the water and small enough to simplify the reflection consideration by the time the overpressure had reached something of the order of 50 pounds per square inch. On this basis then, $W^{\frac{1}{3}}$ scaling was applied to the experimental results to yield the curve for free air pressure against distance.

3.19   Experimental data on pressure against time, on the other hand, as well as that relating the pressure to the distance for higher overpressure than 50 pounds per square inch, are extremely meager. Consequently, an appeal was made to theory to supply this infor-

---

[10] *Ground zero* is the point on the earth's surface vertically below the position of the bomb burst.

mation. The best theoretical treatment available as to the free air blast characteristics of an atomic bomb involved a numerical integration of the hydrodynamical equations. Various assumptions were made as to the initial conditions and in connection with the equation of state of air at high temperatures. The calculations were performed before any atomic bomb had been detonated, and they were very approximate; hence the results for the amount of energy required to produce a given pressure at a specified distance were not in good agreement with experiment. An arbitrary adjustment of the theoretical pressure curve to match that obtained experimentally has been made and the various blast characteristics given in Figs. 3.13a to 3.13e are the result of these manipulations.

C. AIR BURST AND THE MACH EFFECT [11]

GENERAL CONSIDERATIONS

3.20 In the preceding paragraphs, the discussion has dealt with the air blast from an atomic bomb exploded in an infinite atmosphere. In this section consideration will be given to the influence of the height of burst of the bomb on the area of blast damage. The problem is extremely complex and can be solved only in a statistical or average manner. This is so for two reasons: first, the detailed description of a military target can never be completely given, and second, the complete analytical solution of even such a relatively simple problem as the behavior of a shock wave incident on a wall at an oblique angle has never been obtained for all angles. As will be seen later, a solution of the basic problem of shock reflection from a rigid wall can be derived by a combination of theory and experiment. This solution is, however, not readily adapted to yielding the effect of blast in better than an average sense in a more complicated situation. As to the detailed description of the target, not only are the structures of odd shape, but they have the additional complicating property of not being rigid. This means that they do not merely deflect the shock wave, but they also absorb energy from it at each reflection.

3.21 The removal of energy from the blast in this manner decreases the shock pressure at any given distance from the point of detonation to a value somewhat below that which it would have in the absence of dissipative objects, such as buildings. The presence

---

[11] This section is based on work by J. von Neumann and F. Reines done at the Los Alamos Scientific Laboratory.

of such dissipation or diffraction makes it necessary to consider somewhat higher values of the pressure than would be required to produce
a desired effect if there were only one structure set by itself on a
rigid plane.

3.22   The ideal solution to the problem is one in which the required
pressures are calculated for a given explosion and target configuration
by a theoretical treatment of diffraction effects and other sources of
energy losses.   In the absence of an adequate theory, the best procedure is first to derive from theory, or from experiment, the pressure
level required to produce a given degree of damage for a given isolated
structure.   The value so obtained is averaged properly over the actual
distribution of structural types, and then this representative computed
average figure is compared with the average pressure level at which
the damage under consideration has been actually found to occur.
The ratio of these two pressure levels would then express the losses
in question.   This procedure is not practical mainly because the first
mentioned pressure criterion is not sufficiently well known or sufficiently reproducibly defined.   The influence of the losses must therefore be accounted for in qualitative ways, not on an absolute basis,
but rather in the sense of comparing them in two situations—one,
the situation of actual interest, and the other, a standard where the
pressure level corresponding to the observed damage radius is
empirically known.

3.23   The pressures which are actually exerted upon a given structure will have been amplified by reflections from its own or nearby
surfaces and decreased by diffractions around openings and corners.
The former may cause local increases in pressure which will, under
suitable conditions, be quite considerable.   For overpressures of less
than, say, 10 pounds per square inch, the acoustic theory [12] applies in
the main satisfactorily, except for glancing reflections.   According
to this theory any reflection, head-on or oblique, doubles the overpressure at the surface.   It is not difficult to find geometrical arrange-
ments where as many as three such reflections superpose their amplifications, for example, a shock running into a 90° corner, as depicted
in Figs. 3.23a and 3.23b.   In these figures the lines represent the shock
(or reflected) fronts, and the arrows indicate the directions of propagation.   The original (atmospheric) pressure is P, and p is the
overpressure at the shock front.   It is seen (Fig. 3.23b) that there is
a local increase in pressure of four times the initial overpressure in the

---

[12] Acoustic theory is applicable only to waves of small amplitude.

shock, even according to acoustic theory.   Exact shock theory gives
still higher increases.

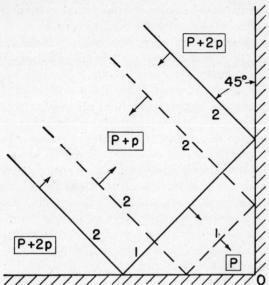

Figure 3.23a.   Two successive positions (later one dotted) of shock pattern
 before original shock reaches corner point at O; 1 indicates original shock and
 2 the shock reflected once.   (*P*=atmospheric pressure, *p*=overpressure.)

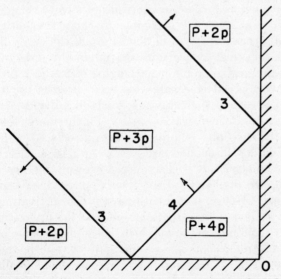

Figure 3.23b.   Shock pattern after original shock has reached O; 3 is shock
 reflected twice, and 4 is shock reflected three times.

3.24   The example cited is a special instance of the more general problem of the pressure increase which may be obtained when an acoustic shock runs into a corner, having a specific angular opening, at a given angle of incidence.   In this general case it can be shown that the pressure increase to be expected is np, where p is the overpressure in the shock wave and n is the number of shocks that have traversed the region; n is determined by the angle of the corner and by the angle of incidence.   The actual pressure amplifications that can be attained are limited by the rarefaction wave from the edges of the necessarily finite wedge.

3.25   In spite of the reality of the local increases it is hopeless to attempt to follow the effects into all their ramifications.   However, these local reflection amplifications and the opposite diffraction shielding effects which necessarily accompany them in neighboring areas, are all perturbations of the main blast phenomenon, caused by the irregularities represented by the target and other structures.   Consequently, an estimate must be made of the formations which can be disregarded as local irregularities not materially affecting the main, average evolution of the shock wave.

3.26   Although there is no exact theory of this phenomenon, there do exist good guiding analogies with acoustics and optics.   It is well known that irregularities with dimensions of less than $\frac{1}{16}$ of a wave length leave reflection "perfect" from the "optical" point of view.   Probably as much as $\frac{1}{4}$ wave length will not affect average intensities significantly, i. e., they are negligible in the sense outlined above.   The linear dimensions of typical houses are of the order of 30 feet to 50 feet and they may conceivably go up to the order of 100 feet.   Hence they are negligible for wave lengths of 120 feet to 200 feet or over, and even in extreme cases for wave lengths up to 400 feet.

3.27   In the case of a shock wave, some difficulty is caused by the absence of a well-defined wave length.   Furthermore, the equations which describe the finite amplitude waves associated with the shock phenomena under discussion are nonlinear.   It is clear, however, that Fourier analysis, as well as any other suitable procedure, will have to assign to the length of the positive phase the essential role of a wave length.   Hence, it is felt to be justified in treating houses as statistically irrelevant perturbations, since at the interesting pressure levels, about 10 pounds per square inch, the positive phase of the shock wave from an atomic bomb has a spatial extension in the neighborhood of 1,000 feet.   These arguments are somewhat qualitative, but they probably do justice to the main features of the situation.

3.28   It may be assumed, therefore, that for the atomic explosions under consideration, houses and other obstructions of comparable dimensions may be treated as small perturbations which do not appreciably affect the main evolution of the blast.   In addition, houses, quite apart from their established "small" size, are also a feeble over-all influence because they cover only a small part of the ground.   Even in "built-up" areas they rarely cover more than 25 percent of the ground, and therefore, the progress of a blast wave along the ground takes place in the main over a smooth surface.   According to these principles, the ground can be treated as a plane reflecting surface as long as its formation is plane from an average topographical point of view.

3.29   The focusing, shielding and other gross effects of hills, valleys, etc., are beyond the scope of the present treatment.   Also, since the density of earth is about 1,000 times that of the air, the transfer of energy through the air into the ground is small, and hence the latter may be treated as a rigid reflector.   A great deal of direct experimental evidence confirming these views for a high burst was obtained at Woods Hole and Princeton during World War II.

3.30   A reasonable idealization is consequently one in which the reflection of the blast from the ground, taken as a rigid, reflecting plane, is to be considered, and all target structures are to be viewed as immersed in the average pressure field thus produced.   Further, as will be seen later (§ 5.26), the damage criterion for atomic explosions is in general the peak pressure.   In consequence of this fact and the preceding discussion, the situation reduces to something relatively simple: in evaluating the damage produced by an air-burst bomb with regard to reflection from the ground, it is only the effect of reflection from a rigid plane on the peak pressure that is significant.

The Height of Burst

3.31   The exact height of the burst above the ground is not important in its effects on the blast received at a point whose distance from the bomb is several times the height of burst.   At distances which are small or of the same order as the height of burst, the fact that the bomb is air burst has a profound effect on the blast characteristics.   In the immediate neighborhood of a ground burst a target suffers extremely high pressures.   For large charges this is, however, not an advantage because it means that the immediate neighborhood would be destroyed more radically than necessary, and the energy so wasted would not be available elsewhere.   In addition to avoiding overdestruction, an air burst at sufficient height minimizes the shielding of remote structures by those near the detonation.

3.32   For atomic bombs there is a further reason for detonation at an altitude.   It is not desirable to let the ball of fire with its enormous temperatures, approaching 1,000,000° C., immediately around the explosion get in contact with matter in bulk, in particular with the ground.   Such contact would result in the loss of much energy in evaporating the earth.   There is a further advantage in an air burst, for such a burst is accompanied by certain forms of blast reflection which would not occur in the case of a surface burst.

3.33   Consider, first, the case of a bomb detonated on the ground. It might be thought that because the shock has a hemispherical shape and always touches the ground at right angles there would be no reflection from the ground.   Actually, this is not true.   If the ground were an absolutely rigid reflecting surface, then the energy normally transmitted to the lower hemisphere in the absence of the ground will not disappear but will be reflected into the upper hemisphere in coincidence with the energy normally sent there in the absence of the ground.   In other words, a bomb detonated on the ground is equivalent to two bombs in so far as the blast in the region above the ground is concerned.   Now twice the charge weight means, in terms of peak pressure, that all pressures are the same for the ground burst charge as for the same charge burst in free air if all distances from the charges are in the ratio of the similarity factor $2^{1/3}$ (§ 3.17).   Comparing pressures at a fixed distance r from the bomb, the peak pressures obtained in the presence of the ground are higher, because of reflection, by a factor of $2^{1/3}$ or $2^{1/2}$, according as the pressure decreases with distance as $1/r$ or as $1/r^{3/2}$.   The $1/r$ law holds approximately, at large distances, i. e., for low pressures, but the variation is something like $1/r^{3/2}$ in the region of interest i. e., 5 to 10 pounds per square inch overpressure.

3.34   Consider, next, the effects of an air burst at distances which are great compared to the height of burst.   It is reasonable to expect that at such distances the height itself, and all phenomena caused by it, ought to have a small influence, and as the distance increases this influence should become entirely negligible.   Hence, at distances which are very large compared to the height of burst the pressure should be amplified by $2^{1/3}$ i. e., 1.26, at most if there is no crater formation, and by an appropriately smaller factor if this occurs.

ACOUSTIC PICTURE OF AIR BURST

3.35 The action of an air-burst charge will first be treated in the acoustic approximation. When the shock sphere hits the ground, it produces a reflected shock. In the acoustic approximation this reflected shock is a part of another, which is congruent to the first one, and behaves as if it were the blast wave coming from a "virtual bomb," situated at the image point of. the real bomb reflected with respect to the ground (Fig. 3.35a). When the shock first strikes the ground,

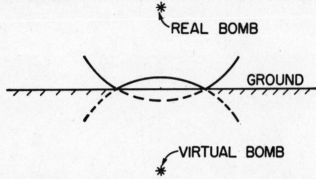

Figure 3.35a. Reflection of spherical shock wave in the acoustic approximation.

it does so at normal incidence, and hence, by acoustic theory doubles the overpressure, i. e., the pressure increases over atmospheric in this region. Even later, when the shock sphere intersects the ground at oblique angles, the laws of acoustics also call for a doubling of overpressure or pressure increase above atmospheric in the twice shocked region at the reflecting surface (Fig. 3.35b). In other words, at all

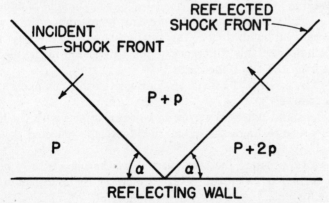

Figure 3.35b. Reflection of shock in the acoustic approximation for larger angle of incidence.

angles of incidence [13] $0° \leq \alpha \leq 90°$, the reflected overpressure is, independently of α, equal to $2p$, where p is the incident overpressure. For $\alpha = 90°$ the incidence is glancing and no reflection in the acoustic sense occurs.

3.36   A chronological representation of the sequence of events as the blast wave expands, is reflected, etc., is given in Fig. 3.36; this shows the appearance, in the acoustic approximation, of the blast pattern as it travels outward from the air-burst bomb. The free air shock overpressures, at successive intervals, are represented by $p_1, . p_2,$

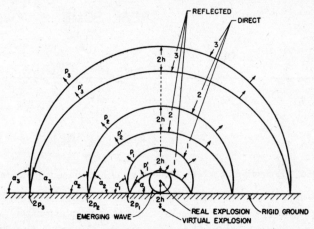

Figure 3.36.   Successive stages in reflection of spherical shock wave in the acoustic limit.

and p_3; the corresponding additional reflected overpressures are p_1', p_2', and p_3', respectively. The latter may be thought of as originating from the "virtual bomb." Since any point above the ground is closer to the real bomb than to the "virtual bomb", p is always greater than p'; however, this difference tends to become negligible as the distance from the bomb increases.

3.37   The essential features of the reflection phenomenon are seen to be as follows:

(a) Incident and reflected waves make equal angles with the ground.

(b) The pressure increases in the incident and reflected waves are equal.

(c) The total pressure increase exerted by the blast at any point on the surface is twice the pressure increase to be expected at the same distance in the absence of the ground.

---

[13] The *angle of incidence,* as used throughout this book, refers to the angle between the normal to the blast front and the normal to the reflecting surface.

(d) The incident and reflected waves have a constant separation, equal to $2h$ at the zenith, where h is the height of burst. At an angle θ from the zenith the separation is smaller; it tends to $2h \cos \theta$ as the wave expands out from the bomb (real and virtual). For $\theta = 90°$, i. e., on the ground, the separation is of course zero, since the incident and reflected waves are necessarily in contact there. Correspondingly, the separation tends to zero as $\theta \rightarrow 90°$, i. e., as the ground is being approached.

(e) As the wave expands, α, the angle of incidence (and reflection), starts at $0°$ and approaches $90°$ in the limit of large distances.

3.38 The variation of the overpressure with time at selected positions in the blast pattern is depicted in Figs. 3.38a and 3.38b. On

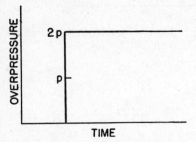

Figure 3.38a. Variation of overpressure with time at a given point on the ground.

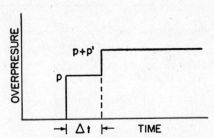

Figure 3.38b. Variation of overpressure with time at a given point above the ground.

the ground there is everywhere a single rise to $2p$, as shown in Fig. 3.38a, but at a fixed height above the ground the increase of pressure occurs in two stages, first to p and then to $p+p'$ (Fig. 3.38b). As the distance from the bomb increases, the time interval Δt between the two shocks tends to zero.

3.39 If, instead of considering the variation of overpressure at a fixed height, it is studied at a number of positions above the ground for which the zenith angle θ is the same, the two-stage increase, first to p and then to $p+p'$, is observed at all points. The time interval Δt decreases with increasing distance from the explosion, approaching a limiting value of $(2h/c) \cos \theta$, where c is the velocity of sound. The same general behavior is found at the zenith, and since θ is here zero, the time interval between the two stages of increase of overpressure tends to $2h/c$ with increasing height above the ground.

3.40 The foregoing results are strictly valid only for shocks with overpressures of infinite duration. Actually, a decay of the overpressure occurs behind the shock because of the finite duration of the explosion; consequently, Figs. 3.38a and 3.38b are changed so as to take the forms of Figs. 3.40a and 3.40b, respectively. The drop

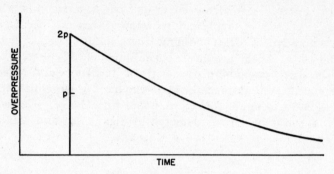

Figure 3.40a.   Variation of overpressure with time at a point on the ground for shock of finite duration.

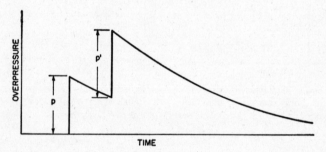

Figure 3.40b.   Variation of overpressure with time at a point above ground for shock of finite duration.

shown in Fig. 3.40b between the pressure rises p and p' may well exceed the second pressure rise p'. However, at or near the reflecting surface, because of the (exactly or approximately) simultaneous arrival of the two shocks in that region, amplification must certainly occur.

Criticism of Acoustic Picture: Formation of Mach Stem

3.41   Certain parts of the acoustic description given here of the blast pattern from a charge burst above a rigid ground are in disagreement, first, with intuition, and second, with the facts. It has been suggested earlier (§ 3.35) that the system of shock source and reflecting wall might be replaced by a real and a virtual source; this would be equivalent to an explosive dipole. It is to be expected that at large distances such an explosive dipole would have the appearance of a single charge having the combined mass. This conclusion is analogous to the result in electrostatics, according to which the field produced by two equal electric charges of the same sign is essentially the field of the total charge when the distance to the point of observation is great compared with the separation between the charges.

3.42 Further, the permanent separation of the original and the reflected shocks in acoustic theory is clearly due to their having the same velocity, i. e., the velocity of sound. Actually shocks of finite strength move faster than sound (Fig. 3.13c). Furthermore, the reflected shock is faster than the original one because it travels through air heated by the former and, hence, has its speed increased relative to it. Consequently, while acoustically the reflected shock is not able to catch up with the incident shock, if the shock has a finite size then it will in reality catch up in regions where the positive phases overlap. Since the two shocks are close together near the ground and in contact at the ground, the positive phases certainly overlap in this region. The reflected shock is therefore faster than the direct shock, and since they become more nearly parallel as time goes on, a merger should sooner or later take place. The shock formed by the fusion of the incident and reflected shocks (see Fig. 2.11) is called the *Mach stem* (§ 3.53).

3.43 It is known from the theory of oblique reflection (§ 3.44) and from experiment that this is the case, and that the overpressure at the fusion shock is about twice that at either of the two original shocks. As the spherical shock expands, conditions become suitable for fusion at increasing distances from the ground. Consequently, the fused portion gradually rises and covers more and more of the shock sphere. It is possible to show that eventually the merger is complete and the two shocks are finally everywhere fused and form a single shock front; the shocks due to the virtual and real bomb will then have merged over the sphere which corresponds to the double charge.[14]

OBLIQUE REFLECTION: DEVIATION FROM ACOUSTIC BEHAVIOR

3.44 A detailed theoretical treatment of the shock wave pattern produced by the reflection of an expanding spherical shock wave from a

---

[14] If the charge is burst at such an altitude that the merger occurs at great heights, say 30,000 feet, then, because of the variation of atmospheric density, neither the original nor the fused shock front will be spherical. However, the present treatment is concerned primarily with effects near the ground and so this point will not be considered here.

rigid plane surface, leading to the derivation of the Mach effect, must start with a description of what happens exactly on the ground where the incident and reflected shocks always intersect each other, and where the reflected shock was originally produced. It will be recalled that according to the acoustic theory a reflection always produces the same increase in overpressure as the incident shock. This result is independent of the angle of incidence up to, but not including, 90° at which angle it ceases to be valid. If the shock is of finite strength. there will be deviations from the acoustic result. Since the acoustic behavior is discontinuous at 90°, deviations from acousticity would be expected to set in earlier than 90°, for the true shock must exhibit some kind of continuous behavior in the neighborhood of 90°. There are, then, two factors which perturb the acoustic behavior; namely, the finite strength of the shock, and the obliquity, especially in the neighborhood of 90°.

3.45   Consider, first, the true behavior of a finite shock for a head-on reflection. The result is usually stated as follows: A shock which hits an absolutely rigid wall will be strengthened more than the acoustic theory predicts. This theory indicates a doubling of overpressure at the rigid wall; for a strong shock, however (see Fig. 3.51), the absolute overpressure on the wall can be as high as eight times the pressure in the incident shock, assuming air to be an ideal gas with a ratio of specific heats, γ, equal to 1.4.

3.46   In the acoustic limit the incident and reflected shocks form a stable configuration regardless of the angle of incidence and of the shock strength. Since the two shocks have the same velocity component parallel to the ground at their point of intersection, the angles of incidence and reflection will also be equal. This is, of course, just the application of Snell's principle of optics in a very simple case (see Fig. 3.35b).

3.47   Consider, now, the case of a finite shock, where the reflected and incident shocks may be of unequal strengths and hence have unequal velocities relative to the air and ground. If the intersection of the two shocks is to remain on the ground, this difference of velocities requires that the reflected and incident shocks make unequal angles with the ground. From the equations of motion it is found that there are as many equations as there are variables and, in general, there are either two solutions or none.

3.48   Consequently, for a given incident shock the reflected shock can be in two positions, one less and one more inclined to the surface (Fig. 3.48). The reflected shock which is steeper turns out to be faster. It can be shown that under these conditions it is the less steep shock which exists, because if the strength of the incident shock is continuously decreased, so that it approaches the acoustic case, it is found that the less steep shock goes over asymptotically to the same strength as the incident shock at the same angle.   The steeper shock, on the other hand, goes over into a finite nonacoustic shock and becomes vertical, i. e., as p incident$\rightarrow 0$, $\alpha_3 \rightarrow \alpha_1$ and $\alpha_2 \rightarrow \pi/2$.   Now since this latter does not actually happen, and is in fact energetically impossible without an external source of energy, it may be assumed, at least in the case of a weak shock, that it is the less steep, weak

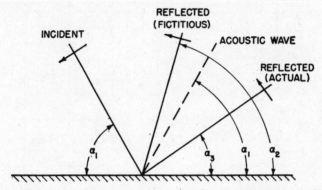

Figure 3.48.   Oblique reflection of plane, finite (nonacoustic) shock wave.

solution which exists.   It might be assumed, by continuity, that the strong reflected shock is forbidden for all incident shock strengths, an assumption supported by the experimental observations of all who have worked on this subject.

3.49   A theoretical consideration of the oblique shock for angles of incidence increasing from 0° towards 90°, reveals that the two solutions for the reflected shock move toward each other.   When the incident shock has reached a sufficient obliquity the two solutions for the reflected shocks merge, forming a Mach stem (§3.42), and beyond this there is no solution.[15] Reflection which occurs within this region is called *irregular reflection*.

The Extreme Angle: Irregular Reflection

3.50   The variations with shock pressure of the limiting or *extreme angle* for regular reflection, where irregular (or Mach) reflection com-

[15] For shocks of any reasonable strength this obliquity is far from 90°; for example, for a shock overpressure of about 1 atmosphere the extreme angle of incidence is about 50°, and even for a shock of 0.1 atmosphere the extreme angle for regular reflection is around 80°.

mences, are of some interest (Fig. 3.50). As the shock is weakened,
the acoustic limit is approached and, therefore, the extreme angle must
be nearer and nearer to 90°. For reasons previously mentioned, as
the angle of incidence becomes close to 90°, deviations from acoustic
behavior should be expected no matter how weak the incident shock.
Both theory and experiment show that such deviations do occur. As

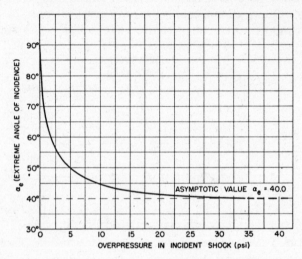

Figure 3.50.   Extreme angle of incidence as function of overpressure in incident
shock wave.

will be seen later, the extreme angle converges to 90° rather slowly,
as the square root of the shock pressure. More interesting is the
fact that as the strength of the shock increases, the extreme angle
decreases from 90°. For 30 pounds per square inch overpressure it
reaches 40°; after this it drops a little, oddly enough, below 40° to
something like 39°, which it reaches at 90 pounds per square inch
overpressure, and then it rises again to 40°, which value it retains for
infinitely strong shocks. This means that for shocks of 30 pounds
per square inch, or greater, the extreme angle has already practically
reached its limiting value of 40°. For 3 to 6 pounds per square inch
overpressure, it is 50° or 60°. Most blast damage by large bombs is
based on peak pressure and is likely to occur between 3 and 6 pounds
per square inch overpressure; for these pressures regular reflection
becomes impossible in the neighborhood of an obliquity of 50° to 60°.

3.51   Another interesting characteristic of irregular reflection is the
variation of the relative overpressure on the surface as a function of

the angle of incidence and the strength of the incident shock. In Fig. 3.51 the relative overpressure is shown as a function of the angle of incidence for strong ($\xi=0$), weak ($\xi=0.7$) and acoustic ($\xi=1.0$) shocks for regular reflection in an ideal gas with γ equal to 1.4.[16] It

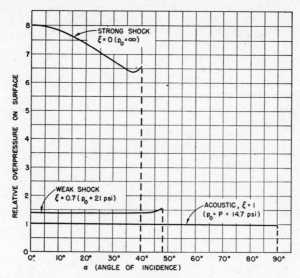

Figure 3.51.   Relative overpressure on surface due to reflection as function of angle of incidence for shocks of different strengths.

will be noted that for a very strong shock the reflected overpressure may be nearly eight times as great as the incident pressure.

Mach Reflection for Plane Shock Waves

3.52   An examination will now be made of the results of exceeding the extreme angle of regular reflection with a plane shock wave. In Fig. 3.52 the incident shock impinges on the wall giving rise to a reflected shock. Adopting the frame of reference which reduces the motion of the point P and the two shocks to rest, then the material will appear to flow through the shocks from left to right as shown. The incident shock causes the material originally flowing parallel to the wall, as indicated at Z, to be deflected toward the wall in the direction of X. The reflected shock renders the flow again parallel to the wall, as at Z'.

[16] The quantity ξ, i. e., the ratio of the (atmospheric) pressure in front of the incident shock, to that (p_0) behind it (atmospheric+overpressure), is called the *shock strength*. Its value tends to zero for very strong shocks and to unity for weak shocks.

3.53 Beyond the extreme angle it is observed that a fusion of the incident and reflected shocks occurs, starting in the neighborhood of P, and the reflected shock overtakes the incident shock. This process originates at the wall and gradually spreads into the volume of the

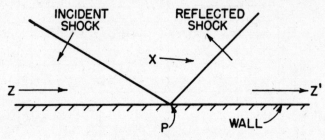

Figure 3.52. Plane shock incident on rigid wall for angle less than the extreme angle.

gas. As it spreads the two shocks merge and form a single shock for a certain distance from the wall, beyond. which they are separate.

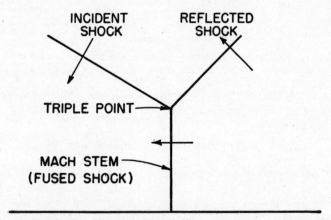

Figure 3.53. Mach reflection: formation of Mach stem.

In the case of irregular reflection, then, the two shocks will no longer look like a V (Fig. 3.52) but like a Y standing on the wall (Fig. 3.53).[17] This is the Mach effect, referred to earlier; the leg of the Y, where the two shocks have merged into a single shock, is the Mach stem. That this species of irregular reflection really occurs was proved, around 1880, by Ernst Mach, after whom it was named. In Mach reflection

[17] For simplicity, the reflected and Mach shock fronts are shown as planar, although this is not necessarily the case.

it is as if reflection were no longer caused directly by the wall but rather by a cushion of air resting on the wall. It has been explored in great detail by hydrodynamical research done during World War II.[18]

3.54 The qualitative picture of Mach reflection is quite simple for the case of a plane shock incident on a wall. Here the incident shock makes a constant angle with the wall. The situation is more complicated in the case of blast produced by a bomb. In the first place, the angle of incidence changes as the shock wave proceeds outward from the bomb. Further, the fact that the shock wave is spherical makes a quantitative difference where Mach reflection occurs, while it introduces no additional features in the case of regular reflection. This is so because regular reflection takes place entirely in the neighborhood of a single point of the wall and, therefore, only local conditions at that point enter.

3.55 The Y type reflection, on the other hand, extends over a finite area and grows up on the shock. Therefore, the properties of the shock in the large area now become relevant. As indicated earlier,

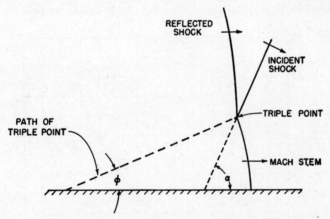

Figure 3.55. Linear trajectory of triple point.

the reflected shock merges with a continuously increasing fraction of the incident shock, and eventually the incident and reflected shocks

[18] J. von Neumann, "Oblique Reflection of Shocks," Bureau of Ordnance E. R. R., No. 12 (1943); H. Polachek and R. J. Seeger, "Interaction of Shock Waves in Waterlike Substances," Bureau of Ordnance E. R. R., No. 14 (1944); P. C. Keenan and R. J. Seeger, "Analysis of Data on Shock Interactions, Progress Report No. 1," Bureau of Ordnance E. R. R., No. 15 (1944); L. G. Smith, "Photographic Investigation of the Reflection of Plane Shocks in Air" (Final Report), OSRD Report No. 6271 (1945); R. R. Halverson, "The Effect of Air Burst on the Blast From Bombs and Small Charges, Part II, The Analysis of Experimental Results," OSRD Report No. 4899 (1945).

may even coincide completely.   Because of the variation of the angle of incidence as the shock wave expands, the height of the *triple point*, that is, the point where the incident, reflected and fused shock fronts meet, varies with distance from the explosion (Fig. 3.55).

3.56   Most of the theoretical and experimental work on the phenomenon, but not all of it, was done in the simpler case of a plane wave incident on a plane wall.   It is found that, in general, the dimensions of the Y in this case are not constant, but that they grow with time.   In other words, while the regular reflection, which produces a V, is stationary, this new kind of reflection is not.   The length associated with the Y is the length of the stem; the V has no stem and no definable size.   In the plane case the stem of the Y grows in time, and the length of the Y stem at any moment defines the duration which the phenomenon must have had from the time of its inception to the time of observation.   It was found both theoretically and experimentally that the shock configuration remains similar to itself in time and the triple point travels a linear path (Fig. 3.55).

3.57   In the region of regular reflection it is clear that the angle of the triple point trajectory is 0°.   It is known that with the onset of irregular reflection the angle ϕ (see Fig. 3.55) made by this trajectory

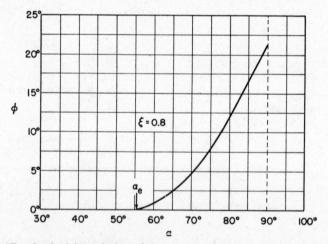

Figure 3.57.   Angle (ϕ) made by triple point trajectory as function of angle of incidence (α) of plane shock.

with the plane surface, for a shock strength ξ of 0.8, is small but becomes greater as the critical angle is exceeded by larger amounts (Fig. 3.57).[19]   Actually, it is very small for a considerable angular

[19] L. G. Smith, *loc. cit.*

interval. For overpressures up to about 7 pounds per square inch, the range in which the most detailed observations are available, the Mach effect begins when the angle between shock and wall is 56°. Even at 66° incidence, the angle of the triple point trajectory with the wall is only 1° to 2°.

3.58   It is seen from Fig. 3.57 that at a certain obliquity, α_e, regular reflection ceases. All forms of reflection occurring after this, i. e., for $\alpha > \alpha_e$, are by definition, irregular. It is believed that irregular reflection at its very inception, i. e., for angles of incidence immediately following α_e, belongs to the type described above as Mach reflection, although it should be mentioned that if the details are studied, there is an interval of a few degrees where the situation is doubtful.

Mach Effect for Spherical Shock Waves

3.59   In the case of a spherical wave, there is no question of edge effects but additional complications arise from the fact that the angle of incidence changes and the shock weakens as it proceeds outward from the center. The increase in the angle of incidence of the expanding spherical shock is, therefore, expected to be accompanied by an increase in the rate of rise of the triple point. This, as well as other features of interest, is shown in Fig. 3.59 which represents the blast pattern for a wave of finite amplitude as it travels outward from an

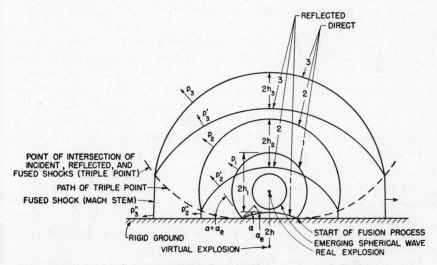

Figure 3.59.   Successive stages in reflection of spherical shock wave of finite amplitude.

air-burst bomb.[20] The general conclusions which may be drawn are as follows:

(a) Incident and reflected waves do not intersect on the ground if the angle of incidence (α) is greater than an extreme angle (α_e). When incident and reflected waves intersect on the ground they do not make equal angles with the ground.

(b) The overpressures in the incident and reflected waves are unequal.

(c) The total overpressure exerted by the blast at any point on the surface varies with the height of burst, the projected distance from the bomb, and the blast energy released by the bomb. It is not obtained, as in the acoustic approximation, by multiplying the free air pressure at the point in question by a factor of two.

(d) The incident and reflected waves have a separation at the zenith which, as the waves expand, at first varies little from the value $2h$ and then decreases to zero as the fusion process proceeds. At an angle from the zenith the separation in the early stages of the expansion is smaller and becomes zero as the two waves fuse, forming the Mach stem.

(e) At distances which are large compared to the height of burst, the direct and reflected waves from an air-burst bomb have fused and proceed outward as a single shock. From complete fusion on, the shock wave appears to have come from double the charge detonated on the ground and in the limit of large distances the Mach stem in the neighborhood of the ground becomes perpendicular to it.

3.60   The variation of the reflected overpressure with time, on the ground, at selected positions in the blast pattern, is shown in Figs. 3.60a, b, and c. It is seen from Fig. 3.60a that when the reflected wave reaches a given point the pressure rises immediately to βp, where p is the incident overpressure, and the *reflection coefficient* β is the ratio of the total to the incident overpressure. The change of β with the angle of incidence for a strong shock ($\xi \approx 0.2$) and a weak shock ($\xi \approx 0.9$) is depicted in Figs. 3.60b and c, respectively.[21]

3.61   At a fixed height above the ground, the overpressure rises in two stages, first to p and then to $p + p'$, as in the acoustic case (Fig. 3.38b). A similar effect is observed in the variation of overpressure with time at a fixed zenith angle. It will be apparent from Fig. 3.59, however, that in both cases the time interval Δt between the two

---

[20] Fig. 3.59 should be compared with Fig. 3.36 for the acoustic limit, i. e., for waves of very small amplitude.
[21] L. G. Smith, *loc. cit.*

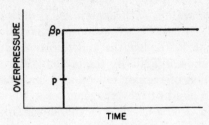

Figure 3.60a.   Reflected overpressure as function of time.

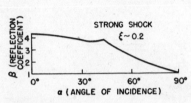

Figure 3.60b.   Reflection coefficient
for strong shock as function of
angle of incidence.

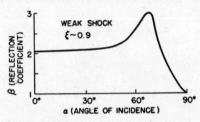

Figure 3.60c.   Reflection coefficient
for weak shock as function of
angle of incidence.

stages will tend to zero with increasing distance from the bomb.   In
the region where Mach fusion occurs there is, of course, always a
single pressure increase.   The modifications necessitated for the case
of a shock having a finite duration are similar to those described in
§ 3.40.

DETERMINATION OF TRIPLE POINT TRAJECTORY

3.62   Experimental determinations of the height of the stem of the
Mach Y have been made using TNT as the explosive.   Despite the
lack of a satisfactory theory, these data, together with the $W^{1/3}$ scaling
law (§ 3.16), make it possible to predict the main features of the
behavior of a reflected spherical blast wave for an atomic explosion.
Inasmuch as the free air pressure-distance curve (Fig. 3.13b), after
taking $W^{1/3}$ scaling into account, differs in these two classes of explosions, the definition of "blast equivalence" in terms of TNT is somewhat arbitrary.   However, it is found that in the range of interest,
i. e., 5 to 10 pounds per square inch overpressure, a suitable value of
W can be found to make the ratio of the peak overpressure produced
in the atomic explosion to the overpressure produced in the "equivalent" TNT explosion nearly unity.   The discussion here will refer to
the peak pressure only, since this determines the damage caused by
large bombs.   With this in mind it is possible to construct tables of

heights of burst by scaling with experimental data on the reflection
of blast waves due to TNT explosions. The following discussion
refers to 1 pound of TNT; lengths and durations are greater for an
explosion of W pounds of TNT by the factor $W^{1/3}$.

3.63   In the region of regular reflection, i. e., when the horizontal
distance d from the point of the explosion is less than d_0, at which the
Mach effect sets in, the sphericity of the shock front introduces no
deviations from the results obtained for plane waves because of the
local character of the reflection phenomenon (see Fig. 3.63a). There-

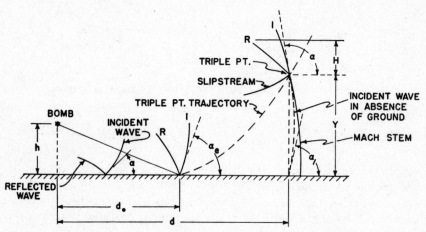

Figure 3.63a.   Spherical shock reflected from rigid ground.

fore, regular reflection theory and shock tube experiments can be used
to determine the dependence of d_0 on the height of burst (Fig. 3.63b).

3.64   For the case of irregular reflection the situation was studied
experimentally. In particular, the triple point was located as follows:
gauges were placed at various heights $(H+Y)$ at a fixed horizontal
distance, d, from the explosion and the differences in the time of arrival
between the direct (I) and reflected (R) shocks were noted (see Fig.
3.63a). An extrapolation of this time to zero gave the height of the
triple point for each height of burst. By repeating the procedure for
various heights of burst h and then scaling the results down to 1 pound
of TNT, curves of Y against h for various values of d were obtained.

3.65   Knowing the geometry of the Mach effect, the next problem
was to connect it with a choice of the heights of burst which maximize
the area over which the pressure exceeds a chosen set of values.
Suppose it is required to find the height of burst, h, which makes a

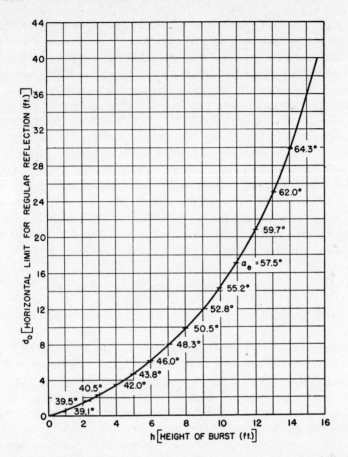

Figure 3.63b.   Calculated limit for regular reflection as function of height of burst
for 1 pound TNT.

given peak overpressure, p, on the ground, occur at the greatest
horizontal projected distance, d.   The procedure would be to measure
p as a function of d for each value of h, and then to plot d as a function
of h for selected values of p.   Such experiments were performed using
TNT.   The value of h for which $d=d_{max}$, is then the height of burst
which yields the greatest distance to a point on the ground for which
the peak pressure has a prescribed value.   This value will, in general,
be in the region of irregular (Mach) reflection.

3.66   Alternatively, if it is required to determine the height of burst
which makes the stem of the Mach Y have a prescribed height, Y, at
a given peak pressure, then for this value of h it is, in general, true

that $d < d_{max}$. The advantage gained by basing h on Y is that the
pressure is increased, not only on the ground but over a vertical region
coinciding with the Mach Y as well. In this way, the average pressure exerted by the blast on a structure is increased, resulting in
increased destruction in regions where the pressure is marginal.

3.67   The situation is somewhat complicated by the variation of
pressure along the stem of the Y. A 15 to 25 percent decrease in
pressure occurs in traversing the stem of the Y from the ground to
the triple point. Because of this variation the mean pressure along
a chosen vertical strip is not rigorously maximized by making the
stem of the Y just tall enough to cover it. As a working approximation, the height of burst will be chosen so as to achieve a desired
stem height at a specific peak overpressure on the ground. By using
an appropriate $W^{\frac{1}{3}}$ scale factor, it is possible to derive tables from
the above experiments for bombs of various energy yields.

Height of Burst and Blast Damage

3.68   In the concluding portion of this chapter, brief consideration
will be given to the bearing of some of the results derived above on
the damage caused by an atomic bomb. First, there is the question
of the relationship between the height of burst and the area of blast
damage. There are two arguments, as explained earlier, which favor
an air burst, quite apart from the influence of oblique reflection.
First, a bomb burst close to the ground is accompanied by cratering
and melting of the ground, and hence there is a loss of energy from
the blast. Second, an air burst avoids much shielding of one structure by another. An undesirable feature of an air burst is the fact
that the bomb is further removed from the target than it would be
if it were burst on the ground. To compensate, there is the fact
that the high-pressure region of a bomb burst on or close to the
ground would overdestroy the target in the near vicinity of the bomb
(§ 3.31). This local overdestruction represents an unnecessary expen-
diture of energy on nearby parts of the target region, thus decreasing
the destruction inflicted on more remote structures.

3.69   The reduction in blast pressure due to elevating the bomb
is, of course, more pronounced for parts of the target which were in
immediate contact with the ground-burst bomb, since they become
removed by at least the height of burst. For more distant parts of
the target the effect of increasing the height of burst is less important,

and at distances which are two or three times greater than the height of burst the change in distance from bomb to target, as a result of increasing this height, is completely unimportant.

3.70   Directly under the bomb, i. e., at ground zero, reflection from the ground partly compensates for the loss in overpressure due to the increase in distance from the bomb to the target area which accompanies an air burst.   The gain in overpressure occasioned by the head-on reflection of a normally incident shock is a factor which would be two if the shock were weak, and between two and eight if the shock is of finite strength (see Fig. 3.51).   For shock overpressures in the region of interest, i. e., 5 to 10 pounds per square inch, this factor is only a little above two.   At increasing distances from ground zero, the increase in the overpressure becomes even larger because of the properties of oblique reflection mentioned previously.   The highest amplification occurs soon after Mach reflection sets in.   After this it drops again as incidence becomes more and more glancing.   Since the blast decays with distance and the free air peak overpressure drops, maximum destruction will occur when the greatest reflection factor is at the point where the blast pressure is just marginal for the particular type of damage.

3.71   Actually, when the target, for example the wall of a house, is struck, it receives two blows if there is regular reflection by the ground in its vicinity: one by the direct and one by the reflected blast wave.   If these two waves are close together they both act as one blast.   If they are far apart, i. e., the angle of reflection is far from 90°, then these two shock waves hit the larger part of the wall with a considerable lag between their times of arrival.   As seen in § 3.37 as long as the reflection is regular the two shocks would arrive simultaneously at the ground but would be separate at all points above the ground, the separation between shocks increasing with distance from the ground.   In this case dissipative and other unfavorable effects may act between the two shocks.   Clearly, the most destruction occurs when the two shocks are merged together, a situation which obtains in the stem of the Mach Y.   If the height of burst of the bomb is such that the stem is about as high as, or perhaps slightly higher than, the target at the distance the pressure starts to drop below the destructive level, the extent of damage should be maximal.

3.72   In Fig. 3.72 the estimated peak overpressure on the ground is given as a function of the distance from ground zero for atomic

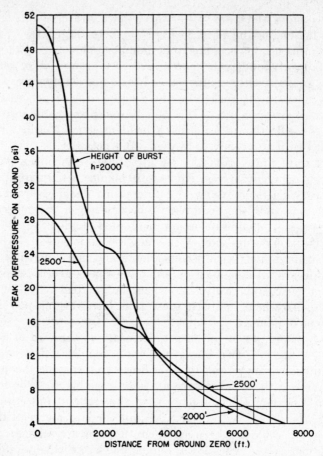

Figure 3.72.   Peak overpressure on ground as function of distance from ground zero for heights of burst of 2,000 and 2,500 feet of nominal atomic bomb.

bomb bursts at altitudes of 2,000 and 2,500 feet above a rigid plane. Irregular (Mach) reflection sets in around 2,000 to 2,500 feet from ground zero, and the Mach stem height at the 10 pounds per square inch peak overpressure is about 50 feet.

CHAPTER IV [1]

SHOCK FROM UNDERWATER AND UNDERGROUND BURSTS

A. INTRODUCTION

4.1   In the present chapter, a qualitative description will be given of the shock phenomena accompanying underwater and underground explosions.   The shock wave, responsible for the major amount of the damage resulting from an underwater burst, will be described in some detail, and numerical estimates will be given of the quantities which are measures of the effectiveness of the shock wave for a nominal atomic bomb.   After the explosion, the gaseous products of the detonation reaction are contained in a bubble, possessing considerable energy (§ 2.38).   As it rises to the surface, it pulsates with the emission of secondary pressure waves, and these waves may contribute to the damage.   The motion of the gas bubble subsequent to the emission of the shock wave and surface effects caused by venting of the bubble to the atmosphere will be considered.[2]   Finally, some properties of the base surge and of the waves due to the shallow underwater burst at Bikini will be described.

4.2   In the case of an underground explosion, the hot gas bubble is formed, just as in air and under water, and a shock wave is propagated through the earth.   Because of the indefinite nature of the latter, a quantitative treatment is much more difficult than for the other types of explosion.   However, there are probably some resemblances between an underground atomic bomb burst and an earthquake which permit useful conclusions to be drawn.   In addition, a certain amount of information has been obtained from direct experiments with conventional explosives.   These subjects will be referred to in the last section of this chapter.

---

[1] Material contributed by S. R. Brinkley, Jr., J. G. Kirkwood, C. W. Lampson, R. Revelle, S. B. Smith.

[2] For a more complete discussion, with special reference to conventional explosives, see R. H. Cole, "Underwater Explosions," Princeton University Press, Princeton, N. J. (1948).

B. PHENOMENA INVOLVED IN UNDERWATER DETONATION

SHOCK WAVE IN AN INFINITE MEDIUM

4.3 A deep underwater burst would approximate quite closely the ideal case of an explosion in an infinite medium, the case which is most amenable to theoretical investigation. In addition, the scaling up of experiments on deep water charges of chemical explosives can be expected to be most reliable in such a case. Since the effect of reflections at the ocean floor can be neglected, it becomes possible to form a reliable estimate of the shock wave parameters. Because of this circumstance, the detailed discussion of underwater shock will begin with a consideration of an explosion in an infinite medium. The theory of the propagation of such a shock wave is comparatively satisfactory, and the fact that the properties of water can be described by a simple equation of state makes possible numerical estimates of shock-wave phenomena that are fairly reliable.

4.4 If pressure is suddenly applied at some localized region of a body of water, a pressure wave will be transmitted through it in all directions. The velocity of propagation of this pressure wave is large, but it is finite because of the finite compressibility of water. If the pressure applied is sufficiently small, the velocity of propagation of the wave is nearly independent of the pressure, depending only on the temperature and density. Such a wave of small amplitude is called an *acoustic wave* (see § 3.23), and the velocity of its propagation is called the acoustic velocity. In sea water at 65° F, the acoustic velocity is about 5,000 feet per second.

4.5 If the geometry of the generating source is such that plane acoustic waves are generated, the motion is said to be one-dimensional, and the resulting waves are propagated without change in amplitude or shape. Such one-dimensional waves are only approximately achieved in real instances. However, if the generating source is spherical, the amplitude of acoustic waves decreases linearly with the reciprocal of the distance from the source, because of the spherical divergence, and the motion of the water is modified, resulting in a phenomenon known as *afterflow*.

4.6 If the time rate of change of the pressure disturbing some localized region of the fluid is small, so that it can react before the pressure has changed appreciably, the fluid may be considered as incompressible. The wave resulting from the disturbance, the propagation velocity of which is infinite in such a fluid, may then be neglected.

4.7   In the water exterior to a detonating explosive, the pressure is so great near the charge that the wave velocity cannot be considered to be independent of pressure.   As a result, the wave profile and the velocity of its motion depend upon the wave amplitude as it is propagated outward from the source.   Consequently, the mathematical description of such waves of large amplitude is considerably more difficult than for the case of waves of small amplitude for which the acoustic approximation suffices.   Further, in the initial stages of the motion of the sphere of detonation products, the rate of change of the pressure is so great that the approximation of incompressible flow does not lead to fruitful results.   At comparatively large distances from the charge, however, the acoustic treatment may be employed to obtain useful asymptotic expressions for the wave parameters. The description of the later stages of the motion of the gas bubble is thus derived from the incompressible approximation.

4.8   By means of the detonation reaction, a chemical explosive is converted into a mass of gas at high temperature and very high pressure.   For the detonation of TNT, the pressure is of the order of 2×10^6 pounds per square inch.   An intense pressure wave in the water is generated by the sphere of detonation products.   As the gas bubble expands, the pressure of the gas falls rapidly and as a consequence the pressure of the water at the gas-water interface decreases correspondingly.   The pressure wave propagated radially outward constitutes the shock wave; its profile is characterized at any given distance from the charge by an abrupt discontinuous rise in pressure to a peak value, followed by a decay which is approximately exponential in form (see Fig. 3.6).

4.9   The velocity of propagation of the shock wave near the charge is several times the acoustic velocity characteristic of waves of small amplitude.   As the peak pressure of the wave decreases, the wave velocity also decreases, and at large distances the wave velocity becomes equal to the acoustic velocity, as for an air shock (§3.13).   As the shock wave is propagated outward, the peak pressure decreases more rapidly than would be predicted for spherical acoustic waves, and the profile of the wave broadens.   These properties are shown schematically in Fig. 4.9 in which the time profile of an underwater shock wave is shown for three (increasing) distances from the charge; the decay that would result from the acoustic laws is indicated by the broken lines.

4.10   As a result of the explosion of an atomic bomb, tremendous temperatures and pressures are realized in a region so small that for practical purposes a point source can be assumed.   The intense radiation of heat results in the very rapid vaporization of large quantities of water. After a few microseconds, there will exist a globe consisting of the fission products together with large amounts of water vapor (§ 2.39). It will be assumed here that for a nominal atomic bomb this gas bubble behaves in a manner similar to that expected from a bubble containing the ordinary detonation products of 20 kilotons of TNT.

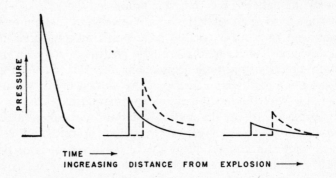

TIME ⟶
INCREASING   DISTANCE   FROM   EXPLOSION ⟶

Figure 4.9.   Variation of pressure-time curve for an underwater shock with distance from the source.

4.11   An analytical representation of the pressure profile of the shock wave at a given distance from the charge, sufficiently accurate for most purposes, is provided by the *peak approximation* in which it is assumed that the pressure-time curve at a fixed distance is given by the relation

$$p = p_m e^{-(t-t_0)/\theta}, \tag{4.11.1}$$

where p is the pressure at time t, p_m is the peak value of the pressure at time t_0, the time of arrival of the shock wave at the point of observation, and θ is a parameter called the *time constant*. The peak approximation provides a good representation of the greater part of the pressure-time curve, failing most seriously at the tail of the wave. By means of this approximation, the complete pressure field associated with the shock wave can be represented by a statement of the variation with distance from the charge of two parameters, namely, the peak pressure and the time constant. It is evident from Fig. 4.9 that the peak pressure diminishes and the time constant θ increases with distance from the charge.

4.12   In the consideration of the effect of the loading on target structures provided by the shock wave, the area under the pressure-time curve is a quantity of importance.   This quantity, called the *impulse*, is a measure of the total magnitude of the load and of its duration.   The manner in which damage is related to the impulse is discussed in a later section of this chapter.   The impulse I is thus defined as

$$I = \int_{t_0}^{\infty} p\, dt, \tag{4.12.1}$$

for a wave whose profile is described by the peak approximation.[3]

4.13   Approximately half of the energy released by the explosion is radiated outward by the shock wave.   As the wave front advances, its total area increases because of spherical divergence and the shock-wave energy per unit area decreases.   This type of energy decay may be called acoustic.   The energy decay of waves of large amplitude is more rapid than that predicted by the acoustic law.   As the water is traversed by the shock wave, a portion of the available energy remains associated with the water in the form of heat.   The amount of energy dissipated is large for waves of large amplitude and small for waves of small amplitude.   This dissipation of energy results in a more rapid decay of the wave amplitude than is predicted by acoustic theory.

4.14   The theory of Kirkwood and Brinkley [4] can be employed for the *a priori* calculation of shock wave-properties.   In addition, it provides a convenient basis for a logical extrapolation to distances near the charge of shock-wave properties measured at large distances from the charge.   In Table 4.14 and Figs. 4.14a and 4.14b, values are given of peak pressure, time constant, impulse, and shock-wave energy in water at various distances from a charge equivalent to 20 kilotons of TNT.   These results, which apply to an infinite medium, i. e., deep water, were obtained by application of the scaling law (§ 3.16) to smaller scale results for TNT. ' Experimental values of the peak pressure were extrapolated to smaller distances by means of the theory, and the theory was also employed to derive results for the impulse and shock-wave energy.   The impulse was calculated on the assumption that the peak approximation to the pressure-time curve applies at all distances.   The first entry in the table corresponds to the radius of a sphere containing 20 kilotons of TNT.

---

[3] For a pressure-time curve of arbitrary form, the impulse may be defined by equation (4.12.1) with the upper limit replaced by t_1, the time at which the excess pressure becomes zero.

[4] J. G. Kirkwood and S. R. Brinkley, Jr., "Theory of the Propagation of Shock Waves from Explosive Sources in Air and Water," OSRD Report No. 4814 (1945); see also, *Phys. Rev. 71*, 606 (1947), *72*, 1109 (1947).

TABLE 4.14. CALCULATED SHOCK-WAVE PROPERTIES FOR THE DEEP UNDERWATER EXPLOSION OF 20 KILOTONS OF TNT

Distance (feet)	Peak pressure (pounds per square inch)	Time constant (milliseconds)	Impulse (lb. sec./in.²)	Shock-wave energy (10³ foot-pounds/inch² of shock front)
45.9	460,000	1.00	460	10,400
50	404,000	1.11	448	8,640
70	249,000	1.57	390	4,170
100	146,000	2.16	316	1,895
150	79,300	2.72	216	762
200	51,900	3.66	190	399
300	29,000	5.14	149	161
500	14,500	7.10	103	52.0
700	9,410	8.34	78.5	25.1
1,000	6,020	9.63	58.0	11.6
1,500	3,680	11.1	40.7	4.91
2,000	2,630	12.0	31.6	2.66
3,000	1,640	13.4	21.9	1.14

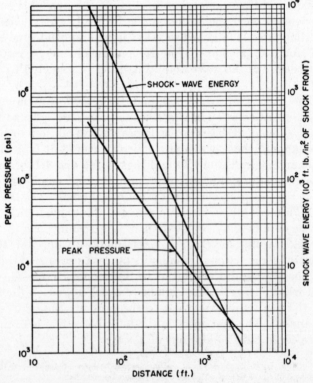

Figure 4.14a. Peak pressure and energy of shock wave as functions of distance from explosion.

4.15 In the previous discussion, it has been assumed that the charge is spherical in shape and that the pressure field resulting from the shock wave is undisturbed by boundary surfaces. For charges of other shape, orientation effects must be considered and a theoretical

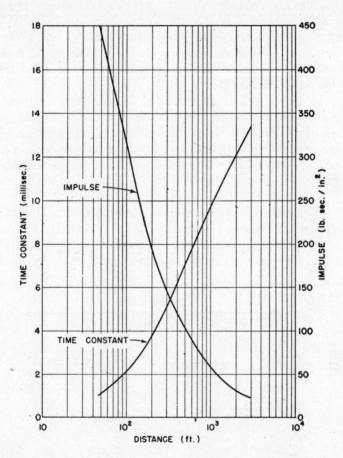

Figure 4.14b.   Time constant and impulse as functions of distance from explosion.

description of the resultant blast wave is much more difficult. However, if all of the charge dimensions are of the same order of magnitude, the results for spherical charges may be taken as representative, and this approximation becomes increasingly good as the distance from the charge is increased.

THE REFLECTION OF UNDERWATER SHOCK WAVES

4.16   In every actual case, the medium in which the shock wave is propagated is finite.   In addition to the natural boundaries afforded by the sea bottom and the surface, there may be artificial boundaries consisting of target vessels, walls, or other obstructions.   The discussion of the propagation of shock waves in an infinite medium applies without modification for times prior to the time at which the shock wave first strikes such a boundary surface.   The pressure field at subsequent times is then modified by the reflection of the shock wave at the boundary surface.[5]

4.17   In Chapter III, an extended discussion was given of the reflections of shock waves at rigid surfaces; this discussion is applicable in all of its details to similar phenomena in water.   The relations that were developed can be applied to the present case, since the equation of state for air, $p = p_0[(\rho/\rho_0)^\gamma - 1]$, is of the same form as the Tait equation for water, $p = B[(\rho/\rho_0)^\gamma - 1]$, where p is the excess pressure.

4.18   Because of the low density of air compared to that of water, the air-water interface can be assumed to be a free surface.   At a free surface, an incident pressure wave is reflected as one of rarefaction (Fig. 4.18).   The advancing pressure wave and receding rarefaction

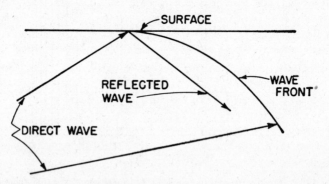

Figure 4.18.   Direct and reflected (rarefaction) wave at surface of water.

wave are then superimposed.   Although the negative peak is smaller than the positive one, it is superimposed upon a late, weak portion of the pressure curve.   The resultant pressure is commonly negative,

---

[5] Experimental observations indicate that inclusion of reflection effects will, in general, not alter the peak pressures in Table 4.14 by more than a factor of about two.

resulting in tension in the water.   Sea water cannot withstand appreciable tension, the upper limit for natural sea water being of the order of atmospheric pressure.   As a result, the tension is relieved by the formation of many small bubbles which prevent a further increase in tension.   This phenomenon is called *cavitation*.

4.19   The form of the pressure-time curve observed at a point near a free surface is shown in Fig. 4.19; this curve is modified in its later

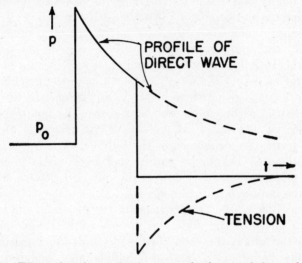

Figure 4.19.   Effect of surface reflection on a shock wave below a free surface.

portions by the reflected rarefaction wave from the surface.   The broken line shows the region of tension to be expected as a result of the reflected wave and the solid line shows the result of cavitation. This effect of the rarefaction wave on the pressure wave is called the *surface cut-off*.   The phenomenon of cavitation and the effects of a free surface on shock waves of finite amplitude have not been adequately described theoretically, in spite of the great importance of these effects on the surface phenomena accompanying an underwater explosion.

4.20   If the water is shallow, pressure waves reflected from the bottom may further complicate the over-all picture.   The description of the pressure field resulting from the superposition of the reflected shock waves from both rigid and free surfaces then becomes very difficult.

4.21   In the description of the surface of the water as a free surface, the density of air is assumed to be negligible compared to that of water. Actually, the density of air is finite, and there is transmission of a relatively weak shock wave across the air-water interface into the air. At the underwater ("Baker") test at Bikini, such a transmitted blast wave was in fact observed.

MOTION OF THE GAS BUBBLE

4.22 After the shock wave has been emitted by an ordinary high explosive, nearly half of the initial energy of explosion remains in the gaseous detonation products. Although the pressure in the gas bubble is then much lower than its initial value, nevertheless it is higher than the equilibrium hydrostatic pressure. The gas bubble thus expands rapidly, and the residual energy of the gas is imparted to the water as potential energy. The water in the neighborhood of the bubble has a high outward velocity, due in part to the excess of pressure existing within the bubble and in part to the afterflow which is characteristic of a spherical pressure wave. Because of the inertia of the water, the expansion of the bubble continues until the gas pressure falls well below the equilibrium hydrostatic pressure. In time, the pressure deficiency brings the outward flow of water to a stop and the bubble begins to contract. During the contraction, the gas pressure is increased, and because of the inertia of the water, the contraction phase of the motion continues until the gas pressure is again greater than the equilibrium hydrostatic pressure. This process may be repeated, and the bubble may undergo repeated cycles of expansions and contractions.

4.23 As a result of the several dynamical conditions which determine the motion, the bubble spends most of its time in an expanded condition, and the pressure of the gas is less than the equilibrium hydrostatic pressure during the greater part of the cycle. The reversal of the bubble motion at the point of greatest contraction occurs so rapidly as to be almost discontinuous in a time scale appropriate to the description of the whole cycle. These features of the bubble motion are illustrated in Fig. 4.23.

4.24 In the case of an atomic underwater explosion, the bubble consists of the fission products and a large amount of vaporized water. It may be supposed that behavior of this bubble simulates that of the bubble formed by the underwater detonation of a chemical explosive. In the simplest case, where the effects of boundaries do not need to be considered, the period of oscillation is quite simply related to the depth and to the energy residual in the gas;[6] it varies as the one-

---

[6] C. Herring, "Theory of the Pulsations of the Gas Bubble Produced by an Underwater Explosion" NDRC Division 6, Report No. C4-sr20-010, OSRD Report No. D-236 (1941).

third power of the energy and the negative five-sixths power of the hydrostatic pressure. The residual energy is proportional to the charge weight or yield, that is, to the energy of the explosion.

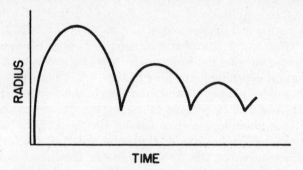

Figure 4.23.   Oscillation of gas bubble under water.

4.25   The theoretical expression for the period T of the first bubble pulse is

$$T = 1.135 p^{1/2} p_0^{-5/6} E^{1/3}, \qquad (4.25.1)$$

where, using consistent, e. g., cgs, units, ρ is the density of the water, p_0 is the total hydrostatic pressure at the level of the detonation, and E is the energy which goes into the bubble pulsations, estimated at 0.4 of the energy of the explosion. For a nominal atomic bomb detonated at a depth of 2,000 feet, the predicted period is 1.9 seconds.

4.26   At the end of its first expansion, the radius of the bubble from an underwater explosion of TNT is given by [7]

$$R_m = 160 (W/p)^{1/3}, \qquad (4.26.1)$$

where R_m is the maximum radius in feet, W is the charge weight in tons, and p is the total hydrostatic pressure expressed in feet of water. For 20 kilotons TNT, the depth at which the globe would just break the surface at its maximum size is 530' feet. At a depth of 1,000 feet the maximum bubble radius is 430 feet; at 1,500 feet the maximum radius is 380 feet; and at 2,000 feet the maximum radius is 340 feet.

4.27   About 40 percent of the energy of explosion, which remains in the gas bubble after the emission of the primary shock wave, is emitted in part in the form of spherical pressure waves generated by the oscillating bubble, and in part it is dissipated due to the effects of

[7] C. Ramsauer, "Die Massenbewegung des Wassers bei Unterwasserexplosionen," *Ann. Physik*, *72*, 265 (1923). The relation has been verified by recent experimental work.

turbulence.   The pressure in the water depends upon the square of the rate of bubble motion, and this is greatest near the point of greatest contraction.   The excess water pressures due to bubble pulsation are, therefore, appreciable only near the time of greatest contraction.   The amplitude of the pressure wave falls off with distance due to the spherical divergence of the wave.   The bubble motion is radically affected by the proximity of the bubble to boundary surfaces; in consequence, the form of the pressure waves attributable to bubble motion depends upon these factors.   The peak pressure of the first bubble pulse is much lower than that of the primary shock wave, being of the order of 10 percent of the latter.   However, the duration of the pulse is much longer than that of the shock wave, and the impulses of the two waves are of the same order of magnitude.   The pressure-time curve of the bubble pulse is shown schematically in Fig. 4.27.   A considerable amount of the energy initially residual in the gas sphere is lost with each pulse, and generally only the first pulse is of appreciable magnitude.[8]

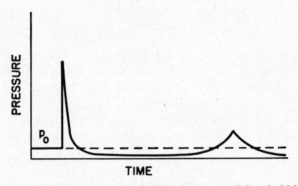

Figure 4.27.   Pressure-time curve for shock wave and first bubble pulse.

4.28   A complete description of the motion of the gas bubble must include a consideration of the effect on the motion of the buoyancy of the bubble.   The theoretical description given by Taylor[9] reproduces the characteristic features of the vertical migration.   The bubble rises slowly during the initial period of expansion and with increasing velocity during the period of contraction; the rate of upward motion is a maximum at the point of greatest contraction.   These characteristics are shown in Fig. 4.28.

---

[8] A. B. Arons and D. R. Yennie, "Energy Partition in Underwater Explosion Phenomena," *Rev. Mod. Phys.*, *20*, 519 (1948).
[9] G. I. Taylor, British Report RC–235 (1941).

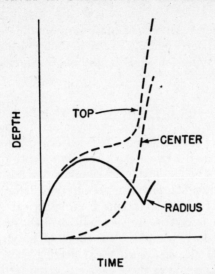

Figure 4.28.   Characteristics of upward motion of gas bubble under water.

4.29   Because of the importance of the effect of gravity on the bubble motion, the simple scaling laws which pertain to the shock-wave phenomena are not applicable.   Approximate scaling laws may be derived from the theoretical treatment of Taylor.   However, these cannot be applied as confidently as in the case of shock-wave phenomena because the theoretical treatment neglects the additional factors affecting the bubble motion.   The effect of varying hydrostatic pressure over the surface of a large bubble is to distort the bubble from a spherical shape into a mushroom shape, with the result that the theoretical estimates of migration velocity are too large. The bubble motion is also affected by proximity of the bubble to rigid surfaces, such as the ground-water interface, to the free surface at the air-water interface, and to deformable or rigid surfaces such as may be provided by a target.   The exact description of these effects is a complicated hydrodynamic problem which must be considered in detail for each particular case.[10]   It may be noted that the bubble is attracted toward a rigid surface and repelled from a free surface during the contraction phase of its oscillations.

4.30   One of the main reasons for interest in the vertical motion of the gas bubble is that for a charge exploded beneath a ship's hull the bubble will have approached the target during its first period. Consequently, the pressure pulse radiated at the end of the period will have a shorter distance to travel and will be more intense upon

---

[10] A complete discussion is given by R. H. Cole, *op. cit.*, Chapter 8.

arrival at the target.   An approximate formula for the total rise during the first period for a bubble of the detonation products of TNT, based upon the assumption that the bubble remains spherical, is

$$\Delta y = 5900 \sqrt{W}/p_0, \qquad (4.30.1)$$

where Δy is the rise in feet during the first period, W is the charge weight in tons, and p_0 is the total pressure at the detonation level in feet of water.   For a 20 kiloton TNT bomb exploded at a depth of 2,000 feet, the predicted rise is 410 feet; at a depth of 1,000 feet, the rise would be 800 feet.   For depths significantly less than 1,000 feet, the bomb would not complete one oscillation before venting to the atmosphere.   Because of deviations from spherical shape, these figures represent an overestimate, as indicated above.

4.31   For very large charges, the effect of gravity predominates over the effects of the free surfaces.   Herring[6] has shown that the ratio of the velocities due to these causes is given by $(5\rho gh/p_0)\,(h/R_m)$, where p_0 is the total hydrostatic pressure at the detonation level, h the depth of this level below the surface, R_m is the maximum radius of the gas bubble, ρ is the density of water, and g is the acceleration due to gravity.   For a 20 kiloton TNT bomb detonated at a depth of 2,000 feet, the upward velocity due to gravity is of the order of 30 times that caused by neighboring surfaces.

SURFACE EFFECTS

4.32   The most spectacular visible effects of an underwater explosion are the most difficult to treat theoretically.   They are intimately related to the geometry of the explosion, and depend in an involved manner on the depth of the burst.   A discussion of these effects must also consider the overall depth of the water and the contour of the bottom if the explosion has taken place in shallow water.   Since their theoretical interpretation is incomplete, only a qualitative discussion of surface effects can be attempted here.

4.33   It was stated in Chapter II that the first observed effect of the shock wave to reach the surface is the appearance of the slick, and this is soon followed by the spray dome.   The latter is thrown up directly over the charge by the reflection of the blast wave at the surface

4.34   If the incident wave at the surface is exponential, the shock pressure decreases rapidly from its peak value.   The head of the reflected rarefaction wave falls progressively behind the head of the

---

[6] C. Herring, "Theory of the Pulsations of the Gas Bubble Produced by an Underwater Explosion," NDRC Division 6, Report No. C4–sr20–010, OSRD Report No. D–236 (1941).

direct pressure wave.   The resultant pressure behind the rarefaction front would thus be less than the hydrostatic pressure p_0 at the detonation level if cavitation did not occur.   Since the cavitation pressure of ordinary sea water is probably close to p_0, cavitation can be expected to result very near the surface in the area covered by the spray dome. According to the approximate formula of Pekeris,[11] the depth Δ at which cavitation occurs is given by

$$\Delta = \frac{p_0 R c_0 \theta}{p_m h (1 - 1.15 c_0 \theta / R)}, \tag{4.34.1}$$

where R is the distance from an explosion at depth h, and c_0 is the velocity of sound.   It is assumed that the incident wave is exponential, the time constant being θ and the peak pressure p_m decaying as $R^{-1.15}$ (§ 4.11).

4.35   This expression indicates that cavitation occurs a fraction of a foot below the surface.   Consequently, it appears that the thin layer of water becomes detached and rises with the velocity of the surface in the form of a spray rather than as a solid sheet.   Kennard [12] has discussed in detail the structure of the region below the surface spray.   It is concluded that the cavitation must spread rapidly downward for a distance that is appreciable but which is only a fraction of the charge depth.   A mass of cavitated water with an upward velocity is thus produced, forming the spray dome.

4.36   The contour of the dome has been studied by a number of writers.   If it is assumed that the peak pressure decays as $R^{-1.15}$, the initial velocity of the dome $u(r)$ at a distance r from its center is related to the initial velocity at the center $u(0)$ by

$$u(r) = u(0) \left[1 + \left(\frac{r}{h} \right)^2 \right]^{-1.07}, \tag{4.36.1}$$

where h is the depth of the explosion.   The dome contour is thus steeper for a shallow explosion than for a deep one.[13]

4.37   As stated earlier, the bubble of hot gases formed in an underwater explosion reaches the surface essentially intact, provided the burst is not too deep.   Here, the pressure of the bubble is relieved, and water rushes into the cavity forming a Monroe-type jet.   This complex phenomenon gives rise to plumes of water spray.

[11] C. L. Pekeris, NDRC Division 6, Report 6.1-sr 1131-1433 (1944).

[12] E. H. Kennard, TMB Report No. 511 (1943).

[13] See R. R. Halverson, W. G. Schneider, and P. C. Cross, OSRD Report No. 6258 (1946).

4.38   The character of the plume depends upon the stage of the bubble motion at which venting takes place, and therefore upon the depth of the charge. If the bubble reaches the surface before its contraction begins, it has a small upward velocity of migration and the venting is, therefore, largely radial. At a greater charge depth, the bubble may reach the surface at its point of greatest contraction and greatest upward velocity of migration. In this case, the water above the bubble is thrown up vertically to form a narrow, high plume. At still greater charge depths, the vertical plume becomes increasingly less developed and radial plumes reappear. As the charge depth further increases, this sequence can be repeated corresponding to different stages of the second bubble contraction, but on a smaller scale because of the decreased energy of the bubble. After more than a few cycles, the bubble has an insignificant residual energy and loses its identity in a mass of turbulent water.

4.39   It is believed that the very large bubble from an atomic explosion does not survive more than about one oscillation. For a relatively shallow burst, the bubble vents while expanding rapidly, and a vertical plume which rises to great heights appears almost immediately (§ 2.42).

C. WAVES PRODUCED BY THE BIKINI UNDERWATER EXPLOSION

PROPERTIES OF THE WAVES

4.40   In the Bikini "Baker" shot, typical of shallow underwater atomic bomb explosions, the first wave to form was a positive crest, followed by a trough which descended as far below the still water level as the crest rose above it. This trough was followed by a train of waves. Near the explosion point the first crest was somewhat higher than the succeeding ones, both above the undisturbed water level and in total height above the succeeding trough. At greater distances from the explosion the highest wave was frequently one of those in the train which followed the first wave. The maximum height in this train passed backward to later and later waves as the distance from the center increased. In almost all cases the height of the second crest was smaller than either the heights of the adjacent crests or the depths of adjacent troughs.

4.41   The number of waves measurable with the instruments used increased from 3 at 2,100 feet from the center to 6 at 10,000 feet, and

14 or more at 22,000 feet from the explosion. In an aerial photograph taken about 5 minutes after detonation over 20 waves can be seen, and the entire area of the lagoon discernible through the clouds is covered with concentric waves radiating from the bomb center. Most of these were apparently too low for instrumental measurement.

4.42   Within 8,000 feet, where the first wave is the highest wave, let H be the maximum height in feet from crest to following trough and R be the distance from the explosion in feet; the relationship $HR=94,000$ can then be used to estimate maximum wave height at any given distance. Beyond 8,000 feet, the empirical equation $(HR)^{0.9}=42,700$ should be employed. The following table [14] gives estimated maximum wave heights from crest to following trough at different distances:

R, Distance (feet)	1,000	2,000	4,000	6,000	8,000	10,000	12,000
H, Maximum height (feet)	94	47	24	16	13	11	9

4.43   The highest wave in the train following the first wave always had the same group velocity, which at Bikini was about 53 feet per second, and succeeding crests became highest as they attained this group velocity (and the corresponding wave length and period).

4.44   Many crests were present as appreciable waves at a considerable distance from the explosion (Fig. 4.44), but at a lesser distance there were only a few waves of measurable height. Since the wave energy travels with the group velocity, the only measurable waves present at any given distance were those that had attained or exceeded a minimum group velocity, determined by the size of the initial disturbance.   At Bikini this group velocity was about 40 feet per second.

4.45   The observed times of arrival of the first wave crest are very well fitted by the equation for velocity of a solitary wave, namely,

$$\frac{dR}{dt}=C=\sqrt{g(d+h)}, \qquad (4.45.1)$$

where C is the wave velocity, g is the acceleration due to gravity, d is the depth, and h is the height of the crest above the undisturbed water level.

4.46   The following values are obtained for the time of arrival of the first crest at different distances from the explosion:

Distance (feet)	1,000	2,000	4,000	6,000	8,000	10,000	12,000
Arrival time (seconds)	11	23	48	74	101	127	154

[14] These results may be assumed to apply to a nominal 20 kiloton TNT energy equivalent atomic bomb. In general, for an explosion in deep water the product HR should be proportional to $W^{1/2}$, where W is the energy release of the bomb. If the distance R is proportional to $W^{1/3}$ (§ 3.10), then H should vary as $W^{1/6}$.

Figure 4.44. Waves from test "Baker" reaching the beach at Bikini. The
maximum wave height at the shore was about 7 feet.

4.47 Owing to the shoaling of the water in the direction toward
Bikini, the velocity of the first wave markedly decreased beyond
12,000 feet and this wave arrived at Bikini, approximately 18,500 feet
from the target center, about 306 seconds after the explosion. Thus
the speed in the last 6,000 feet decreased to about half the value near
the explosion point.

4.48 Times of arrival of the earliest measurable rise of the water
surface due to the first wave, when plotted against distance, approximately fit a straight line with a slope of 80 feet per second, which
intersects the axis of abscissas at about 1,000 feet. Theoretically the
first rise traveled with acoustic velocity and was related to the shock
wave itself. The measured first rise must therefore represent a sudden increase in an already existing slope of the sea surface and is
probably related to the rate of travel of the wave energy. The point
on the back side of the first crest at which the wave surface crossed
the undisturbed water level traveled at about 70 feet per second.

4.49 The time interval between the first and the second crests
was less than 20 seconds at 2,000 feet and increased to 40 seconds at
12,000 feet. That this interval continued to increase with increasing
distance is indicated by the tower photographs from Bikini, which
showed that the second major wave arrived at the beach more than
60 seconds after the first. It is probable that this apparent increase

of 20 seconds between 12,000 and 18,000 feet was due to the dying-out of the second wave, because of the difference between energy (group) velocity and phase velocity.

4.50 The distance between the first and second waves at 2,000 feet from the target center was 1,200 feet. This distance increased with increasing range from the explosion point; at 12,000 feet from the target center it was 2,800 feet.

4.51 Wave length, period, and phase velocity for the second and subsequent waves all increased with time and distance from the center. At any point or time each wave had a period, wave length, and velocity less than that of the preceding wave. The period of the second crest increased from 16 to 24 seconds between 2,000 and 12,000 feet, its wave length increased from 1,000 to 1,700 feet, and the phase velocity increased from 64 to 70 feet. The phase velocity of all crests approached the value $C = \sqrt{gd} = 75$ feet per second as an asymptote.

4.52 In all its characteristics the first wave behaved differently from the succeeding ones. It may be thought of as a long solitary wave, generated directly by the explosion, and receiving its initial energy from the high-velocity outward motion of the water. The subsequent waves were generated impulsively by the collapse of the hole blown in the water. The water rushing in to fill this hole built up a central mound.

4.53 According to the Cauchy-Poisson theory, the mound should have then subsided to the undisturbed level without further oscillation. That this was at least approximately true is shown by the very small number of measurable waves near the explosion point, indicating that the amplitude of the central oscillation diminished very rapidly with time.

Wave Shape

4.54 Twenty-three seconds after the explosion, when the first crest was 2,000 feet from the target center, the average slope from the undisturbed water at the leading edge of the wave to the crest was 1°51′. At 140 seconds the first wave crest had progressed out to nearly 11,000 feet, while the fifth crest was at 5,500 feet. The leading edge of the first wave was then at 12,000 feet and the average slope from this point to the first crest was 0°12′. The highest average slope from trough to crest was 1°23′, on the forward side of the fourth wave.

4.55 From the present data, wave profiles prior to 20 seconds are uncertain. Such a profile near zero time, drawn from the extrapolated positions of the first disturbance and the first crest and trough, suggests that the outer side of the first crest had an average slope of about 15°, while the inner slope was apparently very much steeper. Waves are unstable and break when the average slope from trough to crest much exceeds 15°; hence the first wave was probably breaking as it left the central area.

4.56   At 140 seconds after the burst, there were present only five waves high enough to be recorded by the instruments. Since wave energy is proportional to the square of the wave height, the major part of the total energy of the waves produced by the bomb must at this time have been contained in these five waves. This energy was found to be between 2.6×10^{18} and 3.4×10^{18} ergs or between 0.3 and 0.4 percent of the total energy of a nominal atomic bomb. More than half of the wave energy was in the first wave.

4.57   The first wave peaked up and broke 390 feet off Bikini in water 20 feet deep. The height at breaking was 15 feet, i. e., 2.3 times the height which the wave would have had in deep water at the same distance from the explosion center. This increase in breaker height over deep-water height agreed exactly with the well-known expression for wave behavior in shallow water,

$$h_b = 1.3 \, h_d \left(\frac{d_d}{d_b}\right)^{\frac{1}{4}}, \qquad (4.57.1)$$

where h_b and h_d are wave heights at breaking and in deep water, respectively, and d_d and d_b are the deep-water depth and the depth at breaking.

D.   GEOPHYSICAL EFFECTS OF THE BIKINI UNDERWATER EXPLOSION

CHANGE IN BOTTOM TOPOGRAPHY

4.58   The explosion of the Bikini "Baker" bomb caused a measurable increase in depth of the bottom of the lagoon over an area roughly 600 to 1,100 yards across. The greatest apparent depth difference was 32 feet, but this represents only the removal of a small hill and not a hole 32 feet deep in a previously flat surface. Over an area of 165,000 square yards the bottom was between 20 and 30 feet deeper after "Baker" Day. A deepening of 10 to 20 feet was observed over an area of 260,000 square yards, and of zero to 10 feet over 510,000 square yards.

4.59   The net volume of bottom material removed was estimated to be about 1,420,000 cubic yards, a volume equal to that contained in a 112-yard cube. This volume represents only the *net* amount of bottom material removed from the bomb site, and spread in a thin layer over an area more than a mile in radius. The total, or gross, amount of material originally placed in suspension or blasted out by the bomb is estimated to be 3,680,000 cubic yards. Of this amount, 2,260,000 cubic yards settled back into the crater, partially refilling it.

4.60   Before "Baker" Day, sediment samples collected at the bomb site consisted of coarse-grained algal debris mixed with less than about 10 percent sand and mud. The sand and mud probably resulted from the chemical or bacterial breakdown of the calcareous algal debris. Bottom samples taken after 'Baker" Day near the explosion point were entirely different in character. Instead of algal debris, thicknesses up to 10 feet of mud were found. This "target area mud" had a median diameter of 7.5 microns; 75 percent of the material was less than 20 microns and 25 percent less than 2.5 microns [15] in diameter.

BEACH EROSION FROM WAVES

4.61   A minor amount of erosion of the beach was plainly evident from an examination on the afternoon of "Baker" Day. Some beach material was also carried inland, the farthest debris line in the region of the photographs being about 200 feet from the shore.

4.62   In the process of eroding the beach, the waves set up by the bomb shifted large blocks of beach rock measuring up to $9 \times 5 \times 1$ feet in size. Many of these slabs showed fresh scars several inches across; some were overturned, some broken across, but none, so far as could be determined, were carried more than a few feet from their original positions.

E.   DESCRIPTION OF THE BASE SURGE AT BIKINI [16]

OBSERVED SEQUENCE OF EVENTS

4.63   Immediately after the "Baker" burst at Bikini, the water moving upward formed a conical dome above the previous water level. This soon became a virtually straight-sided column forming the plume (§ 2.42), which continued to expand in diameter until at least 10 seconds after the explosion. On the basis of extrapolation from sur-

---

[15] A micron is 10^{-6} meter or 10^{-4} cm.

[16] The following discussion is based largely upon study and measurements of still photographs taken with automatic recycling aerial cameras at 1 second and 3 second intervals from towers on Bikini, Amen, and Enyu Islands.

face wave measurements it is probable that at its maximum size, the column was considerably larger in diameter than the cavity blown in the lagoon waters.   Above 2,000 feet in altitude, the top of the column was concealed by a roughly equidimensional "cauliflower cloud" which extended up to more than 6,000 feet.

4.64   After the condensation cloud had disappeared, large spike-like jets were seen thrusting out through the sides of the plume.   Photogrammetric measurements show that these jets fell at rates of 32 to 80 feet per second.   It was at first thought that the jets were nearly entirely water because their velocities of fall were considerably greater than the terminal velocity of the largest stable water drop (about 25 feet per second for a drop 0.6 centimeter diameter).   Closer examination showed that after falling 5 to 7 seconds, many of the jets apparently broke up into spray without much increase in volume, and the visible rate of fall greatly diminished.

4.65   Evidently the jets, and therefore also the entire plume, consisted of a relatively small weight of water suspended as drops in air. The suspension of water drops behaved at first like a homogeneous fluid of somewhat higher density than the air outside the column. Exactly similar phenomena have been observed in laboratory studies of the rate of fall of aerosols and liquid suspensions conducted at Stanford University under the direction of P. A. Leighton.   In these experiments, drops of an aerosol or of a liquid suspension were introduced at the top of a glass cylinder into a fluid of very slightly lower density.   The aerosol drops settled at rates up to 10,000 times greater than the velocities of fall of the individual suspended particles they contained, as computed from Stokes's law.   This phenomenon was called "bulk subsidence".   It is an example of the more general class of flow which has been designated as a density current, that is, the flow of a fluid under the action of gravity through another fluid of slightly different density.

4.66   After 10 to 12 seconds, the suspension of water and air over the entire periphery of the column constituting the plume began to fall rapidly.   As this fall continued, the diameter of the water column decreased.   At a height of 450 feet, for example, the diameter changed from 2,050 to 1,500 feet, between 15 and 33 seconds.   Photographs taken 30 to 35 seconds after the explosion seem to show definitely that at this time the remaining part of the column, which was all inside 1,500 feet, was only a tenuous mist.   From this observation, together with the existence of the spike-like jets, and the rapid lateral expansion of the column, in the first 10 to 15 seconds after the explosion, over an area much larger than that of the cavity blown in the water, it is difficult to avoid the conclusion that the plume was an essentially hollow cylinder with walls approximately 300 feet thick. This conclusion is supported by the "hollow" appearance of the cauliflower cloud, as seen from above in some of the aerial photographs.

4.67 As the falling suspension of water in air from the outer part of the column reached the sea surface, it billowed outward and upward as the base surge (§ 2.45). This was first evident between 10 and 12 seconds after the burst. At first the front of the base surge moved outward in all directions with a very high velocity, in excess of 100 feet per second, but this velocity rapidly diminished. Thus, one minute after the explosion, the radial velocity in the cross wind direction was only 47 feet per second; between 2 and 3 minutes later the outward motion had ceased, and the whole mass of the surge was moving slowly down wind at about 10 feet per second, i. e., about 7 miles per hour.

4.68 The front of the base surge at first sloped inward from the water surface. By 60 seconds, the front had assumed the typical rounded profile of a dust cloud or moving fog bank.

4.69 At 12 seconds, the suspended material in the cauliflower cloud began to fall back to the lagoon in large mamillary masses, which attained high settling velocities of more than 50 feet per second. In some cases an abrupt decrease of velocity occurred after an interval, and the plume broke up into a rain curtain. Evidently the same mass subsidence phenomena occurred in the cloud as in the column. The first material from the cloud reached the surface about 1 minute after the detonation, and after 2.5 minutes the cauliflower cloud had dropped nearly all its suspended load into the base surge so that only remnants of it remained aloft. Most of this material fell in an annular area with inner and outer radii of 1,950 and 2,850 feet, respectively. The aerial photographs show part of the lagoon surface inside this annular area after 45 seconds, indicating that at this time there was little suspended material either from the cauliflower cloud or the base surge in the central region. Beyond the annular ring of fall-out from the cloud, the base surge extended over a very large area, with an average outer radius at 3.5 minutes of 8,400 feet.

4.70 For the first 2.5 minutes, the height of the top of the base surge increased irregularly but continuously up to about 1,800 feet. Large irregularities, due to turbulence, in the motion of both the upper surface and the advancing front of the base surge are apparent from the photographs. After 2.5 minutes the top remained stationary in height for nearly a minute while the radial expansion of the surge diminished and finally ceased. Between 3 and 4 minutes the surge began to lift from the lagoon, and after 4.5 minutes its base had lifted 1,500 feet off the water. During and after the lifting process, the surge also thickened, so that its upper surface eventually rose to nearly 6,000 feet. This thickening must have been due to condensation of water in the adiabatically-cooled air pushed up by the base surge as it lifted. Because of this condensation, rain fell from the surge cloud for nearly an hour after the detonation.

VARIATION OF VELOCITY AND DIMENSIONS WITH TIME

4.71   In Fig. 4.71 measured values of the mean crosswind horizontal velocity, mean surface radius, inner radius, and mean height of the base surge are plotted against time for the first few minutes after the detonation. Some of these values, and other data, expressed in metric units are also given in Table 4.71. Over the period from 10 to 200

TABLE 4.71

RADIAL VELOCITY AND DIMENSIONS OF THE BASE SURGE

Time (sec.)	Velocity (cm./sec.)	Outer radius (cm.$\times 10^4$)	Area* (cm.$^2\times 10^{10}$)	Height (cm.$\times 10^4$)	Volume** (cm.$^3\times 10^{15}$)
10	3, 660	3. 7	0. 4	1. 3	—
20	2, 650	6. 6	1. 4	1. 8	0. 15
30	2, 135	9. 2	2. 6	1. 9	. 25
40	1, 830	11. 0	3. 8	2. 1	. 40
50	1, 620	12. 8	5. 1	2. 6	. 55
60	1, 430	14. 4	6. 5	3. 0	. 79
80	1, 160	17. 1	9. 1	3. 7	1. 81
100	945	19. 2	11. 6	4. 5	3. 16
120	795	21. 4	14. 3	4. 8	4. 78
140	700	22. 6	16. 1	5. 5	6. 28
160	580	23. 8	17. 8	5. 5	7. 69
180	490	24. 9	19. 5	5. 5	9. 16
200	365	25. 6	20. 6	5. 5	10. 43

*Total area encompassed by base surge, including central clear region.
**In computing the volume of the base surge cloud, an attempt has been made to take the central clear area into account.

seconds, the crosswind velocity V varied approximately with the inverse square of the time t, being fairly well fitted by the equation

$$V = \frac{C}{(K+t)^2} = \frac{3.3 \times 10^7}{(90+t)^2} \text{ cm./sec.} \qquad (4.71.1)$$

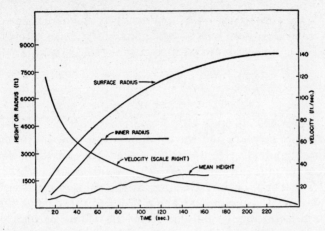

Figure 4.71.   Dimensions and velocity of base surge as functions of time.

4.72   For velocities in the upwind or downwind directions, the wind velocity of 300 centimeters per second must be subtracted from or added to the value for V given in equation (4.71.1).   After 200 seconds, the radial velocity diminished rapidly to zero which was attained at about 240 seconds.

4.73   The mean outer radius corresponding to equation (4.71.1) is given by

$$R = \frac{aK^2 + aKt + Ct}{K^2 + Kt}, \tag{4.73.1}$$

where $a = 4 \times 10^3$.   Introducing numerical values for K and a, it is found that

$$R = \frac{3.6 \times 10^5 + 3.7 \times 10^5 t}{90 + t} \text{ cm.} \tag{4.73.2}$$

Beyond 3 minutes the radius did not appreciably increase and these equations no longer held.

4.74   If R_t is the surge radius at time t, and U is the wind velocity, the distance from the explosion point to the upwind edge of the base surge at any time t will be given by

$$X_{ut} = R_t - Ut, \tag{4.74.1}$$

and in the downwind direction by

$$X_{dt} = R_t + Ut. \tag{4.74.2}$$

4.75   Up to 180 seconds, the area swept by the base surge—including the central region which was apparently clear after the first minute—was, in accordance with equations (4.73.1) and (4.73.2),

$$A=\frac{\pi(aK^2+aKt+Ct)^2}{(K^2+Kt)^2}=\frac{\pi(3.6\times10^5+3.7\times10^5t)^2}{(90+t)^2}\text{ sq. cm.}\quad(4.75.1)$$

4.76   After 200 seconds the area underneath the surge at any instant did not increase, but the total area over which the surge cloud had passed gradually lengthened as the surge traveled downwind (see § 4.79 on probable effects of higher wind speed).

4.77   The height of the base surge at the point of intersection with the plume column remained at about 450 feet throughout the period during which the major fall-out from the plume occurred, that is, between 15 and 33 seconds.   As shown in Table 4.71, however, the average height of the top of the base surge increased continuously up to 140 seconds.   After 140 seconds it remained constant until the entire mass started to lift from the lagoon, at about 210 seconds.

4.78   The apparent volume and mass of the base surge increased continuously from 10 seconds onward (Fig. 4.78).   This increase was

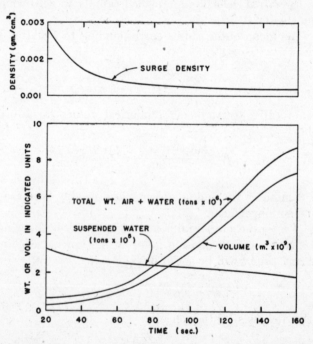

Figure 4.78.   Weight, volume, and density of base surge as functions of time.

due to different causes at different times. Up until 33 seconds, new material was being added as the falling column was transferred into the base surge. Throughout the period of outward expansion from 10 to 200 seconds enormous quantities of air were being engulfed by turbulence at the surface of the surge. Finally, after 200 seconds, condensation took place above the original surge cloud, in the adiabatically cooled air which was forced aloft as the surge rose.

EFFECT OF WIND SPEED

4.79 At Bikini, the wind velocity near the surface was very low, only 5 or 6 miles per hour. An onshore wind of 10 to 15 miles per hour is a more usual daytime situation in a harbor, and winds up to 25 or 30 miles per hour are not uncommon. Such higher wind speeds would have several effects:

(a) The surge would not extend as far upwind at any time.
(b) The surge front would arrive at any downwind point sooner after the explosion, and therefore with higher radiation intensity and higher rate of fall-out.
(c) The area and volume of the surge cloud would be increased by turbulence due to the wind, particularly after the first few minutes when the initial rapid outward expansion of the surge has ceased. Experience with the behavior of smoke over water indicates that

$$R_{wt} = R_{bt} + 0.2Ut, \qquad (4.79.1)$$

where R_{wt} is the actual radius of the surge cloud at any time, t, R_{bt} is the radius it would have had in the absence of wind, and U is the wind velocity.

(d) The total area swept by the surge cloud from its beginning up to any time, t, increases with increasing wind speed. If the total swept area is $A_{\Sigma t}$, then

$$A_{\Sigma t} = \pi R_{bt}^2 + 1.3 R_{bt} Ut + 0.13 (Ut)^2. \qquad (4.79.2)$$

EFFECT OF ATMOSPHERIC CONDITIONS

4.80 The view has been expressed that the base surge phenomenon as observed at Bikini was, at least partly, dependent on the very moist, tropical air-mass prevailing at the time of the explosion. As seen in § 4.65, it is probable that the aerosol constituting the base surge has a somewhat greater density than the surrounding atmosphere. Consequently, the aerosol acted as a meteorological cold-front, and in its outward travel pushed into the ambient air causing this to ascend over the surge front. The tropical air-mass had great thermal instability and its moisture content was such that an ascent of about 1,000 feet would cause sufficient adiabatic cooling to produce cloud condensation. This would explain the steadily increasing volume of the surge as it migrated outward from the center of the explosion.

4.81   At the point where the base surge began to rise off the water, its density, as an aerosol, must have been equal to or less than that of the surrounding air. The ascent then continued as a result of its lower density and was comparable to the rise of an unstable, moist air-mass along a warm front. The development of the strato-cumulus cloud at this stage (Fig. 2.46) is in harmony with the suggestions concerning cloud formation made above.

4.82   Even if the full development of the cloud mass requires a moist atmosphere, it is probable that the initial formation of the base surge, which moves forward at high speed, would be independent of the meteorological conditions. However, it is possible that all the phenomena, exactly as observed in the "Bikini" test, would not occur if an atomic bomb were exploded under water when a dry air-mass is present, or when the atmospheric condensation level is significantly above the height of the initial base surge.

F.   SHOCK FROM UNDERGROUND BURST

UNDERGROUND SHOCK PROPAGATION

4.83   The preceding sections of this chapter have dealt with under-water bursts; in this final section some of the characteristics of under-ground explosions will be considered.

4.84   The detonation of an atomic bomb under the surface of the ground would produce an earth shock which, in its effects, would be somewhat similar to that of an earthquake of small focal depth.[17] The magnitude of the energy release in the underground burst of a nominal atomic bomb would, in fact, be comparable to the energy

---

[17] Some of the seismic effects of the Alamogordo "Trinity" atomic bomb air burst and of the Bikini "Baker" underwater explosion are described by B. Gutenberg, *Bull. Seism. Soc. Amer.*, *36*, 327 (1946) and by B. Gutenberg and C. F. Richter, *Trans. Amer. Geophys. Union*, *27*, 776 (1946), respectively.

developed in a damaging earthquake of scale 5.0 on Richter's logarithmic scale.[18]

4.85 There is, however, a considerable difference in the depths of the focal point of the disturbance beneath the surface of the earth in the two cases. This depth is, in general, very large, of the order of miles, scores or even hundreds of miles in the case of an earthquake, while it would be effectively on the surface for an atomic bomb. These differences are reflected in the period of the seismic waves, their amplitudes, and their decay of intensity with distance from a spot directly above the center of disturbance. The period would be shorter, and the decay with distance somewhat more rapid, for the waves generated by an atomic bomb. Since profound differences exist in the mechanism of propagation of air shock waves and seismic waves generated by explosion, a brief description of the process occurring in an underground explosion will be given.

4.86 The initial stage of an air, water, or underground explosion is the same, namely, the sudden creation of a mass of highly heated and compressed gas which exerts tremendous pressure. This high-pressure gas immediately begins to expand, imparting a high radial velocity to the earth particles adjacent to the charge and producing a large transient pressure in the medium.[19] The high initial velocity of the earth carries it past the point of pressure equilibrium due to inertia, so that after a certain time the motion is arrested and a reverse motion is imparted. If the pressure in the gas bubble were not relieved, the pressure at remote points would decrease to a value equal to the permanent stress in the medium due to the presence of this sphere of high-

---

[18] Richter's magnitude scale, which is based on the logarithm of the amplitude of motion, is related to the energy by the formula

$$M = \frac{1}{1.8} \log\left(\frac{E}{E_0}\right),$$

where M represents the magnitude of the earthquake of energy E, and E_0 is the energy of an earthquake of zero magnitude (taken as 2×10^{11} ergs). The smallest earthquakes felt are of magnitude 1.5, while those of magnitude 4.5 will cause slight damage near the epicenter. Those of magnitude 6 are destructive over a limited area, and magnitude 7.5 is the lower limit of major earthquakes. The results in the appended table give an approximate relationship between the energy and the type of earthquake. The total energy release of a nominal atomic bomb is about 8×10^{20} ergs.

	Energy range ergs	Magnitude of mean
Great earthquakes	10^{26}	8.5
Major earthquakes	$10^{24} - 10^{26}$	7.5
Destructive earthquakes	$10^{22} - 10^{24}$	6.5
Damaging earthquakes	$10^{20} - 10^{22}$	5.5
Minor strong earthquakes	$10^{18} - 10^{20}$	4.5
Generally felt small earthquakes	$10^{16} - 10^{18}$	3.0

For further discussion, see K. E. Bullen, "Introduction to the Theory of Seismology," Cambridge University Press.

[19] See Appendix B.

pressure gas.   There are two factors tending further to reduce the final pressure: one is the cooling of the gas in the bubble due to thermal conduction to the medium, and the other is the relief of pressure due to the break-through of the gas bubble to the surface of the earth, or to the leakage of gas into the surrounding earth.   If the charge is buried at such a depth that the gas pressure is quickly relieved by motion of the medium above the charge, the peak pressure will be reduced.

4.87   The effect of progressively greater depths of burial of an explosive charge is to increase the magnitude of the compressive wave until a depth is reached at which the relief of pressure due to the surface break-through comes after the time of maximum excursion of the adjacent particles in the medium.   Subsequently, relief of pressure exerts no influence on the maximum value of the pressure, and greater depths of burial have little influence on the propagated effects. This result is found experimentally and is consistent with the mechanism described.   The critical depth in earth is predicted to be about 600 feet for a nominal atomic bomb, which is much greater than any practical depth of penetration that could be achieved by bombs or guided missiles.

4.88   The rate of change of the magnitude of the compressive wave with depth of burial of the bomb is such that at practical depths of penetration of a heavy bomb about 35 percent of the maximum potential pressure in the propagated wave will be developed.   The remainder of the potential mechanical energy will be spent in producing air blast, fusing the ground, forming a crater, and in dispersing material from the crater into the air.   A detonation just on the surface would reduce this figure to about 20 percent for propagated seismic effects, leaving about 80 percent of the energy for air-blast production, cratering, etc.

Effect of Soil Characteristics [20]

4.89   The variability of the soil characteristics and the proximity of underlying rock strata introduce additional variables into the underground damage problem over those encountered in air-blast phenomena.   The presence of underlying rock strata relatively close to the surface is a condition which can enhance very appreciably the propagated effects in an underground explosion.   This enhancement comes about in at least two different ways.   The first is a consequence of the reflection of the pressure wave from the rock strata.   Crude calculations show that in normal incidence not more than 50 percent of

[20] For further discussion, see Appendix B.

the energy of the explosion is transmitted from the earth to the underlying rock, and at more oblique angles of incidence this proportion
would probably be less. As a consequence, the wave energy is largely
confined to a thin slice in which the rates of decay are less than they
would be if the slice were not there, since the waves are almost confined to a two-dimensional medium rather than being propagated in
a hemisphere. Another way in which the wave amplitude may be
increased at the larger distances is through energy being transmitted
back up again from the rock, if it happens to be stratified and separated by a lower-velocity medium from the lower rock boundaries.
In this case the rock stratum can also act as a two-dimensional medium
with transmission losses lower than those of earth, so that a portion
of this trapped energy is fed back into the soil stratum above it to
increase its wave motion.

4.90   The experiments on the propagation of explosive effects
through soil have been conducted in places where the underlying rock
strata were as far from the surface as possible in order to reduce the
complexity of the problem.   There is consequently a lack of information as to the magnitude of this enhancement, although its effect has
been detected in a few isolated cases.   The character of the soil is very
important also in attempting to evalutate the probable damage from
underground explosions, but fortunately a considerable amount of
information on this subject has been acquired by experimentation.
It has been found that the range of propagation constants in soil is
very great with light loamy soils at one end of the series and heavy
plastic clays at the other end.   A set of experiments conducted in
Texas and Oklahoma [21] has shown that at equal distances from equal
charges the pressures transmitted by plastic wet-clay soils may be as
great as 50 times larger than those transmitted by light loamy soils.
Similarly, the transmitted pressures through wet clay may be ten times
as high as those transmitted through sandy clay, the latter being taken
as the average soil for this discussion.

4.91   The experiments mentioned above, which were conducted in
soils of several different types, gave measurements of the surface acceleration and displacement and the subsurface pressure as functions
of the distances from the explosive charge.   The connection between
these quantities and the actual damage resulting to surface structures
will be considered, among other matters, in the next chapter.

---

[21] Final Reports on Effects of Underground Explosions by C. W. Lampson, NDRC Report No. A–479, OSRD Report No. 6645 (1945).

CHAPTER V [1]

PHYSICAL DAMAGE (FROM AIR BLAST, GROUND AND UNDERWATER SHOCK)

A. AIR BLAST DAMAGE: GENERAL PRINCIPLES

EFFECTS OF BLAST

5.1 A detailed discussion of the formation and propagation of the shock waves produced from an explosion has been given in earlier parts of this book. As already stated (§ 3.1), the resulting blast represents perhaps the most important aspect of the atomic burst, as far as destruction of property is concerned. In this present chapter consideration will be given to such phases of the behavior of a shock wave as are particularly related to the damage it is capable of doing to various classes of structures. It will be recalled that the essential features of a shock wave are an abrupt rise in pressure, followed by a gradually decreasing pressure, lasting for about a second, and then a suction phase, characterized by a decrease of pressure below normal atmospheric, which lasts for several seconds. Associated with the abrupt rise of pressure in the first phase of the blast wave is an intense wind which persists, but with diminishing velocity, throughout the pressure phase, blowing in the direction of propagation of the blast wave. This wind reverses its direction at the start of the suction phase blowing with a smaller velocity in the direction opposite to its former course, but persisting for a longer period of time (Fig. 5.1). The effect of these winds in the case of blast waves of long duration is to produce a force on the structure for a relatively long time after the shock front has enveloped it and passed by.

5.2 The general nature of the effect of a blast wave on a structure is that of a giant blow due to the sudden onset of pressure, followed by a more or less steady force on the structure, directed away from the source of blast, which lasts until the blast wave envelopes the building. At this time, the onset of a pressure at the rear of the structure reduces the radially directed force to that given by the wind drag, and adds a

---

[1] Material contributed by S. R. Brinkley, Jr., J. G. Kirkwood, D. B. Parker, C. W. Lampson, F. Reines, S. B. Smith, W. E. Strope.

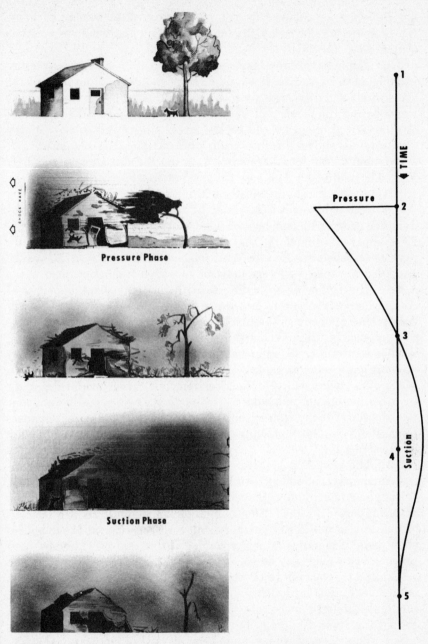

Figure 5.1. Representation of behavior accompanying a shock wave striking a structure.

net squeezing or compressional force to the over-all structure, unless the pressure is relieved by the failure of doors and windows or other structural members.

5.3   The behavior of a blast wave upon striking a cubical structure is depicted in Figs. 5.3a, b, c, and d; these indicate the position of the shock front and of various reflected and diffracted waves at successive times during the passage of the shock.   The impact at the instant of striking is succeeded by the partial envelopment and squeeze of the structure as shown in Fig. 5.3b; the complete envelopment and aerodynamic drag forces are applied during the stages represented by Figs. 5.3c and 5.3d.   It is seen that two factors operate to destroy the structure: the crushing effect of the pressures developed on the structure as it becomes surrounded by the shock wave, and the aerodynamic drag of the air mass or wind motion behind the shock front. It is apparent, therefore, that a properly anchored weak structure may be crushed without being displaced bodily, or if it is weakly anchored a strong structure may move without being crushed.

5.4   The ability of a building to withstand the shock depends, of course, upon its strength, to a lesser degree upon its shape, and upon the number of openings through the building which can serve to relieve the pressure on the outside walls.   The strength, used in this sense, is a general term and is influenced by many factors, some of which are obvious and others are not.   The most obvious indicator of strength is of course massiveness of construction, but this is modified greatly by other factors not immediately visible to the eye, e. g., the resilience and ductility of the frame, the strength of beam and corner connections, the redundancy of supports and the amount of diagonal bracing in the structure.

5.5   The strongest structures are heavily framed steel and reinforced-concrete buildings, while the weakest are probably certain shed-type commercial structures having light frames and long spans of unsupported beams.   Some kinds of lightly-built residential construction also fall in this category, but well constructed frame houses show good resistance to blast damage from ordinary bombs, and presumably would also do so to the blast from atomic bombs.   The resistance to blast of brick structures having load-bearing walls is rather poor; this is probably due to the lack of resilience and to the moderate strength of the connections which are put under stress when the load is applied laterally to the building.

5.6   The effect of shape is not very marked in conventional structures which are generally of a rectangular plan form; a long narrow structure will, of course, be more resistant to blast impinging on the

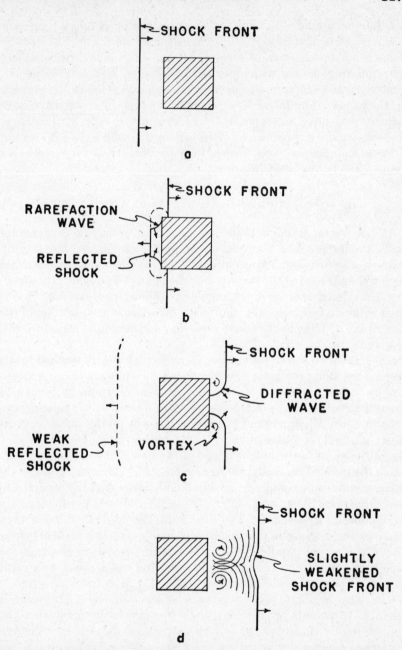

Figure 5.3. Behavior of blast wave upon striking cubical structure: (a) before striking the structure; (b) soon after striking the structure; (c) soon after passing the structure; (d) wave completely past the structure.

end than on the side.   The shape effect is most pronounced in certain auxiliary parts of the structure, such as smoke stacks, which, because of the rapid equalization of pressure around them and their relatively low wind drag, are surprisingly resistant to blast.   They often remain erect when the structures adjacent to them are leveled to the ground. On the other hand, flat surfaces, such as windows in an extensive wall surface, will have no rapid relief of pressure except by breakage. Since they have a short period of vibration, they will have a maximum of stress induced in them, with a high probability of failure even at comparatively low blast pressures.

The Diffraction of Blast Waves by a Structure [2]

5.7   A better understanding of the forces acting on a structure under the impact of a blast wave may perhaps be gained by carrying through a rather detailed examination of the phenomenon occurring during the passage of the wave.   For the sake of simplicity, the structure considered will be a rectangular parallelepiped standing in the open with one face perpendicular to the direction of propagation of the blast wave.   The modifications necessary for an actual structure will be given later.

5.8   It can be shown that a shock wave with a nearly vertical front, propagated along the ground, will set up a flow pattern about a structure on the ground that is essentially the same as would be developed about a structure in free air if the vertical dimensions of the structure were doubled.   The ground plane corresponds to the plane of symmetry of the flow, and neglecting boundary-layer phenomena the flow above the plane is the mirror image of the flow which would exist beneath the plane if the structure were in free air.   Thus, a rigid, rectangular parallelepiped, shaped like a half cube, placed on the ground will have the same flow, and suffer the same diffraction effects, as a rigid cube in free space.   The center of the equivalent cube then becomes the intersection of the ground plane with the vertical center line of the actual parallelepiped.   The term "center of the face" as used here will refer to the equivalent cube and will actually be a point at ground level as described above.

5.9   The incident peak overpressure level of the blast wave is taken as 15 pounds per square inch, a pressure level which would be approximately that required to cause structural damage to a modern reinforced-concrete, windowless type of building.   The dimensions of the structure are taken as 75 feet on each edge of the base and 38

---

[2] See Appendix A.

feet high, which corresponds to a medium sized, three or four story building.

5.10 The expected overpressure-time curve of the incident blast wave, with a superimposed curve which represents the variation with time of the average translational force on the cube per unit area of front face, is given in Fig. 5.10; the derivation of the salient points is described below. It should be noted that this latter curve and the

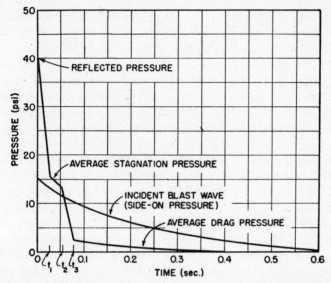

Figure 5.10. Average translational pressure on front face of rigid cube 75-foot edge, approximately 2,600 feet from air burst of nominal atomic bomb.

corresponding one in Fig. 5.15 are first approximations to the actual phenomena taking place, chiefly because the transitional pressures between the various phases of the diffraction phenomena are represented by straight lines whereas it is probable that these regions are more complex and may have superimposed oscillations. A complete interpretation of the phenomena has not yet been developed, but for the elementary structural loadings considered here it seems best to approximate these regions by straight lines. The times computed are those from the onset of the blast to the beginnings of each of the transitional phases referred to above.

5.11 As will be shown later, the pressure is a function of position on the front face, being a maximum at the center and a minimum at the edge. The average of these values when multiplied by the area of the front face would give the force tending to shear the structure from its foundation, or to move it along the surface if it were free to do so.

5.12   The sequence of events which produces the pressure-time curve in Fig. 5.10 is as follows.   At zero time on the graph, the steep-fronted blast wave, shown in the diagram, strikes the face of the structure.   The pressure on the face immediately rises to the reflected pressure, which in the case of a shock wave is greater than the pressure doubling which would be experienced by an acoustic wave (see Fig. 3.51).   Also, at this instant, a rarefaction wave starts from each edge toward the center of the face, traveling with the speed of sound behind a shock of pressure equal to the reflected pressure, signalling the center, in effect, that the wall is not infinite in extent (Fig. 5.3b).   After this set of waves has reached the center, at approximately time t_1, a situation is set up which is similar to that existing on the head of an infinitely long structure parallel to a high-velocity air stream.   A distribution of pressure over the front face occurs in such a way that the intersection of the center line of the structure with the horizontal surface has the so-called *stagnation pressure*,[3] and the edges have essentially the side-on or hydrostatic pressure of the blast wave.   The average of these values is plotted as the average stagnation pressure.   During this time the shock wave is presumed not to have reached the rear edge of the structure.

5.13   At a later instant, indicated by time t_2, which is equal to the length of the structure divided by the velocity of the shock wave, the front of the shock wave reaches the rear edge of the cube and starts spilling in toward the center of the rear face (Fig. 5.3c).   This pressure applied to the rear wall relieves the total translational force on the structure, and after a time interval $t_3 - t_2$, which is approximately that required for the pressure wave to reach the center of the rear wall, the translational force on the structure drops to the value which would be experienced by the parallelepiped of finite dimensions in a steady wind steam.   It is probable that this force, called the *drag force*, is approached in some exponential fashion, and that the time t_3 is actually longer than indicated in Fig. 5.10, but insufficient experimental data exist to determine this time accurately.   Hence, for the purposes of this approximate analysis, it is thought best to indicate it as a time that can be readily calculated, namely, the time required for a signal to be propagated from the edge to the center of the structure at the speed of sound in air at normal temperature and pressure.

---

[3] The stagnation pressure is defined as that pressure of the air existing in the region or regions in which the moving air has been brought completely to rest.

5.14   The time for the drag force to be established is proportional
to the size of the structure, so that a relatively small structure, such
as a smoke stack or an isolated girder, suffers the high reflected
and stagnation pressures for an exceedingly brief time.   Experience
has shown that these two types of structures are extremely resistant
to blast, and if they are strong enough to withstand the drag force
of much lower intensity but of much longer duration, they will not
be damaged.

5.15   The forces considered above are not those that cause failure
of structural details such as front and side walls or roofs, but are
largely applicable to the shearing force on the foundations or to the
flexure of the frame of a steel building.   The force on a panel or
section of the front wall will vary somewhat with its position on the
wall, but taking the case of a section near the center of the front face,
the overpressure in the direction of propagation of the blast wave
will be similar to that shown in Fig. 5.15.   Here the pressure rises

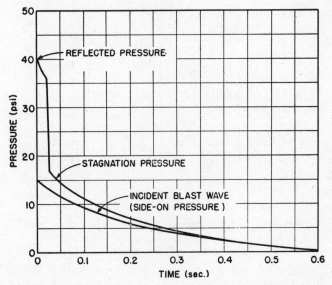

Figure 5.15.   Pressure on panel near center of front face of rigid cube.

instantly to the reflected pressure, falling off in time as that of the
blast wave decreases.   At a time approximately equal to that required for the rarefaction wave from the edge to reach the center,
the pressure drops to the stagnation pressure of the blast wave.   The
stagnation pressure decreases as the pressure in the blast wave decreases until it becomes nearly identical with the side-on or hydro-

static pressure of the wave. The pressures on the side panels which are parallel to the direction of propagation of the blast are nearly the same as the side-on pressure of the blast wave.

5.16 The calculated reflected pressure, stagnation pressure, and drag pressure divided by the drag coefficient [4] as a function of the peak overpressure in the blast wave are indicated in Fig. 5.16. These values, which exist immediately behind the shock front, may be useful in computing the behavior of different structural configurations to the impact of a blast wave whose duration is long compared to the period of vibration of the structure.

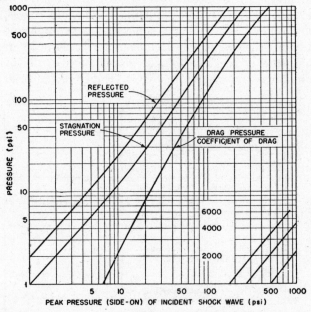

Figure 5.16. Reflected pressure, stagnation pressure, and drag pressure as functions of peak pressure of incident shock wave.

THE EFFECT OF ANGLE OF IMPACT OF SHOCK WAVE

5.17 The impact of the blast wave on a surface at angles other than normal might be expected to produce a different reflected pressure and consequently a different force on the surface than would a head-on impact. Such is, indeed, the case, but the differences in pressure are rather small and almost inconsequential up to angles of

---

[4] The drag pressure p_d is equal to $c_d u^2 \rho$, where c_d is the coefficient of drag, u is the particle velocity, and ρ the density; the quantity plotted in Fig. 5.16 is p_d/c_d. If c_d were unity the ordinates would give the drag force per unit area of the structure.

incidence of the order of 40°.   At this angle, which corresponds roughly to the extreme angle at which regular reflection gives way to Mach reflection (§ 3.50), there is a change in the character of the effect; the pressure then changes quite rapidly toward the "side-on" pressure which will be that experienced by the surface when it is parallel to the direction of motion of the blast wave.   The characteristics of these changes of reflected pressure with angle form a subject of considerable interest to investigators since certain features of the effect have not been satisfactorily explained.[5]

5.18   Reference to Fig. 5.18, which gives the reflection coefficient

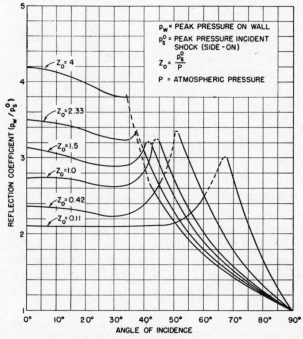

Figure 5.18.   Reflection coefficient as function of angle of incidence for shocks of different strengths.

(§ 3.60) as a function of the angle of incidence of the shock wave, shows certain regions of the curve in the vicinity of the extreme angle as dotted.   These dotted regions were placed on the figure mainly to show which curves join together.   They are not intended to indicate anything other than very approximate values of the pressures, since the hydrodynamical phenomena in this region are not at all well understood.   The detailed explanation of the nature of these

[5] L. G. Smith, "Photographic Investigation of Plane Shocks in Air", OSRD Report No. 6271 (1945).

curves is the same as that given in Chapter III, dealing with the reflection of the shock wave from the ground when the bomb is detonated in the air. The formation and growth of a Mach Y, when the extreme angle of incidence is exceeded, is characteristic of this class of reflection phenomena and serves to complicate the nature of the diffraction effects associated with the passage of a blast wave about a structure. Even though the effects may be changed in detail, it is not believed that any profound changes in the magnitudes or durations of the quantities will occur to invalidate the approximate analysis given previously, if allowance for the reflection coefficient is made according to Fig. 5.18.

THE VARIATION OF THE PRESSURE WITH TIME

5.19   The variation of the pressure behind the shock front with time over a limited pressure region may be represented by a simple empirical equation of the form (cf. equation (4.11.1))

$$p_s = p_s^0(1-t/t_0)e^{-t/t_0}, \tag{5.19.1}$$

where p_s is the overpressure in the shock wave at the time t, p_s^0 is the peak overpressure (side-on), and t_0 is the duration of the positive phase of the blast wave.

5.20   This equation gives the approximate form of the variation of pressure behind the shock front for blast pressures not exceeding about 25 pounds per square inch. While it is not exact, it may be sufficiently good to allow a designer to estimate the drag and stagnation pressures on a structure after the wave has been diffracted, using the simplified theory given above. More accurate semiempirical formulas for the pressure-time relation can be written; however, their form is somewhat more complicated and their use is probably not warranted in rough calculations.[6]

---

[6] A formula given by K. O. Friedrichs ("Formation and Decay of Shock Waves", Inst. of Math. and Mech., New York University, IMM–NYU–158) for a plane blast wave, modified to take account of the divergence of a spherical wave front, gives at low pressures a more accurate representation of the pressure as a function of time in the positive phase of the wave than does equation (5.19.1). This modified formula may be written as

$$Z = \frac{35}{9} \frac{\sigma}{\lambda} (1 + \tfrac{1}{2} \sigma),$$

where

$$\sigma = \frac{\sigma_0(1-x)}{1+\sigma_0 x},$$

and

$$\sigma_0 = \left[\left(1 + \frac{18}{35} Z_0 \lambda \right)^{1/2} - 1 \right].$$

In these equations Z_0 has the same significance as in Fig. 5.18, Z is equal to p_s/P, x is t/t_0, and λ is the scaling factor (§ 3.17) equal to $(r/W^{1/3})$, where r ft. is the distance from the explosion, and W is the energy yield expressed in pounds of TNT.

5.21   The values of the expected duration (t_0) of the positive phase of a shock wave from an air burst of a nominal atomic bomb can be obtained from Fig. 3.13e.   These values may be used in the formula for the pressure-time relation to give the shape of the shock wave at any distance up to 2 miles.   It must be remembered, however, that the pressures on a structure will be dependent on its size and orientation relative to the wave front as well as on the pressures in the wave itself.

5.22   In Fig. 5.22, which can be derived by combining Figs. 3.13b

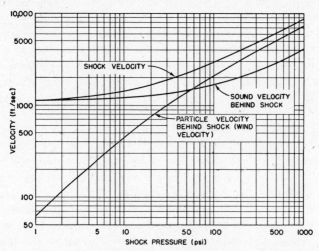

Figure 5.22.   Shock velocity, sound velocity, and particle velocity behind shock as function of shock pressure.

and 3.13c, is shown the shock velocity, particle velocity (equal to the wind velocity), and the speed of sound behind the shock as a function of shock pressure.   These values, which are based on a nominal sound velocity in free air of 1,130 feet per second, may be useful in determining the approximate pressure-time curve for a given structure following the method used to derive Figs. 5.10 and 5.15.

Blast Damage Criteria

5.23   The relatively long duration of the blast wave from an atomic bomb, which is of the order of a second, compared with a few milliseconds for a conventional bomb, introduces a significant modification into any calculations of damage radii that may have been derived from extrapolation of data from conventional high-explosive bombs.   Due to the comparatively large size of the structures relative to the length of the blast wave of ordinary bombs the impulse received by the structure is very nearly proportional to the impulse of the incident blast wave. This comes about because the relief of pressure afforded by the diffraction effects from the edge arrives too late to be effective, and the pressure on the face is proportional to the pressure in the shock wave itself. Consequently, the building receives practically the full impulse of the blast.

5.24 In the case of the atomic bomb this situation does not hold, since the comparatively great length (about 1,000 feet) of the blast wave relative to the dimensions of ordinary structures permits the full effects of diffraction to come into play. As a result, the variation with time of the pressure incident on the face of the structure is governed by the diffraction effects from the edges. The impulse received by the structure is, consequently, a function of the size of the structure and of the peak pressure (Fig. 5.10), rather than being proportional to the impulse of the incident blast wave.

5.25 From this point of view it appears that an actual building which fails when subjected to a prescribed impulse in a time which is short compared with the duration of the positive phase, will actually fail while being subjected to the stresses induced by an essentially constant pressure. A relatively large building with a strong wall facing the blast will not fail according to a peak pressure criterion but will follow a different criterion, that of impulse (§ 4.12). Viewed in another way, the structure is always destroyed by the impulse it actually receives from the blast wave, but a large enough bomb continues to maintain pressure in a region long after the structure is destroyed. It can be shown that for these long blast waves the total translational impulse received by the structure is roughly proportional to the volume of the structure when other conditions are constant.

5.26 It should perhaps be mentioned that even though impulse causes failure, no amount of impulse will be effective if the pressure associated with it is below a critical value. As the structure becomes larger and weaker the damage criterion changes from the requirement that the peak pressure exceed a critical value to the requirement that both the peak pressure and impulse available from the blast must exceed critical values. However, the peak pressure criterion is generally valid under the conditions which optimize damage in the air burst of an atomic bomb, because most buildings are relatively small.

5.27 An interesting point arises in connection with the damage criteria considered above relative to the area of blast damage due to an air burst. According to the scaling laws in Chapter III, the distance at which a given overpressure is achieved in an explosion varies roughly as the cube root of W, the energy release. The area over which the shock pressure exceeds a certain value, say 10 pounds per square inch, is thus approximately proportional to $W^{2/3}$. If the peak pressure is the criterion of damage, as it is for atomic bombs, because of the length of the shock wave, then the area of destruction may also be supposed to vary as $W^{2/3}$. In other words, if the energy release of the bomb is doubled, the blast-damaged area is increased by $2^{2/3}$, i. e., by a factor of less than 1.6.

5.28 If the impulse were the blast damage criterion, the effective radius of the bomb would increase more rapidly than $W^{1/3}$. Dimensionally, impulse involves the product of pressure and time (§ 4.12), and not only will the distance for a given pressure increase, but the time will also increase with the energy release of the bomb. Experimental data with ordinary high explosives indicate, in fact, that the radius of damage, where impulse. is the criterion, varies roughly as $W^{2/5}$. A doubling of the energy release would thus mean an increase by a factor of about 1.6 in radius and 2.5 in the area of blast damage.

5.29 It is apparent that, in this respect, the atomic bomb is at somewhat of a disadvantage as regards the increase in destructiveness with the size, i. e., energy release, of the bomb. It might seem to be more economical, from the standpoint of blast damage, to use less powerful bombs, with shorter wave lengths, so that the impulse, rather than the peak pressure, is the determining factor. However, as seen in § 1.43, the quantity of fissionable material in an atomic bomb must exceed a certain critical amount if it is to be at all effective, so that it does not appear to be possible to take advantage of this impulse criterion.

GROUND SHOCK DAMAGE

5.30 The burst of an atomic bomb in the air at such a height as would be expected to give maximum air-blast damage would exert a fairly large reflected pressure, of the order of 25 to 50 pounds per square inch, on the ground directly underneath the burst. This pressure would not be relieved by diffraction and would consequently exist for a period of time equal to the duration of the blast wave itself, although the rate of decay with time would be more rapid. Such a loading suddenly applied to the ground surface would cause it to act to some extent as would a bowl of jelly were a finger to be placed rather gently but suddenly in the center. The surface waves radiating out from the center produce what is termed *ground roll*, which, for an air burst, is a somewhat minor oscillation of the surface sufficient to be felt but insufficient to cause any damage. However, the pressure acting on the earth's surface will be transmitted downward, with some attenuation, to any superficially buried object in the ground. These pressures might damage certain structures buried at a shallow depth. Some air-raid protective structures may fall in this category, but they could be designed to withstand the pressure if desired.

5.31   In general, it can be said that the ground shock effects from an air-burst bomb will probably be negligible at a distance, and that even directly underneath the burst, moderately strong underground structures will not be appreciably affected. Certain public utilities, such as sewer pipes and drains, at shallow depths may be damaged by the earth movement, but metal pipe would probably not be disrupted except where exposed to air blast.

Factors Influencing Blast Effect

5.32   The general effect of blast on structures varies with a number of factors. First, the pressure-time curve for the structure as a whole, or for a particular element being investigated, must be known. As described in the preceding sections of this chapter, the pressure-time curves will be dependent upon the distance from the explosion, the direction and vertical angle from the explosion, the shape and size of the structure, and the equalization of pressure by local failure. Next must be considered the response of the structure and its various elements to the applicable time-pressure curve. There are two general approaches to such an investigation. The first method is to analyze the structural frame or elements elastically and determine their periods of vibration and response to the applied loads. This will indicate whether the structure will be strained beyond the elastic limit, and something of the probability of failure. If, however, the structure is strained beyond the elastic limit it no longer behaves elastically; plastic deformation occurs and this is of vital interest in determining whether the structure will survive. The capacity to absorb blast energy beyond the elastic limit is far greater than that within the elastic limit; consequently, the second method, namely, analysis of the plastic response, is more important if some deformation can be accepted.

5.33   A more detailed consideration is essential if a reasonable approach is to be made to an analysis of existing structures and to the subject of design to withstand blast effects. In order to facilitate this analysis, the various factors governing loads resulting from air blast will be examined.

(a) *Distance.*—The peak pressure varies with distance as shown in Fig 3.13b; further, as stated earlier, particularly in Chapter III, at a distance determined by physical factors involved there is produced a Mach effect which increases the blast pressure.

(b) *Height of Burst.*—Outside the region in which the Mach effect is operative, the vertical angle formed by a line to the explosion and the horizontal plane will have a marked influence on damage. With increasing vertical angle there will be increased roof loads and a smaller lateral component. At greater distances from the point of burst the lateral component will assume greater significance. It may be presumed that the height selected for the burst will depend upon the resistance of structures and other elements related to the effects of the blast (§ 3.68 *et seq.*).

(c) *Direction of Blast.*—The direction from which the blast comes will affect the loading on the structure. For example, a long building with the blast normal to the long dimension would receive quite a different loading than would be the case if this dimension were in the direction of the blast. The angle made by the blast front with the walls of the structure will also influence the results.

(d) *Form Factors.*—The shape and size of the structure will be major factors in affecting the loading. The width of the exposed face of a rectangular structure will determine the time required to reach the stagnation pressure at the center, i. e., t_1 (Fig. 5.10), and the length of the structure along the radius from the explosion will determine the time required for the shock wave to proceed from the front to the back face, i. e., (t_2-t_1); the width of the back face will establish the time for the waves proceeding from each side to meet, i. e., (t_3-t_2). If, instead of being rectangular, the shape were rounded, somewhat less time will be required for the various stages described above. When the condition has been reached where drag forces predominate, good aerodynamic forms will reduce these forces materially.

In connection with the above, it will be of interest to consider the effect of the blast waves on different kinds of structures and structural elements. In the case of the building 75 feet square and 38 feet high, the pressure-time curve has already been developed (Fig. 5.10). For a relatively slender structure, such as a smokestack or the chord of a bridge, the first two phases will occur in a very short space of time, and from then on the drag force only need be considered. This brings up the question of form factors of smaller elements. The drag on various structural shapes due to the wind caused by the explosion is not readily available and will have to be estimated in the absence of wind-tunnel tests. However, it is believed that the interest in aerodynamic effects may result in such information being developed.

(e) *Pressure Equalization.*—There are certain portions of structures that are much less resistant to blast than others. Window panes, light siding, and other weak elements will fail in a very short space of time. When this occurs the pressure will tend to equalize on the inside and the outside of the structure, thus reducing the effect on the structure as a whole.

5.34 There are certain modifying factors in addition to those listed above which must be considered in particular cases, viz, (a) the shielding effect of structures which lie between the source of blast and the building under consideration, and (b) the reflection of blast pressure under certain circumstances which involve large flat areas adjacent to the structure. It is intuitively obvious that the degree of shielding provided by a structure is a function of its size and proximity to the shielded object, but a quantitative evaluation of this factor for a given geometrical situation is less obvious. In the case of such long-duration blast waves as are produced by an atomic explosion, the main effect of a shielding structure of moderate size will be to reduce the impac-effect of the blast and the blast wind. This reduction will probably be appreciable only if the distance to the shielding structure is less than two or three times the height or width of the shielded object, depending on which of these is the smaller.

5.35 Where the radial distance between structures is less, the net translational force on the building may be reduced by a factor which is dependent on the size and shape of the shielded structure. For example, a long structure lying parallel to the blast, which has its near end shielded by a structure of comparable size but reasonably close, will experience a translational force which is not very different from that experienced by the shielding structure if allowance for differences in radial distances is made. The reason for this is that the diffracted pressure between the structures builds up nearly to the stagnation pressure experienced by the shielding structure before the blast wave reaches the end of the shielded structure. If this structure were very short radially, so that the blast wave reached the end very soon after the onset of pressure, the translational force would be appreciably less. In either case, the net compressive or squeezing force on the structure would be modified relatively little by the presence of the shielding structure.

5.36   The conclusion to be reached is that in the case of the long-duration blast waves from an atomic bomb, the shielding due to adjacent structures is much less important than it is in the case of explosions of conventional bombs where the size of the building relative to the length of the blast wave is much larger.   The greater height of burst of the atomic bomb will also tend to reduce the shielding effect of one building on another, especially at relatively short distances from ground zero.   The observations made in Japan after the atomic bomb explosions support these general conclusions. Special cases of shielding of one structure by another, and of shielding due to topography of the land in Nagasaki will be referred to later (§ 5.48 et seq.).

5.37   The effect of reflection of pressure from adjacent structures is not very important, except in a few instances when the vertical angle of the blast wave is such as to trap the blast in deep narrow canyons formed by high buildings in certain streets in very large cities.   Similar large vertical angles may cause a downward direct blast pressure, followed by a reflection of the blast, over water surfaces, in such a way as to load bridges, first in a downward and then in an upward direction, thus initiating a vibration cycle which may result in failure.

5.38   The second consideration in determining probability of damage is that of the response of the structure.   The factors affecting resistance to damage are believed to be the following:

(a) *Rigidity.*—The greater the resistance offered to deformation the greater the energy required to produce damage.   For example, a building designed for earthquake resistance, stiffened by diaphragm walls and having continuity at joints, will be less damaged than one designed for a conventional wind load.

(b) *Redundancy.*—Portions of the structure not ordinarily considered in design, that will nevertheless resist deformation of the structure, may play a large part in reducing damage.

(c) *Ductility.*—Damage involves plastic deformation generally.   Consequently, the more ductile the materials the greater the possible deformation without failure.

5.39   With this brief discussion of the relevant factors, an analysis may now be made for two conditions, namely, elastic and plastic deformation.

(a) *Elastic Deformation.*—The period of application of load resulting from the explosion of a nominal atomic bomb will be, in general, many times the natural period of vibration of the structural elements and may be substantially greater than that of the entire structure. If the pressure-time relation and the periods of the structural elements are known, it is possible to determine the maximum stresses. Tests indicate that under dynamic load conditions somewhat higher stresses are permissible than under static load. For reinforced concrete, for example, preliminary information shows that the factor may be 1.3 times the stress permitted for an equal static load. Thus, it is possible to determine whether a structure will withstand elastically a given dynamic load by calculating the stress, and determining how it compares with the static elastic limit multiplied by 1.3.

(b) *Plastic Deformation.*—The foregoing method is useful if permanent deformation cannot be accepted. It seems unlikely, however, that such an assumption is justifiable in view of the tremendous forces involved and the fact that repeated damage in any one area is unlikely. From a military standpoint, for example, it has been concluded that deformation which did not prevent a tank or ship from operating successfully was acceptable. Similarly, in a protective structure it has been considered that damage which did not interfere with its continued effective use was permissible. What will be acceptable in the case of buildings, bridges, and other structures is an individual problem. It is clear, in any event, that deformation to the point of imminent collapse is definitely undesirable, but in each case some lesser deformation will be acceptable. Hence, it seems more logical to base analysis of probable damage on plastic deformation to some established limit. It must be determined how the structure would deform after passing the elastic limit as a result of a given loading and what the resisting forces would be.

During the period of application of the blast, when the blast force exceeds the resisting force, the structure would be accelerated. Knowing the applied and resisting forces, the period of application of such forces and the mass, it is possible to calculate the velocity at the end of the period of acceleration. Conversely, knowing the momentum and resisting forces at the end of the acceleration phase, the time required to come to rest can be calculated. From these calculations the total deformation will be established. Should such deformation be within the limits set by separate investigation of acceptable damage, then the structure may be considered to have satisfactory resistance.[7]

B. AIR BLAST DAMAGE: JAPANESE EXPERIENCE [8]

GENERAL OBSERVATIONS

5.40 The discussion so far has dealt mainly with the general principles of blast damage. The actual effects on buildings, bridges, utilities, and housing to be expected from the detonation of a nominal atomic bomb will now be considered. Information obtained from surveys of Nagasaki and Hiroshima will be used as a primary guide, but reference will also be made to structures of types that were not found in the blasted areas of these cities. In addition, differences in construction practice, which affect the comparison to be made between Japan and the United States, will be taken into account.

5.41 Before proceeding with the detailed descriptions, attention may be called to an important difference between the effects of an atomic bomb blast and those due to a conventional, high-explosive bomb. The great power of the former results in a unique destruction feature called *mass distortion* of buildings. An ordinary explosion will usually damage only part of a large structure, but the atomic blast can engulf and flatten whole buildings. Further, because the shock wave of an atomic explosion is of relatively long duration (§ 5.23), most structural failures occur during a small part of the positive phase while the pressure is essentially constant.

5.42 An examination of the areas in Japan affected by atomic bombing shows that small masonry buildings were engulfed by the oncoming pressure wave and collapsed completely. Light buildings and residences were totally demolished by blast and fire. Manufacturing buildings of steel construction were denuded of roofing and siding, and only the twisted frames remained. Nearly everything above ground at close range, except reinforced-concrete smoke stacks, was destroyed. Some buildings leaned away from ground zero as though struck by a hurricane of stupendous proportions. Telephone poles were snapped off at ground level carrying the wires down with them, and gas holders were ruptured and collapsed.

5.43 Many buildings, that at a distance appeared to be sound, were found on close inspection to be damaged and gutted by fire.

---

[7] See Appendix A.

[8] United States Strategic Bombing Survey, "The Effect of the Atomic Bomb on Hiroshima, Japan," Vols. I, II, and III (1947); "The Effect of the Atomic Bomb on Nagasaki, Japan," Vols. I, II, and III (1947).

There were many evidences, in fact, of the effect of radiant heat in starting fires and in scorching and drying out materials that were not highly combustible.   This aspect of damage due to an atomic explosion will be described more fully in Chapter VI.   Telephone poles were charred and granite surfaces were etched by heat and by the sand blasting due to the high winds carrying abrasive material.   All vehicles at close range were damaged by blast and were burned out. Most important, in this connection, was that water pressure was lost by the breaking of pipes, mainly as a result of the collapse of buildings, thus greatly increasing the additional destruction by fire.

5.44   It may be pointed out that certain structures were designed to be earthquake-resistant, which probably made them stronger than their counterparts in the United States, while other construction was undoubtedly lighter than that in this country.   However, contrary to popular conceptions concerning the flimsy characteristics of the Japanese residences, it is the considered opinion of a group of highly qualified architects and engineers who surveyed the atomic bomb damage that the resistance to blast of American residences in general would not be markedly different from those in Hiroshima and Nagasaki.

5.45   From the observations made in Japan it is possible to draw some conclusions relative to the blast damage to be expected at various distances from ground zero for an air burst of a nominal atomic bomb.   These conclusions, based on the assumption that the height of burst is such as to inflict maximum damage (§ 3.68), are conveniently summarized in the form of Table 5.45.[9]   It is true that substantial variations will occur because of differences in building design and construction, and so the data in the table are based on a supposed "average value" for the strength of the structure.   The inclusion of the values of peak (side-on) blast pressure, blast-wind velocity, and duration of the pressure phase of the blast wave gives a basis for the association of the different degrees of damage with the pressure and duration.   This should provide a rough comparison of the theoretical calculations on structural resistance with actual observation.

5.46   The various types of damage and the radii within which they may be expected to occur are given below:

(a)   *Virtually complete destruction* will occur out to a radius of approximately one-half mile from ground zero, corresponding to an area of destruction of about three-quarters of a square mile.

---

[9] The values of wind velocity, duration of shock wave, and peak overpressures at various distances, obtained by calculation and extrapolation from data for TNT bombs, are for an assumed height of burst of 2,000 feet over a flat terrain (cf. Fig. 3.72). Approximate estimates of peak pressures made in Japan some time after the explosions are in fair agreement.

TABLE 5.45

Wind velocity (mph)	Duration (sec)	Overpressure (psi)	Miles	Feet	Damage
					Limit of light damage at 8 miles.
50	1.25	1.5			12,000←Light damage to window frames and doors, moderate plaster damage, complete window damage.
			2.25		
60	1.23	1.7			11,000←Flash charring of telegraph poles. Roof and wall covering on steel frame building damaged.
			2.0		←Partial damage to structures in area.
70	1.20	2.0			10,000←Blast damage to majority of homes. Severe fire damage expected. Flash ignition of dry combustible materials.
			1.75		
80	1.15	2.4			9000←Heavy plaster damage
					←Moderate damage to area.
100	1.12	2.9	1.50		8000←Severe damage to homes, heavy damage to window frames and doors, foliage scorched by radiant heat.
125	1.06	3.6			7000
			1.25		←Structural damage to multistory brick buildings.
160	0.98	5.2			6000←{ Severe damage to entire area. / Severe structural damage to steel frame building. 9-inch brick walls moderately cracked.
			1.0		←Electrical installations and trolley cars destroyed. / ←Multistory brick building completely destroyed.
200	0.90	7.4			5000←12-inch brick walls severely cracked.
					←Steel frame building destroyed (mass distortion of frame). / ←Light concrete buildings collapsed.
270	0.77	10	0.75		4000←Reinforced concrete smoke stack with 8-inch walls overturned. / ←Roof tiles bubbled (melted by heat). / ←18-inch brick walls completely destroyed.
380	0.62	16			3000
			0.50		Virtually complete destruction of all buildings, other than reinforced concrete aseismic design.
550	0.45	24			2000←{ Limit of severe structural damage to earthquake-resistant reinforced concrete buildings. / Reinforced concrete building collapsed, 10-inch walls, 6-inch floor.
			0.25		←Mass distortion of heavy steel frame buildings. Loss of roofs and panels.
800	0.37	36			1000←Decks of steel plate girder bridge shift laterally.
					0 Air Burst of an Atomic Bomb.

(b) *Severe damage*, defined as major structural damage that would result in collapse or liability to collapse of the building, will occur out to a radial distance which is slightly in excess of 1 mile from ground zero. This corresponds to an area of 4 square miles in which the damage ranges from severe to destructive.

(c) *Moderate damage*, short of major structural damage but sufficient to render the structure unusable until repaired, will occur out to a radius of about 1⅝ miles, giving an area of 8 square miles in which the damage ranges from moderate to destructive.

(d) *Partial damage*, will be inflicted out to a radius of approximately 2 miles, adding 4 additional square miles of damage area, and making a total of 12 square miles subject to some degree of damage in excess of plaster damage and window destruction.

(e) *Light damage*, which is mostly plaster damage and window breakage, may extend out to a radius of 8 miles or more, giving a light damage area of the order of 200 square miles. Actually these distances, at which window and light plaster damage will be inflicted, vary appreciably with the meteorological conditions at the time of the detonation and may be considerably greater under conditions which provide a temperature inversion in the lower atmosphere.[10]

5.47   The data given above are for the explosion of a nominal atomic bomb with an energy release equivalent to that of 20 kilotons of TNT. As stated in § 5.26, since the peak overpressure of the shock wave is the criterion of blast damage for an atomic bomb, it may be supposed that the limiting distances from ground zero for various types of damage, especially the larger distances, will vary approximately as the cube root of the energy of the bomb. The distances in Table 5.45 for various kinds of damage would thus have to be multiplied by $(W/20)^{1/3}$ to give the approximate effects to be expected from an atomic bomb of W kilotons TNT equivalent energy release.[11]

---

[10] In the Report of the British Mission to Japan on "The Effects of the Atomic Bombs at Hiroshima and Nagasaki", it was estimated that in a British city, such as London, the Nagasaki bomb would have (1) caused complete collapse of normal houses to a distance of 3,000 feet from ground zero, (2) damaged beyond repair out to 5,280 feet, (3) rendered uninhabitable without extensive repair out to 7,920 feet, and (4) rendered uninhabitable without minor repairs out to 13,200 feet.

[11] The results are shown in Fig. 12. 13, where the energy release, in terms of TNT, is plotted against the distances at which moderate (2.7 psi) and severe (5.2 psi) damage may be expected.

Effect of Shielding

5.48   The general experience in Japan provides support for the view expressed in § 5.36, that the effect of one building in shielding another from blast damage due to an atomic bomb would be small. There was some slight evidence of such shielding, for example in the medical school in Nagasaki, where a group of buildings apparently afforded each other mutual protection, but on the whole the shielding of one building by another was not appreciable.   An interesting case of indirect shielding by a structure was observed in connection with the workers' houses to the north of the torpedo plant in Nagasaki, and about 6,000 to 7,000 feet from ground zero.   The damage to these houses was not nearly as bad as was suffered by other houses which were 1,000 feet or more further from the explosion.   It seems that the destruction in the torpedo plant had weakened the blast somewhat, and its full power was not restored until it had progressed some distance ahead.

5.49   Several instances of shielding were noted in Nagasaki due to the presence of hills (Fig. 5.49).   It was partly the shielding by the hills in the center of the city that resulted in a smaller area of devastation in Nagasaki than in Hiroshima, in spite of the fact that the atomic bomb used in the former case was not less powerful. However, the hills provided effective shielding only at such distances that the blast pressure was becoming critical for a particular structure, that is, when the pressure was barely sufficient to cause its collapse.

5.50   Houses built in ravines at Nagasaki pointing well away from the center of the explosion were essentially unharmed, but others at similar distances in ravines pointing toward the explosion were severely damaged.   In a small hamlet to the north of Nagasaki, about 8,000 feet from ground zero, a distinctive variation in the intensity of damage could be seen corresponding with the shadows thrown by a sharp hill.

5.51   A striking example of shielding was provided by a hill about 8,000 feet southeast from the center of the explosion in Nagasaki. Here the buildings, which were of the European type, were on the reverse side of a steep hill, and the damage was light, mainly to plaster and windows.   At the same distance to the south-southeast of the city, where there was no shielding by hills, the destruction was considerably greater.   All window frames, windows and doors were damaged; there was also heavy plaster damage and cracks appeared in brickwork.

Figure 5.49. *Upper photo:* Residential areas at Nagasaki shielded by hills (bare area in foreground is a firebreak). *Lower photo:* Similar residential area, not shielded, reduced to rubble. Roadway was cleared of debris before the photograph was taken.

LONG-RANGE BLAST DAMAGE

5.52   One of the curious features of blast damage caused by a large explosion, not necessarily that of an atomic bomb, is that appreciable effects are sometimes observed at considerable distances from the bomb burst, while some intermediate regions are largely unaffected. It appears that under suitable meteorological conditions, there is a focusing of incident and various reflected shock waves which may result in causing blast damage at certain points as far as 50 miles from the explosion.   Some of the necessary conditions appear to be temperature inversion (§ 2.27, footnote) at a relatively low altitude, surface winds of low velocity, and a region of high atmospheric pressure.

5.53   Long-range blast damage was observed, to some extent, as a result of the atomic bombing of Japan.   For example, the barracks sheds at Kamigo, nearly 5 miles south of ground zero in Nagasaki, collapsed to ground level, although other buildings close by remained completely intact.   In Hiroshima, the general limiting radius for the displacement of roof tiles was about 8,000 feet from the bomb burst, but some cases of displacement occurred as far out as 5 miles.

MULTISTORY REINFORCED-CONCRETE FRAME BUILDINGS

5.54   In the preceding paragraphs the discussion of damage has been somewhat general in nature.   Consideration will now be given to the kind of damage inflicted on specific types of structures.   There were many multistory, reinforced-concrete frame buildings in Hiroshima and a smaller number in Nagasaki (Figs. 5.54 a and b).   They varied in resistance to blast damage according to design and construction, but generally suffered remarkably little damage, particularly those designed for resistance against earthquakes.   After the severe earthquake of 1923 a code was established for all new construction to reduce earthquake damage.   The height of buildings was limited to 100 feet and design for a lateral load of 0.1 times gravity was required.   In addition, the recognized principles of stiffening by diaphragms and improved framing to provide continuity were specified. The more important buildings were well designed and constructed according to the code, but some were built without much regard for its requirements.

5.55   Close to the explosion the vertical component of blast was more important so that there was heavy damage caused by the downward force exerted on the roof.   Depending upon its strength, the roof was pushed down and left sagging or failed completely.   The

Figure 5.54a. *Upper photo:* Reinforced-concrete frame building, 700 feet from ground zero, 2,100 feet from point of explosion; external walls intact. *Lower photo:* Interior of above burned out; note sagging of roof and spalling of plaster by fire.

Figure 5.54b. *Upper photo:* Reinforced-concrete frame building, 5,300 feet from ground zero. *Lower photo:* Interior of above practically undamaged, except for windows.

remainder of the structure was less damaged than similar buildings further from ground zero because of the smaller horizontal force.

5.56   At greater distances the lateral force was proportionately greater and produced the following effects:

(a) *Failure of the roof slab by lateral compression causing it to buckle.*— This was apparently caused by the force applied to the side of the building which in turn was transferred to the roof tending to push it back.   Since the roof was restrained by connections to less affected portions- of the building, it failed in compression (Fig. 5.56*a*).

Figure 5.56*a*.   Reinforced-concrete building, about 1,700 feet from ground zero, showing cracked roof slab and parapet walls.

(b) *A similar failure in floor systems.*—Failure usually occurred in the bay between the first row of interior columns and the affected wall (Fig. 5.56*b*).   Buckling was usually upward.

(c) *Cracking of concrete and overstressing of concrete and steel at haunches and connections.*—This effect was apparent in a large number of buildings and is readily explained by the tremendous lateral force applied (Fig. 5.56*c*).

Figure 5.56b.   Buckling and cracking of beams in reinforced-concrete building, about 1,700 feet from ground zero.

Figure 5.56c.   Second floor of reinforced-concrete frame building, 1,900 feet from ground zero, showing fractured third-floor beams, and failure of columns at windows.

(*d*) *Failure of columns by shearing action.*—Columns in the first story were cracked diagonally (Fig. 5.56*d*). This was probably caused by the higher shearing force in the first story resulting from the lateral pressure on the building.

Figure 5.56*d*.   Typical examples of column failure in reinforced-concrete frame building, 1,900 feet from ground zero.

(*e*) *Failure of exterior walls.*—On the side toward the blast, walls were dished inward. The degree of such action depended upon the distance from ground zero and the strength of the wall. It was also affected by pressure equalization resulting from failure of windows (Fig. 5.56*e*).

(*f*) *Failure of floors.*—Floors were most affected by direct blast in those cases where pressure equalization was not possible. For example, the floors over inclosed basements were pushed downward when higher floors were undamaged (Fig. 5.56*f*).

(*g*) *Miscellaneous effects.*—In addition to the structural damage described above, there was heavy damage to false ceilings, plaster and partitions. Such damage occurred in varying degrees out to a distance of 12,000 feet in Nagasaki. Glass window panes were broken up to the same distance. Brick and other facings from buildings were blown off, even when the structures themselves were not seriously damaged. These effects are extremely important because of the large number of casualties caused by missiles and flying glass, and blockage of the streets by debris (Fig. 5.56*g*).

Figure 5.56e.   Reinforced-concrete frame building, 5,900 feet from ground zero, showing crushing of concrete panel walls on side facing the explosion.

Figure 5.56*f*. Reïnforced-concrete building, 1,500 feet from ground zero. Floor slab and beams of first floor collapsed into basement.

Figure 5.56*g*. Debris blocking streets after the atomic bomb explosion at Hiroshima.

Multistory Steel-Frame Buildings

5.57   There was only one building of this type on record (Fig. 5.57). This was in Nagasaki at a distance of 4,500 feet from the bomb burst. The only part of the structure not classified as being of heavy construction was the roof which was of thin concrete supported by unusually light steel trusses. The downward failure of the roof, which was dished 3 feet, was the only structural damage in the building. Reinforced-concrete buildings at the same distance were also undamaged, but there is insufficient evidence to permit conclusions to be drawn as to relative resistance of the two types of construction.

Industrial Buildings and Equipment

5.58   In Nagasaki there were many steel buildings used for manufacturing, and these were generally of the shed type, with some of the sawtooth design (Figs. 5.58a and b). Roofs and siding were of corrugated sheet metal or of asbestos cement. In some cases there were rails for heavy gantry cranes, but generally cranes were of low capacity. Construction was generally comparable to that in the United States. The first effect of blast was to strip off the siding and roof material, but since this did not occur instantaneously, a large impulsive force was applied to the frame. Severe damage occurred up to a distance of 6,000 feet.

5.59   There were several types of failure of such structures. Close to the explosion the buildings were pushed over bodily, and at greater distances they were in many cases left leaning away from the source of the blast (Fig. 5.58a). The columns being long and slender offered little resistance to the lateral force. Sometimes columns failed by a combination of lateral force, causing flexure, at the same time that an increased downward load came from the vertical component of blast on the roof. This caused buckling and collapse. Roof trusses were buckled by compression resulting from blast on the exposed side of the building.

5.60   A difference was noticed in the effect on the frame depending upon whether a frangible material, like asbestos cement, or a material of high tensile strength, such as corrugated sheet iron, was used for roof and siding. Asbestos cement broke up more readily and transferred less force to the steel frame with less structural damage.

5.61   Fire produced heavy damage to unprotected steel members so that it was impossible to tell exactly what the blast effect had been. In general, the steel frames were badly distorted and would have

Figure 5.57.   At left and somewhat back of center is shown the only multistory steel-frame building exposed to atomic bombs.   It was in Nagasaki, 4,500 feet from ground zero.

Figure 5.58a. Light steel-frame industrial building, 1,800 feet from ground zero. Corrugated iron roof and wall sheathing were stripped by the blast, and the combustible contents destroyed by fire.

Figure 5.58b. Industrial building with sawtooth roof truss, about 5,000 feet from ground zero. Damage by blast and fire was severe.

been of little use even though siding and roofing material had been available for repairs.

5.62 In some industrial buildings wood trusses were used to support the roofs. These were more vulnerable to blast because of poor framing and connections and were readily burned out by fire. Concrete columns were employed in some cases with steel roof trusses; the columns were more resistant to buckling than steel because of the smaller length-to-diameter ratio.

5.63 Damage to machine tools (Fig. 5.63) was caused by debris in reinforced-concrete sheds in particular, by fire in wood-frame structures, and by dislocation and overturning caused by damage to the structure. In many cases the machine tools were belt-driven, so that the distortion of the building pulled the machine tool off its base, damaging or overturning it.

5.64 Stacks are of special interest (Fig. 5.64). Those of reinforced concrete were particularly resistant to blast; this can be accounted for by their shape and size, which permitted the blast to equalize quickly, their long period of vibration, and their strength. Steel stacks performed fairly well, but being lighter in weight and subject to crushing were not comparable to reinforced concrete. Well constructed masonry stacks also withstood damage reasonably well.

Buildings With Load-Bearing Walls

5.65 Small buildings of this type with light walls collapsed. Larger buildings with cross walls and of somewhat heavier construction were more resistant but failed at distances up to 6,200 feet (Figs. 5.65a and b). Cracks were observed at the junction of cross walls and side walls when the building remained standing. It is quite apparent that this type of building possesses none of the characteristics that would make it resistant to collapse when subjected to heavy lateral load.

Timber-Framed Buildings and Housing

5.66 While the quality of the workmanship in framing wood buildings was high, little attention was paid to engineering principles. Mortise and tenon joints were weak points and connections in general were poor (Fig. 5.66a). Timbers were dapped out excessively or splices were put in improper locations. In general, the construction was not well adapted to resist wracking action. Housing collapsed

Figure 5.63. Steel-frame light engineering shop, 3,300 feet from ground zero. Machine tools rendered useless by fire, blast, and debris.

at Nagasaki up to a distance of 7,500 feet and there was structural damage up to a distance of 8,600 feet. Roofs, wall panels, and partitions were damaged out to a distance of 9,000 feet (Fig. 5.66b).

Figure 5.64. General view of area of destruction of engineering factory, about 5,000 feet from ground zero, showing smokestacks still standing.

Bridges

5.67   There were a number of kinds of bridges exposed in Hiroshima and Nagasaki. Those of wood were burned in most cases, but the steel-girder bridges suffered little damage. One bridge, only 260 feet from ground zero, which was a girder type and had a reinforced-concrete deck, showed no sign of any structural damage. It had apparently deflected and rebounded, causing a slight movement. Other bridges at greater distances suffered more lateral shifting. A reinforced-concrete deck was lifted from the supporting steel girders of one bridge, due presumably to the reflected blast wave from the water below (Figs. 5.67a, b, and c).

Figure 5.65a. *Upper photo*: Building with load-bearing walls, 600 feet from ground zero, 2,100 feet from the point of explosion. *Lower photo*: Interior of above, showing buckling of wall and combustible material burned out.

Figure 5.65b. *Upper photo*: Building with load-bearing walls, 5,200 feet from ground zero. Load-bearing wall away from the blast collapsed. *Lower photo*: Interior of above, showing damage due to blast and fire. (Compare with Figure 5.54b for a reinforced-concrete building at about same distance from ground zero; both buildings were in Hiroshima.)

Figure 5.66a.   *Upper photo*: Wood-frame building, 8,000 feet from ground zero, showing rupture of columns at points where windows or other horizontals were mortised in.   *Lower photo*: Detail of above, showing typical column failure. (Note mortise and tenon joints at wall plate.)

Figure 5.66b. Blast damage to wooden dwelling about 5,000 feet from ground zero.

Figure 5.67a. Plate-girder bridge, about 1,000 feet from ground zero, 2,230 feet from point of explosion. The bridge received severe damage, but continued to carry highway, pedestrian, and street-car traffic. (The picture was taken after debris had been cleared from the roadway in the foreground.)

Figure 5.67b. Steel-plate girder, double-track railway bridge, about 840 feet from ground zero, 2,150 feet from point of explosion. The plate girders were moved about 3 feet by the blast; the railroad tracks were bent out of shape and trolley cars were demolished, but the poles were left standing.

Figure 5.67c. Reinforced-concrete bridge with T-beam deck, 2,330 feet from ground zero. Part of deck was knocked off the pier and abutment by the blast, causing one span, 35 feet long, to drop into the river. The remainder of the bridge was almost undamaged.

UTILITIES

5.68   In Nagasaki the public utility system was comparable to that in an American city of 30,000 population except that open sewers were used. Damage to the water supply essential for fire fighting was of the greatest significance (Figs. 5.68a and b). This was not caused by failure of the underground mains, but by loss of pressure through breakage of pipes in houses and buildings, except in one case described below. Earth surface depressions up to 1 foot in depth were observed at scattered points in a filled-in area at a maximum distance of 2,000 feet from ground zero. This caused a series of fail-

Figure 5.68a.   Four-inch gate valve in water main broken by debris from brick wall at 1,100 feet from ground zero.

ures of 12-inch cast-iron water pipes 3 feet below grade, the breakage being probably caused by unequal vertical displacement. There was no serious damage to reservoirs and water-treatment plants as they were located at too great a distance.

5.69   Utility poles were destroyed by blast or fire, and overhead utilities were heavily damaged at distances up to 10,000 feet. Underground electrical conduits were little affected. Switch gear and transformers were not damaged directly by blast but by secondary effects, such as collapse of the structure in which they were located or by debris (Fig. 5.69a).   Motors and generators were damaged by fire. Gas holders were heavily damaged by blast at 6,600 feet and the escaping gas was ignited but there was no explosion (Fig. 5.69b).   Gas mains suffered no observable damage.   Street railway equipment was heavily damaged by fire and blast (see Fig. 5.67c); buses and automobiles were, in general, also damaged by blast and were burned out at shorter distances (Fig. 5.69c).   As an example, an American made car was heavily damaged and burned at 3,000 feet, while one at 6,000 feet suffered only minor damage.

Figure 5.68b.   Damage to portion of 16-inch water main, carried on bridge, about 1,200 feet from ground zero.

SHELTERS

5.70   Caves were used to a large extent for shelter although there were many timber, semiburied shelters with an earth cover of about 18 inches.   These were not particularly well built, yet in some cases they survived at a distance of 900 feet and none was damaged beyond half a mile (see Fig. 12.52a and b).

Figure 5.69a. Electric substation, 2,400 feet from ground zero; switch racks, transformers, and other equipment damaged. (The corrugated iron sheathing was stripped from the walls by the blast, rendering contents of building vulnerable to fire.)

Figure 5.69b.   Destroyed gas holder, 3,200 feet from ground zero.

Figure 5.69c.   General view, about 3,000 feet from ground zero at Nagasaki, showing wrecked automobiles in foreground.

C. PROBABLE EFFECTS IN THE UNITED STATES

REINFORCED-CONCRETE FRAME BUILDINGS

5.71   While the destructive effects observed in Japan (§§ 5.54–5.56) are comparable in general to those to be expected in the United States, there are some differences that are worthy of discussion.   Furthermore, there is the question of damage to the larger bridges of many American cities for which there is no direct guide from damage to the small bridges in Japan.   Reinforced-concrete buildings of earthquake-resistant design withstood the blast quite well.   These buildings were designed for a lateral force equal to 10 percent of the vertical load. When pressure is applied tending to displace the top of the building with respect to the foundation, the resulting action is roughly the same as that which would arise if seismic forces moved the foundation against the inertial resistance of the structure.

5.72   The multistory buildings in this country are generally designed to withstand a wind load of 15 pounds per square foot.   For an average six-story, reinforced-concrete, frame building this would be roughly equivalent to 2 percent of the vertical load.   On this basis, American reinforced-concrete buildings would be much less resistant to collapse than those designed for earthquake resistance in Japan. No firm conclusions can be drawn on this subject, however, as most buildings have lateral strength far in excess of that required to withstand a 15 pounds per square foot wind load.

5.73   In the eleven Western States of this country, the building codes provide for the design of structures to resist horizontal, earthquake forces varying from 2 to 16 percent of the vertical load, which is usually taken as dead load plus half the vertical design live load. There are three earthquake zones, the Pacific coast area having the highest requirements.   The design specifications, as stipulated in the building codes, are similar to those for wind loads, with a 33 percent increase in the allowable working stresses.   These buildings would be proportionately more resistant as the ratio of horizontal to vertical load increases.

STEEL–FRAME BUILDINGS

5.74   The effect on steel-frame buildings, such as multiple storied office and hospital structures, should be approximately the same as that on reinforced-concrete buildings, except that steel has a somewhat greater energy absorption capacity than reinforced concrete.   This is due to the fact that with usual design stresses the work necessary to produce failure in steel is greater in proportion than in reinforced concrete. Consequently, tall buildings having heavy steel frames, constructed so as to provide good continuity at connections, and a long period of vibration, should withstand the effect of blast quite well.

INDUSTRIAL TYPE BUILDINGS

5.75   American steel industrial buildings would probably fare no better than those in Japan. The sawtooth roofs designed as rigid frames would be especially vulnerable to blast damage.

HOUSING

5.76   Tests made on typical housing of wood-frame construction with conventional bombs up to 500 pounds and at various distances indicate a high degree of resistance against blast beyond 30 feet. While no direct interpretation of these results can be made with regard to the blast from a large explosion, which would have quite different characteristics, it is believed that the radius of material structural blast damage would not exceed 7,500 feet. This is slightly less than that in Nagasaki where the severe damage to houses extended to a distance of 8,500 feet.

BRIDGES

5.77   In Japan bridges withstood vertical blast loads quite well, and there is no reason to believe that other bridges of the same type would not behave in a similar fashion. In fact, it is probable that all bridges would be quite resistant to blast. Lateral loads, even if excessive, would affect the less important structural members of the bridge. For example, if the bracing designed to withstand wind loads were overstressed, its repair or replacement would not be nearly so serious as if chord members were affected. The actual lateral loads are difficult to calculate, particularly as the blast-wind velocities may be close to that of sound. However, in this case the drag pressure only will be of great importance, and there will be relatively small effect from the incident blast because of the comparatively small size of the members. Wind-tunnel tests would be necessary to provide accurate data on drag coefficients. Pending availability of such information, it is suggested that an analysis be made using the usual design areas for wind load, and that the impulsive forces be calculated for each member in accordance with the method given in § 5.7 *et seq*. The total transient load at each panel point could then be tabulated and a calculation made with regard to the resulting stresses.

D. AIR BURST OVER WATER

CONCLUSIONS BASED ON BIKINI OBSERVATIONS

5.78   From the data obtained in the Bikini "Able" air burst over water it appears that, allowing for the difference in the height of burst, the variation of the peak pressure of the shock wave with the horizontal distance from the point of burst is very similar to that found for an air burst over land.   Consequently, it may be concluded that the general nature of the damage to houses and other buildings and installations on shore, at specific distances from the bomb burst, will be much the same as described in earlier sections of this chapter.

5.79   Some mention may be made here of damage which might be expected to ships and their contents as the result of an air burst over water.   The destruction would be due almost entirely to the shock wave in air, there being little transmitted through the water, for a reasonable height of detonation.   This distinguishes an air burst from one taking place underwater, as will be seen later.   From the results observed at Bikini it appears that up to about 2,500 to 3,000 feet horizontal distance from the explosion, vessels of all types will suffer serious damage or will be sunk (Figs. 5.79a and b).   Moderate damage will be experienced out to 4,500 feet, and minor damage may be expected to occur within a radius of 6,000 feet.

5.80   Because of the shock wave transmitted through the air, exposed structures, such as masts, spars, radar antennae, etc., may be expected to suffer damage.   This would be very severe up to 3,000 or 3,500 feet from the explosion.   Within the same radius light vehicles and airplanes (Figs. 5.80a and b) on the ships and other light structures and electronic equipment will be seriously damaged.

5.81   Ship machinery would probably remain intact within the range in which the ship survives.   The principal exception is blast damage to boilers and uptakes, and this will account for most cases of immobilization.   Boilers may be expected to suffer heavy damage out to 2,700 feet, moderate damage to 4,000 feet, and light damage to nearly 5,000 feet.

5.82   A certain amount of shielding from the shock is experienced by equipment in the interior of the vessel.   The damage to such

Figure 5.79a. The light, aircraft carrier U. S. S. *Independence*, located within 2,600 feet of surface zero at the Bikini "Able" test. The flight deck was broken in several places and the four stacks were demolished. Fire broke out on the hangar deck, adding to the general destruction.

Figure 5.79b. The Japanese cruiser *Sakawa* was severely damaged both above and below the water line by the "Able" explosion at Bikini. The ship sank on the day following the test.

equipment can thus be minimized by closing all exterior openings
when an atomic bomb attack appears possible.

Figure 5.80a.   The stern deck of the U. S. S. *Nevada*, within 2,000 feet of surface
zero, damaged by the "Able" burst at Bikini.

E.   DAMAGE FROM UNDERGROUND BURST

COMPARISON WITH EARTHQUAKE DAMAGE

5.83   The fundamental principles, as far as they are known, of the
behavior of shock waves due to underground explosions in soils of
different types were described in Chapter IV.   In this section an
attempt will be made to assess the structural damage that might be
expected from an atomic bomb detonated under the surface of the
earth, although there are no actual experiences upon which to base
the conclusions.   It might appear that use could be made, by appropriate scaling, of data obtained from TNT explosions, but this approach
has not proved too satisfactory.

Figure 5.80b.   Damage to a Navy seaplane on the U. S. S. *Nevada*, within 2,000 feet of surface zero.

5.84   The analogy between an atomic bomb explosion and an earthquake was mentioned in § 4.84, and it seems that some significant information may be secured in this manner.   From surveys made after the San Francisco earthquake of 1906, a scale of damage, which was correlated with the horizontal acceleration in terms of the force of gravity, was developed; this is reproduced in Table 5.84.

5.85   It is probably true that acceleration alone is not a very good index of the damaging power of an earth wave, since acceleration will not produce appreciable damage unless it is accompanied by sufficient motion to cause reasonably large displacements.   The displacement that would damage a structure severely is, of course, connected with the acceleration and the degree of differential motion that occurs. It would be reasonable to believe that a structure if handled gently,

TABLE 5.84

EARTHQUAKE DAMAGE SCALE*

Grade A.—Very violent (greater than 0.4 gravity).**

Grade B.—Violent (0.3–0.12 gravity).

Fissuring of asphalt; destruction of foundation walls and under-pinnings of structures; the breaking of sewers and water mains; displacement of street car tracks

Grade C.—Very strong (0.12–0.08 gravity).

Brick wall or masonry badly cracked with occasional collapse; frame. buildings lurched or listed on fair or weak underpinning; general destruction of chimneys and masonry, cement or brick veneers; considerable cracking or crushing of foundation walls.

Grade D.—Strong (0.08–0.02 gravity).

General but not universal fall of chimneys; cracks in masonry and brick walls; cracks in foundation walls; a few isolated cases of lurching or listing of frame buildings built up on weak underpinning.

Grade E.—Weak (less than 0.02 gravity).

Occasional fall of chimneys and damage to plaster, partitions, plumbing, etc.

---

*Physics of the Earth, Part VI: Seismology, Bulletin of the National Research Council, No. 90 (1933).
**The accelerations given in the table are those in a horizontal direction.

so that inertial forces are negligible, could stand very large displacements if every part received the same amount of movement. But if either or both of these conditions is not met, then damage may result. Failures of the foundation walls may occur due to earth pressure alone acting hydrostatically, but it is the differential earth pressures, which are in turn functions of the shape and length of the pressure wave, that are responsible for the accelerations imparted to the building substructure.[12] It is seen that the quantities are so interlinked that any real separation of the effects is impractical. Nevertheless, since inertial forces, differential movements and hydrostatic pressures are agents that act to produce failures of the structure in different ways, it may not be too unrealistic to attempt to set up criteria of damage based on these three quantities, and to compare them with such information as is available to see if they are consistent.

5.86   From Table 5.84 it is seen that appreciable damage corresponding to that from a strong (grade D) earthquake, which is ap-

---

[12] Because of the great length of the shock wave in an atomic bomb burst, many buildings have dimensions which are small compared with the positive part of the wave (§ 5.23). The motion of the earth and the back and front of a structure will thus be much the same, and the differential earth pressures may be small.

proximately equivalent to an underground atomic bomb burst (§ 4.84), occurs at accelerations between 0.08 and 0.02 times gravity in the horizontal direction. The geometrical mean of these accelerations is 0.04, which is taken as the limiting acceleration for appreciable damage. Lacking comparable information on the other agents of damage, they may be determined at the distance at which this value of the acceleration would occur, and the magnitudes compared with available data concerning the resistance of typical structures to these factors. The possible influence of underlying rock strata has been neglected, but the equation of pressure in terms of distance used is that which applies to somewhat greater depths of burial of the charge; hence, the effects may be partially compensating. The distance at which the horizontal acceleration has a magnitude of 0.04 times gravity has been computed for a sandy-clay soil and for a dense plastic clay, since they represent roughly the average and extreme in soil transmissibilities. The results of these computations are given in Table 5.86.

TABLE 5.86

ESTIMATED EFFECTS OF HORIZONTAL ACCELERATION

Distance	Acceleration	Motion	Reflected pressure
1,800 feet (sandy clay)_____	0.04 g	2.2 ft.	16 psi
5,000 feet (plastic clay)_____	0.04 g	0.3 ft.	14 psi

5.87 It will be noted that the pressures, for the given acceleration, are approximately the same at these two distances for the two soil types, but that the amplitude of motion is greater for the sandy clay at the nearer distance. This greater movement, when accompanied by the same acceleration, would be expected to cause greater damage. It has been suggested by H. O. Wood [13] that the measure of destructive intensity should be the product of the acceleration and the amplitude of motion.

ESTIMATE OF ATOMIC BOMB DAMAGE

5.88 The calculations indicate that destructive earth-shock effect would probably occur to a radial distance of 1,350 to 3,300 feet from the point of underground explosion of an atomic bomb, while appreciable damage to walls, chimneys, and foundations would be expected up to distances of 1,800 to 5,000 feet from the origin. The limits of the radial distance for light damage would range from roughly 2,700 to 10,500 feet on the basis that 0.01 g is the horizontal acceleration

---

[13] See reference to Table 5.84.

necessary to accomplish it. It appears, therefore, that the damage to be expected from an underground detonation is less than that from an air burst. As a rough generalization, it has been estimated that a bomb dropped from the air, and which penetrated to a depth of 40 to 50 feet below the surface before exploding, would cause blast damage over radii of about one-half to two-thirds of the radii for corresponding damage due to an air burst. However, as indicated in § 4.89, the reflection of the shock wave from rock strata at depths of less than 200 to 300 feet beneath the point of detonation, would probably result in an appreciable increase in the area of damage.

5.89   A detailed analysis of the probable damage suffered by a particular structure will have to be based on the response of the structure to the oscillatory motion imparted by the ground roll, and to the pressures and shearing actions experienced by the subsurface portions of the building. Generally speaking, the size, mass, and possible attachment to rock will be factors that tend to reduce its motion while imparting greater stresses to the foundation structure. It seems probable that displacements of the order quoted above would produce damage to any underground structure such as subways or foundations.

5.90   Wall-bearing buildings would undoubtedly collapse at considerable distances from ground zero and would be the most hazardous to occupy. Wood-frame buildings would resist reasonably well depending on the method of support. Brick piers would fail as would brick chimneys. The probable result would be the shifting of the structure on its foundations with the possibility of dropping it to the ground if supported on brick piers.

5.91   All underground utilities would suffer greatly from the displacements and pressures exerted, particularly sewer, gas, and water mains. Electrical mains would suffer much less due to their ductility, but above-ground lines would be damaged by tower and pole distortion which might result in the breakage of the wires.

5.92   If a nominal atomic bomb were dropped in such a manner as to explode at a depth of approximately 50 feet in ordinary soil, a crater about 800 feet in diameter and 100 feet in depth would be produced.[14] The shape and size of the area over which the expelled material would be spread will be governed to a great extent by the strength and direction of the wind. Tests on relatively small scale charges of TNT, of the order of 2,500 pounds in weight, indicate distributions of appreciable quantities of crater material to a radius of 1 mile downwind and about 0.2 mile upwind. The ordinary scaling

---

[14] For further discussion, see Appendix B.

laws cannot be applied in this case due to the influence of gravity, but it is probable that for a nominal atomic bomb these distances would be increased by a factor of four or more, depending on the wind velocity. (The wind velocity in the experiments cited varied from 15 to 20 miles per hour.)

5.93   The material expelled from the crater would be expected to be highly radioactive, due to the presence of trapped fission products and of material activated by neutron irradiation, and would constitute a hazard of the type discussed in Chapter VIII.

F.   DAMAGE FROM UNDERWATER BURST: GENERAL PRINCIPLES

Introduction

5.94   It was seen in the first part of Chapter IV that the explosion of a bomb under water is accompanied by the formation and propagation of a shock wave. A proportion of the shock passes into the air at the surface of the water, but most of the energy is transmitted through the water. It is consequently capable of causing blast damage, just as in the case of an air burst or of an underground explosion. The data in Table 4.14 and Fig. 4.14a, calculated for a 20 kiloton charge of TNT, indicate that the peak overpressures due to a shock wave in deep water [15] can in fact have very high values, much higher than those attained in an air burst, even at considerable distances from the explosion.

5.95   A theoretical analysis of the factors causing damage in an underwater burst is very complicated. Consequently, only a qualitative discussion of the subject will be given here. The only information of value is that derived from the atomic bomb burst in the Bikini "Baker" test.

5.96   The effect of the explosion on a structure is ultimately determined by the dynamical properties of the structure and by the complete pressure distribution in the surrounding water. However, since the pressure distribution is extensively modified by the structure itself, the structure and water must be considered together as a single dynamical system. Further, the cases of most interest are those in which the structural material is stressed beyond its elastic limit, so that permanent deformation or rupture results. The plastic state is incompletely understood, particularly under conditions of dynamic loading, and so the analysis has been carried out for several highly

---

[15] The results refer to an infinite medium, which may be regarded as equivalent to deep water.

idealized situations. From the results it is possible to draw conclusions of a general and somewhat tentative nature.

5.97 The pressure at an infinite surface with incident plane waves can be determined from a consideration of the incident and reflected waves. However, in the more general case of a deformable surface of finite extent, the analysis involves the physical concept of diffracted spherical waves, originating at points on the periphery of the surface, superimposed on the incident wave. In many instances of deformable surfaces, the resultant pressure becomes negative because of the deformation. Since water cannot withstand appreciable tension except under special conditions, cavitation results and the motion of the surface is modified (§ 4.18).

Effect of Characteristic Times

5.98 In idealized cases,[16] it is found that the damage resulting from pressure waves depends markedly on the dimensions and certain characteristic times. The quantities which are significant are the time constant of the incident wave (§ 4.11), the natural response times, e. g., the plastic time, of the structure, and the diffraction times measuring the time required for diffracted pressure waves to be propagated distances of the order of the dimensions of the structure.

5.99 If the time constant of the pressure wave is large compared to the characteristic times of the structure, the effect of the wave simulates that of an applied static pressure, and in the case of the shock wave or of bubble pulses, peak pressures are the significant parameters (cf. § 5.23 *et seq.*). In scaling up the damage in this case, the correct scaling factor is the cube root of the explosion energy yield or charge-weight equivalent. On the other hand, if the time constant of the pressure wave is small compared to the characteristic times of the structure, the motion of the structure is determined by the impulse of the wave. The latter condition is realized for large structures of slow response and only if the structure is sufficiently rigid, so that cavitation does not occur before rarefaction pressures are equalized by diffraction waves. The scaling factor for distance in this case is the two-thirds power of the explosion energy or weight of equivalent charge (§ 5.28).

5.100 If cavitation occurs because of substantial plastic deformation before the equalization of negative pressures by diffraction waves,

---

[16] The plastic deformation of circular plates under various constraints has been studied by J. G. Kirkwood and J. M. Richardson, "The Plastic Deformation of Circular Diaphragms under Dynamic Loading by an Underwater Explosion Wave," OSRD Report No. 4200 (1944). This work is summarized, and references to other authors are given, by R. H. Cole, "Underwater Explosions," Princeton University Press, Princeton, N. J., 1948, Chapter 10.

a considerable amount of energy may be stored as kinetic energy of the structure and cavitated water, and later used in plastic deformation. Under these circumstances, the shock-wave energy becomes the significant parameter in a discussion of damage, and the theoretical scaling factor for distance is the square root of the explosion energy or equivalent charge weight. It appears that a scaling factor of approximately the two-fifths power of the explosion energy leads to a better fit of the data, but a variation with the type of structure is to be expected.

5.101   It has been shown that the duration of the shock wave in water for a nominal atomic bomb is of the order of 35 milliseconds, if the wave is unaffected by surface cut-off. This time is approximately an order of magnitude greater than the characteristic times for component plates of capital ships. Therefore, if the target is far enough removed from the surface to be unaffected by the cut-off during the times for which damage occurs, the peak pressure becomes the parameter significant in the prediction of damage. The damage distance can then be expected to scale as the cube root of the explosion energy.

DEPTH OF EXPLOSION

5.102   The depth of the explosion is of importance in a consideration of the damage resulting from the shock wave. If the target is on or near the surface, e. g., a ship's hull, the shock wave will reach the surface at some point before reaching the target. It has been seen that the reflected wave from the surface will be a rarefaction wave. Thus, the shock arrives at the target followed immediately by the rarefaction wave, and the high pressures following the shock front are cut off. Therefore, greatest damage will occur if the rarefaction wave does not get nearer the shock front than the distance within which are found the necessary excess pressures for damage. Since pressures lasting about one-half the significant elastic time of the structure make the most important contribution to damage, the first few milliseconds of the pressure-time curve must be kept intact for greatest effectiveness. If the shock-wave velocity is approximately acoustic, the charge depth for maximum damage radius is readily estimated.

5.103   The geometry of this situation is shown in Fig. 5.103. The angle β can be computed from the depth below the surface of the bottom of the target hull and the distance corresponding to that portion of the pressure-time curve which the characteristic times of the hull plates require in order that the shock wave may be unaffected by the reflected rarefaction wave. It then follows that if $\alpha = (180 - \beta)/2$, the depth of the explosion should be sin α times the distance at which the damage is to be effective, i. e., the lethal radius.[17]

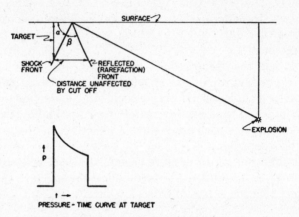

Figure 5.103.   Geometry and pressure-time curve of shock wave at target due to an underwater explosion.

5.104   Curves have been given for the distances at which TNT charges of 500 to 5,000 pounds cause serious flooding of typical capital vessels. Whether or not such flooding is to be considered lethal depends upon so many factors of design as to make generalization unprofitable. A consideration of these data and application of the scaling law to the nominal atomic bomb leads to the conclusion that the distance of serious flooding may be taken to be of the order of a half mile. If it is assumed that the bottom plates of the vessel are 30 feet under the surface, and that the length of the shock wave at this depth which must be effective before the pressure cut-off by the rarefaction wave is 30 feet, then the considerations of the last paragraph indicate that maximum damage will result if the explosion takes place about a quarter mile below the surface.

5.105   With a shallow explosion in deep water, the effects are more complicated. For targets near the charge, the angle of incidence of the shock wave will be great enough so that the pressure of the wave is not significantly affected by the surface cut-off. At greater distances, however, the angle of incidence becomes less and a greater portion of the pressure-time curve of the shock wave is affected.

<hr>

[17] This analysis is due to J. von Neumann.

This situation is illustrated in Fig. 5.105. Ultimately, the duration of the surviving positive portion of the compound wave becomes equal to or less than the characteristic times of the target structure. The significant parameter for damage is, then, the positive impulse of the compound wave, if the structure is sufficiently rigid, or the energy,

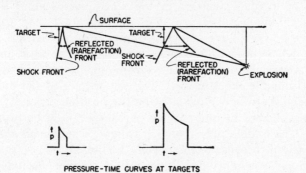

PRESSURE-TIME CURVES AT TARGETS

Figure 5.105.   Pressure-time curves of shock waves at targets at increasing distances from underwater explosion.

if cavitation occurs. Detailed consideration must be given to the geometry of the target area and to the location of the vessels within the area.   The pressure-time profile of the shock wave incident on a particular target vessel will depend upon the general configuration of the area and also upon the location of the vessel within the area. For these reasons, it is difficult to estimate a damage radius for such a shallow explosion.

5.106   For a shallow burst in shallow water, the picture is further complicated by the participation in the damage of shock waves reflected from the ocean floor.   At Bikini, two pressure pulses were observed which were of approximately step profile, due to cut-off, and of the same order of intensity, and which were separated by a few milliseconds.

5.107   It is probable that maximum lethal damage radius is achieved by a properly oriented deep charge in deep water, and that the effect of a different orientation or of shallow water is to decrease the damage radius.   Therefore, the figure of about one-half mile, estimated as the maximum radius for serious damage, may be taken to represent an upper limit for the more complicated cases of shallow shots in deep or shallow water.

Bubble Pulse and Waves

5.108   Approximately half of the available energy of an explosive is contained in the primary blast wave. Although up to a third of this energy may be dissipated as heat within distances for which damage is significant, the shock wave is the source of the largest amount of available energy in the water surrounding the charge. Secondary bubble pulses are of greater duration than the primary shock wave; they have impulses comparable to that of the shock wave, but have much lower peak pressures. The total energy radiated by secondary bubble pulses is consequently much less than that derived from the shock wave. The importance of the bubble pulse for damage is strongly dependent on the position and state of motion of the gas sphere in reference to the surface, the bottom, and the target. The bubble pulse may contribute to supplementary damage particularly if, because of migration, the bubble is close to the target when the pulse is emitted. In general, it may be concluded that the bubble pulse is of significance only if the arrangement of charge, target, and other surfaces is favorable.

5.109   It may be mentioned that, in particular cases, serious mechanical damage may result from some of the surface effects. Thus, at certain firing depths, surface waves may be formed of sufficient height to overrun nearby shore installations or to swamp vessels (§ 4.40 *et seq.*).

G. UNDERWATER BURST DAMAGE: BIKINI EXPERIENCE

Shock Wave in Water

5.110   The evidence from the Bikini ("Baker"), shallow underwater, atomic bomb explosion is that the shock wave transmitted through the water was the major cause of damage to the ships in the lagoon. From the observations made at the time certain general conclusions can be drawn, and these will be outlined here. The nature and extent of the damage to a surface vessel will vary with the distance from the point vertically above the bomb burst, i. e., from surface zero, with the ship type, its orientation with respect to the position of the explosion, and whether it is operating or riding at anchor.

5.111   It is expected that the lethal or sinking range of all types of surface vessels will be very much the same, and will be in the neighborhood of 1,200 to 1,800 feet from surface zero, for a shallow underwater burst of a nominal atomic bomb. Some ships will probably be sunk out to 2,700 feet, but others in this range will suffer considerable structural damage. Serious loss of efficiency is to be anticipated within a radius of 3,600 feet from surface zero. Even at this distance the peak pressure of the underwater shock wave will be over 500 pounds per square inch. Submerged submarines will probably be lost out to 2,700 feet from the explosion.

5.112 The principal types of damage experienced on ships due to the shock wave in water from a shallow explosion will be weakening of the ship girder, damage to fittings and equipment essential to watertightness, and damage to machinery, electrical and similar equipment, foundations, and piping. In addition to damage to the external surfaces, severe shock effects will be transmitted through the hull to interior structure and equipment. Heavy equipment will receive more damage than light equipment, but shock-mounted equipment will generally survive.

5.113 Boilers and main propulsive machinery will suffer heavy damage out to 2,250 feet, moderate damage to 2,700 feet, and light damage to 3,300 feet from surface zero. Auxiliary machinery associated with the propulsive equipment will not suffer as severely. For practical purposes, 3,000 feet may be taken as the expected radius of immobilization. Vessels underway may be expected to suffer somewhat more severe machinery damage than vessels at anchor.

5.114 In spite of the very high peak pressures which, as seen above, are extremely damaging to ships, and possibly also to piers and breakwaters, it is believed that other harbor and shore installations would not be seriously affected by the shock wave transmitted through the water. Of course, vessels sunk at or near piers, or thrown against them by the shock wave would decrease the effectiveness of the harbor. In addition, the influence of the air shock must be taken into consideration, as will be shown below.

Shock Wave in Air

5.115 Although the major portion of the shock due to a shallow underwater atomic explosion is propagated through the water, a not inconsiderable amount is transmitted as a shock wave in the air. The data obtained at Bikini indicate that the energy of the air shock for a shallow underwater burst of a nominal atomic bomb would be roughly equivalent to 4 kilotons of TNT, and such a shock would, of course, be capable of producing extensive destruction.

5.116 The shock wave transmitted through the air will undoubtedly cause some damage to the superstructure of ships on the water, but this will probably not be very significant in comparison to the harm done by the underwater shock.   The main effect of the air blast would probably be felt on land, if the bomb were exploded not too far from shore.   It has been estimated that at 2,000 feet from surface zero the peak pressure of the air shock due to the underwater burst was 10 pounds per square inch, and at 1 mile it was still more than 2 pounds per square inch.   With these data in mind, an examination of Table 5.45 will show that a shallow underwater atomic bomb burst taking place within something like half a mile from shore would cause serious damage to harbor facilities and to warehouses and other structures near the water.   Appreciable damage would, of course, occur some distance away.

5.117   By making use of the approximate scaling law relating the bomb energy to the radius of the area of destruction, as outlined in § 5.47, it would appear that the shallow underwater explosion of a nominal atomic bomb would produce damage of the various types referred to in Table 5.45 up to distances a little more than half those given there for an air burst.   In other words, the underwater burst would cause virtually complete destruction or severe damage up to a little over one-half mile from surface zero, and partial damage would extend out to somewhat over 1 mile.   Light damage, that is, mainly cracking of plaster and window breakage, would occur for a distance up to 4 miles away.   This means that if the bomb was detonated under water over 1 mile from shore, the structural damage on land would not be serious.

5.118   The plume following an underwater explosion (§ 2.42) consists largely of spray, and so its ability to cause physical damage to a ship is somewhat in doubt.   It appears certain, however, that the large waves formed at Bikini (§ 4.42) were responsible for some of the devastation following the atomic bomb burst.   Fairly unequivocal evidence for major damage to the U. S. S. *Saratoga* due to water-wave action is obtainable from the series of photographs taken at 3-second intervals.   Nine seconds after the explosion the photographs show the stern of the *Saratoga* rising on the first wave crest at least 43 feet above its previous level.   The radar mast is bent over but the island structure is apparently unaffected by the shock wave.   Shortly afterward the ship was obscured from view by the base surge.   When the ship again became visible the central part of the island structure was seen to be folded down onto the deck of the carrier.   It appears probable that soon after the first rise the *Saratoga* fell into the succeeding trough and was badly hit by the breaking crest of the second wave.

5.119   In view of the damage caused by waves to ships, it appears probable that similar destruction would be caused on shore if the underwater bomb burst took place in sufficient proximity. From the results obtained at Bikini (§ 4.42), where the water was moderately deep, it can be estimated that at 1 mile from surface zero the maximum height of the wave formed in the water, from trough to crest, was about 20 feet. Even at a distance of 2 miles, the wave height reached a maximum of 10 feet. For an explosion taking place in shallow water, the waves at the same distances might be twice as high. Such waves breaking over the shore could do serious harm to port facilities and warehouses.

H. DEEP UNDERWATER BURST

5.120 If the detonation of an atomic bomb took place about 1,000 feet below the surface of the sea in deep water, underwater shock would account for the major damage to ship targets. Within about 2,000 feet of surface zero, the surface wave phenomena would also contribute greatly to ship damage.

5.121 It is estimated that severe damage to merchant-type hulls and light naval craft would extend out to about 3,000 feet, but heavy, multiple-bottom craft would probably survive as close as 2,000 feet from surface zero. Shock damage to machinery resulting in immobilization may extend out to 4,500 feet. The general types of damage ensuing from a deep underwater burst will approximate those following from a shallow burst, as described above, since the effects would be due to the shock wave transmitted through the water.

5.122 Apart from damage caused by waves, it is believed that, with the possible exception of piers and breakwaters, little harm would result to harbor and shore installations as a consequence of a deep underwater explosion of an atomic bomb.

CHAPTER VI [1]

THERMAL RADIATION AND INCENDIARY EFFECTS

A. INTRODUCTION

THERMAL RADIATION FROM ATOMIC BOMB

6.1 It was pointed out in Chapter I that the radiations from an atomic explosion may be divided into two major categories, namely, thermal and nuclear radiations. These two types of radiation have vastly different characteristics, and hence will be discussed separately. In the present chapter the subject of thermal radiation which, as the name implies, refers to the radiation emitted from hot materials by virtue of their elevated temperature, will be considered. Although blast is responsible for most of the destruction caused by an atomic bomb, thermal radiation can make a significant contribution to the total damage, by producing skin burns in living organisms and, to a lesser extent, by igniting combustible structures and hence initiating fires.

6.2 An important difference between an atomic and a conventional explosion is that the energy liberated per unit mass is much greater in the former case. As a consequence, the temperature attained is much higher, with the result that a larger proportion of the energy is emitted as thermal radiation at the time of the explosion. An atomic bomb, for example, releases roughly one-third of its total energy in the form of this radiation. For the nominal atomic bomb discussed in this book, the energy emitted in this manner would be about 6.7×10^{12} calories, which is equivalent to about 8 million kilowatt hours. It is evident that this enormous amount of radiant energy would be expected to produce considerable damage.

6.3 In order to evaluate the hazard due to thermal radiation it is necessary to understand its character as well as its effects. In this chapter, the theoretical principles will be described, and the radiation laws, which are fundamental to an understanding of the subject, will be outlined. Since the essential criterion of damage due to burning

[1] Material contributed by H. L. Bowman, S. Glasstone, J. O. Hirschfelder, A. Kramish, R. M. Langer, J. L. Magee, F. Reines, B. R. Suydam, W. L. Whitson.

is, in many cases, the total radiant energy falling upon unit area, this quantity will be given some attention.

Temperature and Radius of Ball of Fire

6.4   As indicated in Chapter II, in the early stages of an atomic explosion, radiation and shock phenomena are closely related. At about 0.1 millisecond after the detonation, the ball of fire consists of an isothermal sphere of about 50 feet radius, having a temperature of about 300,000° K.[2] Because of the ease with which radiation can travel inside the sphere, no appreciable temperature gradients exist within it, and the temperature, as well as the pressure and density, is uniform.   At this stage the shock front coincides with the surface of the isothermal sphere (§ 2.9).

6.5   As the explosion proceeds, the shock front expands at a rate faster than the isothermal sphere, heating the air it engulfs.   This shock-heated air is quite opaque to the high-temperature radiation; consequently, the radiation front engulfs new, i. e., shock heated, air relatively slowly.   Throughout this stage, then, there is a very hot inner core, i. e., the isothermal sphere, bounded by the radiation front; next comes a layer of much cooler, shock-heated air, and at its outer boundary there is the shock front itself.   For reasons to be given below, under these conditions transport of energy by the shock wave is faster than by radiation.

6.6   The foregoing phenomena have been subjected to a theoretical treatment and from this many valuable quantitative results have been obtained.   The theory will not be presented here, but use will be made of some of the conclusions.   The curves in Fig. 6.6, based partly on theory and partly on experiment, show the variation with time of the radius (R) of the ball of fire, and of its approximate apparent (or surface) temperature (T).   When due allowance is made for the necessary approximations in applying the theory, on the one hand, and for experimental errors, on the other hand, the results are in satisfactory agreement.

6.7   It will be seen from the figure that the surface temperature of the ball of fire falls rapidly to a minimum, as mentioned in § 2.13, around 2,000° K, within little more than one-hundredth of a second from the detonation of the atomic bomb.   This is followed by an increase to somewhat over 7,000° K, at the second maximum, after which the surface temperature falls steadily.   A general qualitative interpretation of these results can be given on the basis of the optical

---

[2] All temperatures in this chapter are absolute temperatures in degrees Kelvin (° K); they are equal to the respective centigrade temperatures + 273°.

properties of air.   It depends on the fact that at temperatures above 2,000° K, heated air radiates quite strongly, while at lower temperatures it is transparent to, i. e., does not absorb, thermal radiation and does not radiate.

6.8   As the shock front expands in the early stages of the explosion, its strength decreases, and the surface temperature falls rapidly to-

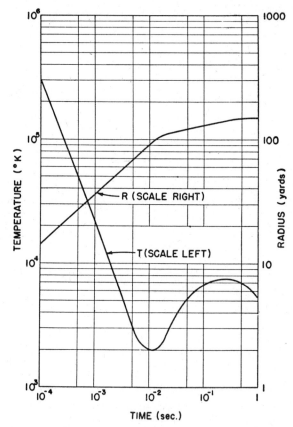

Figure 6.6.   Temperature and radius of ball of fire as function of time after explosion.

ward the minimum.   The shock front is then radiating essentially as an incandescent black body, but the rate of emission of radiation, which is proportional to $T^4 R^2$ (§ 6.19), falls off, in spite of the increase in the radius R of the ball of fire, because of the rapid decrease in the surface temperature.   Soon the temperature of the shock front becomes so low that the air is no longer incandescent; this represents the breakaway point (§ 2.11).

6.9   Since it cannot radiate, the shock front cannot now absorb radiation, and so the air behind the shock front, which has a higher temperature, begins to be seen.   Thus, the apparent, or surface, temperature, having reached a minimum, commences to increase. The shock now ceases to play any further part, as far as radiation is concerned, and the rise of surface temperature continues until that of the hot core of the isothermal sphere is attained.   This gives the second maximum which subsequently falls, due to cooling of the hot gases by radiation and expansion.

6.10   The formation of oxides of nitrogen in the air surrounding the ball of fire is of interest in connection with the optical properties described above.   For temperatures between 2,000° and 5,000° K the equilibrium concentrations of nitric oxide and nitrogen dioxide in the air are between 1 and 5 percent.   Below 2,000° K, the equilibrium concentration is negligible, and above 5,000° K, the oxides are dissociated into atoms.   Thus, if the air is heated by the shock wave to this temperature range, the oxides of nitrogen are formed.   Nitrogen dioxide is a brown gas which is opaque to visible radiation, and it is possible that the presence of this substance in the shock front contributes to the low surface temperature near the breakaway.   It is estimated that in the explosion of a nominal atomic bomb something of the order of 100 tons of nitrogen dioxide are formed, and this was believed to be responsible for the peach color of the rising cloud observed in the Bikini "Able" test (§ 2.18).

TRANSPORT OF RADIATION

6.11   Before proceeding to a more detailed consideration of the radiation emitted by an atomic bomb, brief reference will be made to a matter of some interest.   It has been mentioned (§ 6.5) that the reason why the ball of fire becomes separated from the isothermal sphere is that at a certain temperature transfer of energy by shock is faster than by radiation.   Since radiation consists of photons [3] traveling with the speed of light, it is not obvious why transport of energy as radiation should be slower than by the shock wave.

6.12   A simplified explanation of the situation may be developed by considering an isothermal sphere of air at a temperature of 30,000° K

---

[3] According to the quantum theory, electromagnetic radiation is propagated in the form of *photons*, each carrying energy hc/λ, where h is Planck's constant (§ 6.15), c is the velocity of light, and λ is the wave length of the radiation.

expanding by radiative transport alone into cold air. By means of Planck's quantum theory, which is considered below (§ 6.15), it can be shown that in such a sphere as much as 70 percent of the radiation is concentrated in the region of wave length less than 1,860 Å. In cold air the average mean free path of the photon for this radiation emitted by the hot sphere is of the order of 0.01 cm. or less.[4]

6.13   Now, the process of radiative transport proceeds somewhat in the following manner. On the average, each photon travels with the velocity of light for a distance of one mean free path and then it is absorbed by a molecule, atom, or gaseous ion present in the air which becomes excited. This entity remains in the excited state for a certain time, before returning to its ground state and emitting another photon. After this photon is emitted it moves off in a random direction, and the adsorption and emission of photons by the air molecules, etc., is repeated.

6.14   Because of the short mean free path of the photons of radiation of wave length less than 1,860 Å, and also on account of the fact that the photons move in a random path—the so-called "random walk"—the effective rate of diffusion is very small. In other words, the velocity of transport of radiation is low for the bulk of the radiation from the hot sphere; therefore, the rate of transport through cold air will be relatively small. However, on account of its much greater mean free path, the small fraction of the radiant energy of longer wave length, i. e., in excess of about 1,860 Å, will be propagated with the velocity of light.

B.   RADIATION FROM THE BALL OF FIRE

RADIATION LAWS

6.15   The spectrum of the thermal radiation from the ball of fire, assuming it to be a black body radiator,[5] is related to the surface temperature by Planck's radiation law. If $\epsilon_\lambda d\lambda$ denotes the energy density of radiation in the wave length interval λ to $\lambda + d\lambda$, the law states that

$$\epsilon_\lambda = \frac{8\pi hc}{\lambda^5} \cdot \frac{1}{e^{hc/\lambda kT} - 1},$$
(6.15.1)

---

[4] The mean free path of a photon, i. e., the mean distance it travels before absorption by a molecule, is equal to the reciprocal of the absorption coefficient. Radiations of wave length less than 1,860 Å are strongly absorbed (§ 6.17), and so the mean free path is very short.

[5] The assumption that the ball of fire radiates as a black body is made from theoretical considerations only, for the spectral distribution of the radiation has not been determined. It may be mentioned that it is known from experiment that the continuous background in the radiation from the sun follows the black body distribution law, and there are reasons for believing that the conditions in the ball of fire are even more favorable for the emission of black body radiation.

where c is the velocity of light in vacuo, h is Planck's quantum of action, k is Boltzmann's constant, i. e., the gas constant per molecule, and T is the absolute temperature. The values of the energy density, in ergs per cm.^{3} per Å, as calculated from equation (6.15.1) for three different temperatures, are plotted in Fig. 6.15 as a function of the

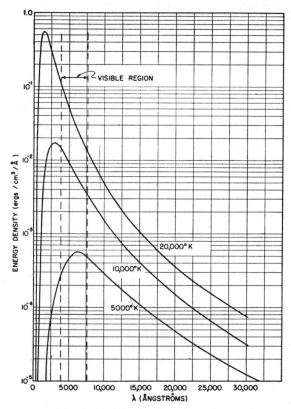

Figure 6.15.   Energy density of black body radiation as function of wave length for different temperatures according to Planck's equation.

wave length.   The curves show how markedly the radiant energy is concentrated into the short wave length region of the spectrum.

6.16   A second law of the black body radiation is required at this point.   When a black body is heated to an absolute temperature T, each unit area of its surface radiates energy at a rate proportional to the fourth power of the temperature.   This law, the Stefan-Boltzmann law, then states that the flux of radiant energy, that is, the rate at which the energy passes through 1 square centimeter of the surface of a black body, is given by the expression

$$\Phi_b = \sigma T^4, \tag{6.16.1}$$

where, according to the Planck theory,

$$\sigma = 2\pi^5 k^4 / 15 h^3 c^2 \tag{6.16.2}$$

$$= 5.67 \times 10^{-5} \text{ erg cm.}^{-2} \text{ sec.}^{-1} \text{ deg.}^{-4}.$$

RADIATION FLUX AND ILLUMINATION

6.17   From the two radiation laws stated above, it is possible to calculate the flux of radiant energy into an absorbing surface located

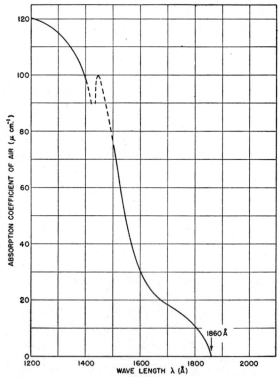

Figure 6.17.   Absorption coefficient of radiation by air as function of wave length.

at any distance from the ball of fire, provided the transmission characteristics of the air are known.   On the basis of ultraviolet absorption measurements in air, it can be stated that, for present purposes, cold air is opaque to radiations of all wave lengths shorter than 1,860 Å and is transparent for longer wave lengths. This is apparent from Fig. 6.17 which gives the absorption coefficient as a function of the wave length;[6] it is seen that at 1,860 Å the coefficient has decreased almost to zero, the actual value being 0.0044 cm.$^{-1}$.

6.18   The fraction f_0 of the total radiation emitted which can penetrate a significant distance in air can therefore be defined by

$$f_0 = \frac{\int_{\lambda_0}^{\infty} \epsilon_\lambda d\lambda}{\int_0^{\infty} \epsilon_\lambda d\lambda}, \qquad (6.18.1)^{[7]}$$

where λ_0 is 1,860 Å, and ϵ_λ is the Planck function. Since ϵ_λ is given by the Planck equation (6.15.1), the indicated integrations can be performed, and the values of f_0 for different temperatures can be calculated. The results so obtained are shown in Fig. 6.18; they may

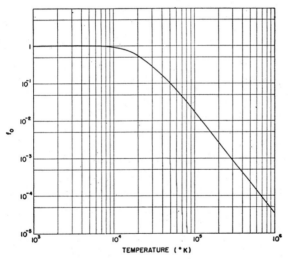

Figure 6.18.   Fraction of radiation penetrating the air as function of temperature of ball of fire.

be taken as representing f_0 as a function of the surface temperature of the ball of fire. It will be noted from this figure that for temperatures

---

[6] Absorption data given by E. G. Schneider, *J. Opt. Soc. Amer.*, *30*, 128 (1940).

[7] Because cold air is not completely transparent to wave lengths greater than 1,860 Å, this equation may be applied only for distances of a few meters from the ball of fire. The corrections necessary for greater distances are considered below (§ 6.21 *et seq.*)

less than 10,000° K, that is, for times greater than about 10^{-3} seconds after the explosion, the value of f_0 is essentially unity.

6.19   The rate at which energy passes through the whole of the spherical surface of the ball of fire, that is, over a solid angle of 4π, is given by equation (6.16.1) as $\sigma T^4 \times 4\pi R^2$, where R is the radius of the ball.   Since only the fraction f_0 of this penetrates the air, the rate at which the radiant energy reaches all points on a spherical area at a moderate distance from the point of detonation is $f_0 \sigma T^4 \times 4\pi R^2$. The radiant energy flux ϕ per unit area at a distance D is then obtained upon dividing by the total spherical area $4\pi D^2$, so that

$$\phi = f_0 \sigma T^4 \left(\frac{R}{D}\right)^2. \qquad (6.19.1)$$

6.20   From equation (6.19.1) the illumination or flux at a given point, distant D, can be computed for various times after an atomic explosion, using the values of R and T from Fig. 6.5 and of f_0 from Fig. 6.18.   In order to avoid plotting values for individual distances, the quantity ϕD^2, which is equal to $f_0 \sigma T^4 R^2$, is given in Fig. 6.20

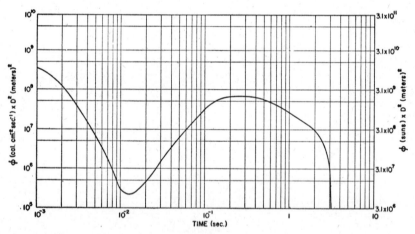

Figure 6.20.   Illumination of ball of fire as function of time after explosion.

as a function of the time; the energy flux is in calories per square centimeter per second, and the distance is in meters.   From the curve, the energy flux at any given moderate distance at a specific time can be readily determined.   These values, with some modification for transmission of the radiation over long distances, can be used to calculate the total thermal energy from an atomic bomb falling on unit area as a function of distance.

6.21 It will be observed that the smallest time interval after the explosion for which data are given in Fig. 6.20 is 10^{-3} second, and hence the values of f_0 are effectively unity, as stated in § 6.18. Therefore, the ordinates in this figure actually represent $\sigma T^4 R^2$. As seen above, the total rate at which energy is radiated from the ball of fire is $\sigma T^4 \times 4\pi R^2$ and, consequently, the ordinates in Fig. 6.20 give its radiation flux (or illumination) per unit solid angle after various time intervals.

6.22 In order to obtain some indication of the magnitude of the illumination, it is convenient to introduce a unit called a *sun*; this is defined as a flux of 0.032 calories per square centimeter per second, and is supposed to be equivalent to the energy received from the sun at the top of the atmosphere. The ordinates at the right of Fig. 6.20 give the values of ϕD^2, with ϕ in suns and D in meters.

6.23 At the luminosity minimum, the value of ϕD^2 is about 6.8×10^6 sun-meters^2, so that at this point the ball of fire, as seen at a distance of about 2,600 meters, i. e., 1.6 miles, should appear about as bright as the sun. Actually, it will be somewhat less bright, to an extent depending on the clearness of the air, because of atmospheric attenuation to be considered below.

SCATTERING AND ABSORPTION

6.24 The discussion so far has referred to the behavior of the radiation in the interior and in the immediate vicinity of the ball of fire. For this purpose it was justifiable to consider cold air as being transparent to all wave lengths longer than 1,860 Å, as the mean free path of such radiation is many meters. This simplified treatment of atmospheric transmission fails, however, when the radiant fluxes to be expected at great distances are required. It is necessary, therefore, to inquire into the transmission characteristics of air for radiation in the neighborhood of the visible region of the spectrum, i. e., for wave lengths exceeding 1,860 Å.

6.25 There are essentially two processes by which a beam of light may lose energy in penetrating air, namely, scattering and absorption. Two different types of scattering are important: scattering by individual air molecules, and scattering by dust or water droplets which are suspended in the air. The molecular, or Rayleigh, scattering is always present and is a function of the air density (or molecular concentration), to which it is in fact proportional; that is, it depends on the air temperature and the altitude above sea level. In addition, the intensity of Rayleigh scattering is proportional to the reciprocal fourth power of the wave length. Scattering of an entirely different sort occurs when there are particles such as dust or water droplets, e. g., fog or haze, in the air. As this type of scattering is essentially a diffraction process, the frequency law is dependent on the particle size in a complicated way. Again, the amount of such scattering is proportional to the concentration of scattering centers.

6.26   The other process for energy loss from a light beam is by absorption by the atoms or molecules of oxygen, nitrogen, water, etc., present in the air. This is relatively unimportant except in the near ultraviolet and in the infrared region, where water vapor absorbs quite strongly. In addition, there may be some absorption of ultraviolet radiation by ozone which is produced by interaction of gamma rays from the atomic explosion with atmospheric oxygen. As a result of Rayleigh scattering and the absorption in the near ultraviolet region of the spectrum, the transmission of light of wave length from 1,860 to about 3,000 Å is greatly reduced. This becomes more marked with increasing distance from the explosion, so that no radiation of wave length less than 3,000 Å is observed at distances greater than 5 to 10 miles.

ATMOSPHERIC ATTENUATION

6.27   Consider a point source of light in an infinite homogeneous atmosphere and suppose this source to be surrounded with a sphere of arbitrary radius. Of all the photons which leave the source, some will travel in straight lines and cross the spherical surface, some will be scattered, once or more, but will still eventually cross the sphere, and some photons will be absorbed and hence lost. The photons which are absorbed and lost will however heat the air within the sphere, and this heated air will eventually emit its excess energy in the form of longer wave length radiation. The net effect will thus be that all of the energy radiated from the source will eventually cross the spherical surface.

6.28   It might be concluded from this example that the radiant energy from an atomic bomb will eventually penetrate any thickness of air with no attenuation. This is far from being the case. In actual fact, the bomb will not be surrounded by a homogeneous atmosphere, for the concentration of scattering centers in the air above the burst decreases in density with increasing altitude and the atmosphere is bounded below by the earth. The point of interest here is only the attenuation of the radiant energy measured in a horizontal direction. The variation in the concentration of scattering centers with altitude leads to the conclusion that radiation can penetrate vertically more easily than horizontally. For example, a horizontal light beam travels through a denser medium than does a vertical beam, and hence it loses more energy by scattering than it gains. Further, most of the radiant energy is lost once it strikes the ground. Scattering, then, leads to attenuation of the radiant energy; analogous reasoning shows that absorption has a similar effect. Energy is thus lost from the horizontal radiation by selective upward scattering and by absorption in the ground.

6.29 Another mechanism for loss of radiant energy may be found in convection currents. The hot ball of fire does not radiate away all of its energy, for the heated gases are lighter than the surrounding air and they consequently rise, eventually carrying a part of their energy high into the atmosphere. For this reason, much of the radiant energy lost by absorption is never regained by re-radiation.

6.30. The theoretical treatment of scattering and absorption is extremely complex and will not be attempted here. It appears, however, that allowance for atmospheric attenuation, due to absorption and scattering, may be made, to a reasonable approximation, for each spectral component of wave length λ, by means of the exponential factor $e^{-k_\lambda D}$, where k_λ is the attenuation coefficient for the specified wave length. For a source which is not monochromatic it is necessary to integrate over all wave lengths from 1,860 Å to infinity, but for most purposes it is more convenient, and reasonably satisfactory, to use a somewhat less accurate, but simpler, mean attenuation factor e^{-kD}, where the coefficient k is the value of k_λ averaged over the spectrum of wave lengths from 1,860 Å to infinity.[8]

6.31 The fact that k_λ depends on the wave length leads to an alteration of the spectrum of the radiant energy with distance. Generally, it can be said that Rayleigh scattering preferentially removes energy from the short wave lengths, and that water vapor absorbs much of the infrared. The value of the mean attenuation coefficient k will usually vary from about 2 kilometers^{-1}, i. e., 2 km.$^{-1}$, in a dense haze to 0.10 km.$^{-1}$ in an exceptionally clear atmosphere. The relation-

---

[8] Because of the considerations referred to in §6.26, the mean attenuation factor λ will vary with the distance from the explosion. At moderately close distances, where the effects of the radiation in causing skin burns and initiating fires are important, k_λ should be averaged over all wave lengths from 1,860 Å to infinity, as stated above, although the range from 2,000 Å to infinity is probably adequate. But at distances in excess of 5 or 10 miles, depending on the state of the atmosphere, the lower limit of wave length is about 3,000 Å, since the attenuation of radiation in the range from 1,860 to 3,000 Å is then very considerable.

ship between k and the visibility range, i. e., the horizontal distance at which a large dark object can be seen against the horizon sky, is

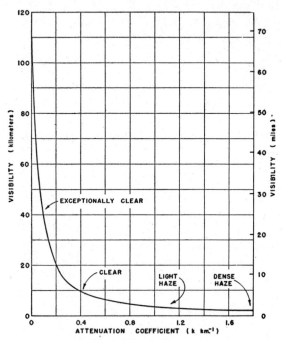

Figure 6.31.   Attenuation coefficient of radiation by air as function of visibility.

depicted in Fig. 6.31.   When the air is exceptionally clear, i. e., k is 0:1 km.$^{-1}$, the visibility range is seen to be about 40 km. or 25 miles. On an average clear day, k may be in the vicinity of 0.2 km.$^{-1}$, but in general, especially in large cities, the visibility range is usually not more than 10 km., i. e., 6.2 miles, and k is then about 0.4 km.$^{-1}$.

6.32   In many cases, atmospheric transmission may be complicated by temperature inversions and by low-lying clouds.   In such circumstances, the problem of transmission with scattering and absorption through a stratified atmosphere arises.   This problem is very complex and an adequate treatment is not possible here.

6.33   In order to make allowance for atmospheric attenuation, in the manner indicated above, the expression for the radiant flux at a distance D from the explosion, without attenuation, as given by equation (6.19.1), is multiplied by the mean attenuation factor e^{-kD}; the result is

$$\phi = f_0 \sigma T^4 \left(\frac{R}{D}\right)^2 e^{-kD}. \tag{6.33.1}$$

Since the flux ϕ is the rate at which energy crosses a unit area of a surface, the total thermal radiation energy Q delivered per unit area at a given distance will be obtained by integration with respect to the time (t); thus,

$$Q = \int_0^\infty \phi(t)\,dt \tag{6.33.2}$$

$$= \frac{e^{-kD}}{D^2} \sigma \int_0^\infty f_0 T^4 R^2 dt. \tag{(6.33.3)}$$

6.34 If the values of f_0, T and R are known as functions of time, and the attenuation coefficient k is available, it would be possible from equation (6.33.3) to determine the total thermal energy delivered per unit area at any distance D from an atomic explosion. Although this method is quite general, it is not simple to use, and hence an alternative procedure may be adopted. This depends on a knowledge of the total energy emitted by the bomb as thermal radiation.

6.35 Let E be the total thermal radiation energy produced in an atomic explosion; then, if there were no atmospheric attenuation, the energy delivered per unit area at a distance D would be given by $E/4\pi D^2$. If this is multiplied by the attenuation factor e^{-kD}, the result is equivalent to Q as given by equation (6.33.3); thus,

$$Q = \frac{E}{4\pi D^2} e^{-kD}. \tag{6.35.1}$$

The value of E is not known precisely, but for a nominal atomic bomb it may be taken as 6.7×10^{12} calories, as stated in § 6.2.

6.36 By means of this equation, it is possible to calculate the amount of thermal radiation energy delivered per unit area at any distance from an atomic explosion, for a specific value of the mean attenuation coefficient. The latter is usually expressed in km.$^{-1}$, as seen above, and so the distance D in the exponent should be in kilometers. On the other hand, if the unit area is to be 1 sq. cm., then D in the denominator will be expressed in centimeters. The results of these calculations for several values of k are plotted in Fig. 6.36. The damage caused by thermal radiation is largely determined by the total radiant energy delivered to unit area (§ 6.49). Hence, the information contained in Fig. 6.36 should provide the basis for estimates of expected damage at various distances from an atomic bomb explosion under different atmospheric conditions (§ 6.50).

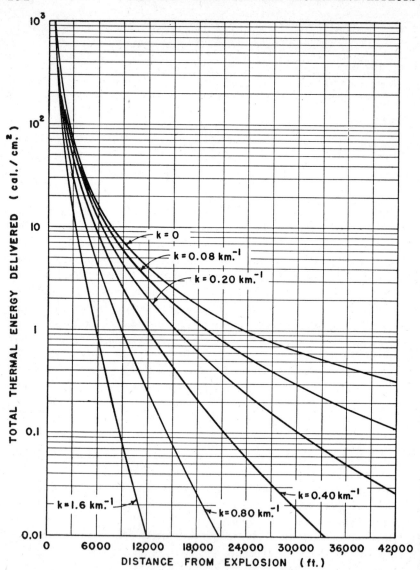

Figure 6.36.   Total thermal energy delivered as function of distance for different atmospheric visibilities.

SCALING LAWS

6.37   The calculations in the earlier portions of this chapter have dealt specifically with the thermal radiation from a nominal atomic bomb of 20 kilotons TNT equivalent energy release. In order to determine the corresponding results for a bomb of different energy yield, scaling laws may be employed. A precise treatment can be made with the aid of equation (6.33.1) together with the scaling laws given in Chapter III. However, the same conclusions may be reached in an alternative manner.

6.38 Consider two bombs whose total energy releases are W_1 and W_2. It is reasonable to assume that the fraction of energy liberated as thermal radiation is approximately independent of the total energy; hence, $E_2/W_2 = E_1/W_1$, where E_1 and E_2 are the respective thermal radiation energies. Making use of equation (6.35.1), it follows that at a given distance from the explosions

$$\frac{Q_2}{Q_1} = \frac{W_2}{W_1},\qquad (6.38.1)$$

where Q_1 and Q_2 are the total amounts of radiant energy falling on unit area in the two cases. This result represents a scaling law which states that the total radiant energy crossing a unit area located at a specified distance from the explosion is proportional to the total energy released by the bomb.

6.39 It is of interest to compare the distances D_1 and D_2 at which the atomic explosions of total energy W_1 and W_2 have the same effect as far as the thermal radiation is concerned; i. e., $Q_1 = Q_2$. By equation (6.35.1)·

$$Q_1 = \frac{E_1}{4\pi D_1{}^2}\, e^{-kD_1}\qquad (6.39.1)$$

and

$$Q_2 = \frac{E_2}{4\pi D_2{}^2}\, e^{-kD_2},\qquad (6.39.2)$$

and if these are set equal to one another, it follows that

$$\left(\frac{D_2}{D_1}\right)^2 = \frac{E_2}{E_1}\, e^{-k(D_2 - D_1)}.\qquad (6.39.3)$$

It was assumed above that the thermal radiation energy is a definite proportion of the total energy release W; hence,

$$\left(\frac{D_2}{D_1}\right)^2 = \frac{W_2}{W_1}\, e^{-k(D_2 - D_1)}.\qquad (6.39.4)$$

6.40 The ratio $(D_2/D_1)^2$ may be taken as the ratio of the areas damaged by thermal radiation in the two explosions; it is seen from equation (6.39.4) that this would be equal to the ratio of the respective energy releases if it were not for the exponential attenuation factor. In comparing two bombs which are not too large nor too different in size, the exponential factor is nearly unity and the thermal-damage areas are approximately proportional to the energy releases.   If, on the other hand, one of the two bombs being compared is very large, the exponential factor becomes increasingly important, so that, beyond a certain size, further increase of the energy release of the bomb has little effect on the thermal damage area.

6.41   It will be recalled from § 5.27 that the ratio of the areas damaged by shock wave is approximately proportional to the two-thirds power of the energy release of the bomb.   Hence, for bombs which are not too large, the thermal damage area increases more rapidly with the energy of the bomb than does the area damaged by blast. For large bombs, however, the latter increases more rapidly than the former.

6.42   Although equation (6.39.4) is useful in showing how the damage area due to thermal radiation varies with the energy release, a simpler, but equivalent, scaling procedure can be used to provide information of practical value.   In order to obtain the effect of a bomb of energy release equivalent to W kilotons of TNT, the appropriate value of the energy received per unit area, read from Fig. 6.36, is multiplied by $W/20$, since the results in this figure refer to 20 kilotons TNT equivalent energy.   Some curves obtained in this manner, taking the attenuation coefficient k as 0.1 km.$^{-1}$, are given in Fig. 6.42; they show the distances from the explosion at which specific amounts of energy are received, per unit area, as a function of the energy released in the explosion.   Similar curves can, of course, be readily obtained from Fig. 6.36 for other values of the attenuation coefficient.

C.   THERMAL RADIATION EFFECTS

ABSORPTION OF THERMAL RADIATION

6.43   It was seen in the preceding sections of this chapter that because of the high temperatures attained in an atomic explosion, the bomb resembles the sun—except for it being much nearer—in the respect that a very large amount of energy is emitted as thermal radiation.   With a conventional high-explosive bomb, not only is the total energy release much smaller, but the proportion of energy that appears as radiation is also very much less than for an atomic bomb.

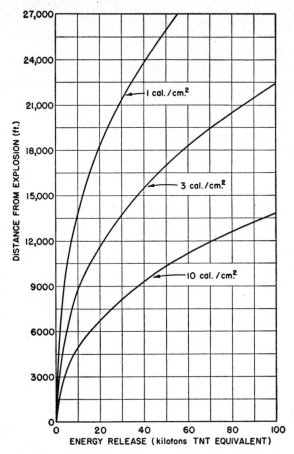

Figure 6.42. Distance from explosion at which definite amounts of thermal energy are delivered as function of energy release of bomb.

Consequently, the thermal radiation effects of a conventional bomb are insignificant, but in an atomic explosion they are of great importance. The resulting phenomena are novel, at least as far as bomb detonation is concerned, and therefore merit some discussion.

6.44   The proportion of the thermal radiation emitted in a particular atomic explosion that reaches the earth's surface depends on the distance from the burst and the clarity of the atmosphere (cf. Fig. 6.36). Because of absorption by the constituents of the air, this radiation will lie almost exclusively in the spectral region of wavelengths exceeding 1,860 Å.   That is to say, it will consist of ultraviolet (from 1,860 to about 3,850 Å), visible (3,850 to 7,600 Å), and infrared radiations (beyond 7,600 Å).

6.45 When the radiation falls on matter, part may be reflected, part will be absorbed, and the remainder, if any, will pass through, ultimately to fall on other portions of matter. It is the radiation which is absorbed that is important for the present purpose. The extent of this absorption depends on the nature of the matter and also upon its color. A black material will absorb a much larger proportion of the thermal radiation falling on it than will the same material when colored white.

6.46 Some of the radiation absorbed, particularly that in the ultraviolet spectral region, may produce chemical reaction, but most of the absorbed thermal radiation is converted directly into heat.[9] As a result the temperature of the absorbing material rises, and harmful consequences may ensue. It has been estimated, for example, that in the atomic bomb explosions in Japan, which took place some 2,000 feet above the surface of the earth, the temperature at ground zero, due to thermal radiation, was probably between 3,000° and 4,000° C. It is true that the temperature fell off rapidly with increasing distance from the burst, but the effects were definitely noticeable as far as 2 miles away or more.

6.47 An important point in connection with the thermal radiation from an atomic bomb is not only the amount of energy in this radiation, but also the fact that nearly the whole of it is emitted in an extremely short time, about 3 seconds from the initiation of the explosion. In other words, the intensity of the radiation, which is a measure of the rate at which it reaches a particular surface, is very high. Because of this high intensity, the heat accompanying the absorption of thermal radiation is produced rapidly, most of it in the surface of the body upon which it falls. Since only a small proportion of the heat is dissipated by conduction during the short interval, high surface temperatures are attained. If the emission (and absorption) of the same amount of thermal radiation occurred over a much longer period, the surface temperatures would be considerably lower, and the consequent damage much less, although the total amounts of radiation absorbed and of heat produced would be unchanged.

---

[9] Actually the energy of all radiations from an atomic bomb, both thermal and nuclear, will ultimately appear as heat, but with the nuclear radiations the conversion is very indirect and may take an appreciable ime.

CRITICAL ENERGIES

6.48   The most important physical effects of the high temperatures due to the absorption of thermal radiation are, of course, ignition or charring of combustible materials and the burning of skin.   The ignition of materials involves a large number of factors, and it is, in general, very difficult to establish definite conditions under which such burning will or will not occur.   Somewhat similar considerations apply to skin burns.   However, it seems to be established, at least as far as wood charring and skin burns are concerned, that if the heat is supplied at a rapid rate, as would be the case for the absorption of radiation of high intensity, the essential criterion is the total energy received per unit area.

6.49   The general nature of the results obtained for the charring of wood is shown diagrammatically in Fig. 6.49.   The ordinates

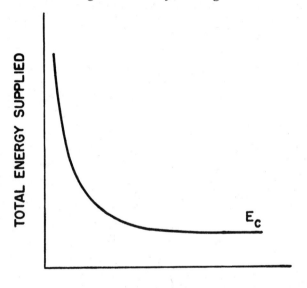

RATE OF ENERGY SUPPLY·

Figure 6.49.   Total energy necessary for ignition of wood as function of rate of supply.

represent the total amount of energy supplied as heat per unit area of the wood, and the abscissas give the rate of heat supply per unit area.   It is seen that as the rate of heat supply increases, the total energy necessary to produce charring at first decreases, and then reaches a constant limiting value. This means that, assuming the heat to be supplied sufficiently rapidly, as it is by the thermal radiation from an atomic bomb burst, there is a certain minimum or critical quantity of heat energy per unit area, represented by E_c, which is necessary to produce charring of wood. Apparently, the same criterion is applicable to skin burns, and probably to other phenomena associated with high surface temperatures.

6.50 Experiments have been made to determine the apparent critical heat energies required to produce certain effects in various materials, by supplying radiant energy of high intensity, i. e., at a high rate, about 55 calories per square centimeter per second, from a carbon arc-lamp. The conditions may be regarded as resembling those accompanying an atomic explosion. Some of the results obtained have been approximated and recorded in Table 6.50; in the last two columns of this table are given the actual distances, as estimated from Fig. 6.36, from a nominal atomic bomb burst, at which the respective energies would be attained for two different values of the atmospheric attenuation coefficient (§ 6.31). On an average clear day k may be regarded as lying between 0.2 and 0.4 km.$^{-1}$ (see Fig. 6.31). The corresponding distances for bombs of different energies can be estimated by using the scaling laws given in § 6.42. It should be noted that the distances quoted represent those from the bomb burst; the corresponding distances from ground zero would be somewhat less, depending on the height of burst.

6.51 Some of the data quoted, especially for wood and textiles, are rough averages, for there are appreciable variations with the nature of the wood, its dryness, treatment, e. g., paint, varnish, etc. The color and type of the textile material also have an influence on the observed critical heat energy. However, the values do give an indication of what is to be expected as a result of thermal radiation from an atomic explosion.

6.52 From the figures in Table 6.50, it may be concluded that exposure to thermal radiation from a nominal atomic bomb, on a fairly clear day, would lead to more or less serious skin burns within a radius of about 10,000 feet from ground zero. This is in general agreement with the experiences in Japan, which will be referred to below. However, in spite of its great range, protection from thermal radiation is easily achieved. The rays travel in straight lines, and so only direct exposure, in the open or through windows, would lead to harmful consequences. Shelter behind almost any object, such as anywhere in the interior of a house, away from windows, of course, or behind a tree, or even protection of one part of the body by another so

TABLE 6.50*

CRITICAL ENERGIES AND DISTANCES FROM ATOMIC
EXPLOSION

Material	Effect	Critical energy	Effective distance	
			$k=0.2$ km.$^{-1}$	$k=0.4$ km.$^{-1}$
		cal./cm.^{2}	Feet	Feet
Skin	Moderate burns	3	10, 000	8, 400
	Slight burns	2	12, 000	9, 600
White paper	Chars	8	7, 000	6, 000
	Burns	10	6, 300	5, 400
Black paper	Burns	3	10, 000	8, 400
Douglas fir	Chars	8	7, 000	6, 000
	Burns	11	5, 900	5, 200
Douglas fir (stained dark)	Burns	3	10, 000	8, 400
Philippine mahogany	Chars	7	7, 300	6, 300
	Burns	9	7, 150	6, 150
Maple (black)	Chars	8	7, 000	6, 000
	Burns	25	4, 300	3, 800
Cotton shirting (gray)	Scorches	8	7, 000	6, 000
	Burns	10	6, 300	5, 400
Cotton twill	Scorches	10	6, 300	5, 400
	Burns	17	5, 100	4, 400
Gabardine (green)	Brittle	7	7, 300	6, 300
	Burns	10	6, 300	5, 400
Nylon (olive drab)	Melts	3	10, 000	8, 400
Rayon lining	Scorches	3	10, 000	8, 400
	Burns	8	7, 000	6, 000
Wool serge (dark blue)	Nap gone	2	12, 000	9, 600
	Loose fibers burn	7	7, 300	6, 300
Worsted (tropical khaki)	Nap melts	4	9, 100	7, 600
	Burns	15	5, 400	4, 700
Rubber (synthetic)	Burns	8	7, 000	6, 000
Lucite	Softens	72	2, 400	2, 300
Bakelite	Chars	75	2, 400	2, 300

*The critical energies have been adapted from measurements made at the Material Laboratory, New
York Naval Shipyard.

as to avoid direct exposure to the atomic ball of fire, would be effective.
Only fairly close to ground zero would the thermal radiation be expected to penetrate clothing, and so parts of the body covered in this
way are generally safe from thermal radiation burns.

SKIN BURNS DUE TO THERMAL RADIATION

6.53 One of the striking facts connected with the atomic bombing
of Japan was the large number of casualties attributed to what have

been called "flash burns", caused by the instantaneous thermal radiation [10]. It has been estimated that 20 to 30 percent of fatal casualties at Hiroshima and Nagasaki were due to such burns, as distinct from those who suffered the more familiar flame burns. Thermal radiation burns were recorded at a distance of 7,500 feet from ground zero at Hiroshima and as far as 13,000 feet at Nagasaki. The incidence of these burns, as might have been expected, was inversely related to the distance from the explosion.

6.54   A very distinctive feature of the thermal radiation burns was their sharp limitation to exposed areas of the skin facing the center of

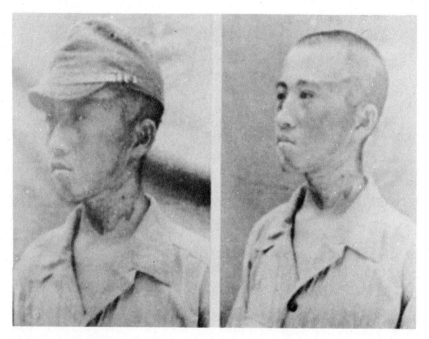

Figure 6.54.   Partial protection against thermal radiation at 6,500 feet from ground zero produced "profile" burns.   The cap was sufficient to protect the top of the head against flash burn.

the explosion; they were consequently sometimes referred to as "profile burns" (Fig. 6.54).   This is due to the fact mentioned above that the radiation travels in straight lines, and so only regions directly exposed to it will be affected.   A striking illustration of this behavior

---

[10] The physical and physiological aspects of these "flash burns" due to rapid heating of the skin differ to some extent from those of ordinary flame burns (see Chapter XI).

was that of a man writing before a window. His hands were seriously burned, but his face and neck, which were not covered, suffered only slight burns because the angle of entry of the radiation was such as to place them in partial shadow.

6.55 Although thermal radiation burns were largely confined to exposed parts of the body, there were a few cases where such burns occurred through one, and very occasionally more, layers of clothing. Instances of this kind were observed only near the center of the explosion. Where burns did occur through clothing, these tended to involve regions where the clothes were tightly drawn over the skin, at the elbows or shoulders, for example, while areas where the clothing

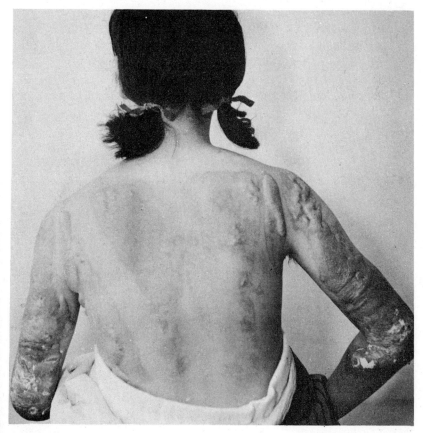

Figure 6.55a. The skin under the areas of contact with clothing is burned. The protective effect of thicker layers can be seen on the shoulders and across the back.

fitted loosely were unharmed (Fig. 6.55a). Finally, because white or light colors reflected the thermal radiations, they generally afforded better protection than dark clothing. Thus, it was not unusual to find burns through black clothing, but not through white material worn by the same individual (Fig. 6.55b).

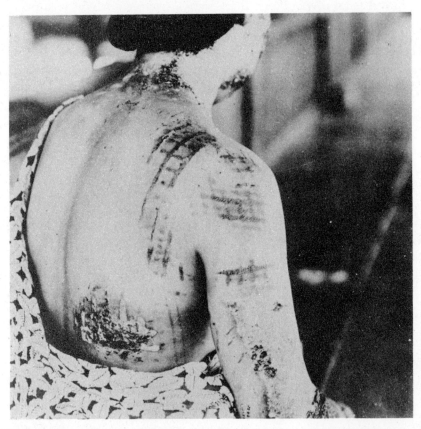

Figure 6.55b. The patient's skin is burned in a pattern corresponding to the dark portions of a kimono worn at the time of the explosion.

RELATIVE IMPORTANCE OF INFRARED AND ULTRAVIOLET RADIATIONS IN SKIN BURNS

6.56   In the foregoing treatment the influence of the total absorbed radiation has been considered as being due to its conversion into heat. The resulting high temperature then presumably causes chemical changes to take place which manifest themselves as skin burns. It is well known, however, that ultraviolet radiation, in the wave length region of 1,860 to 3,400 Å, can cause erythema, i. e., reddening of the skin, in moderate doses, leading to painful blistering for higher doses. These effects are probably due to direct chemical action of the radiation of short wave length and are not related to the heat produced. Since the radiation from an atomic bomb contains a fair amount in the ultraviolet region, it is of interest to consider how much this might contribute to skin burning.[11]

6.57 By using the Planck equation (6.15.1), the energy emission as a function of wave length at various temperatures can be calculated, as shown in Fig. 6.15. From a knowledge of the atmospheric absorption coefficients of radiations of different wave lengths, in the range from 1,860 to 3,400 Å, the proportion of energy within this range that reaches the earth at various distances from a given source, e. g., an atomic bomb, can be estimated.[12] In this way it has been found that the energy in the range of interest is a maximum fraction of the total at a temperature of 10,000° K; the contribution is less at higher and lower temperatures. Consequently, instead of attempting to integrate the energy in the range of 1,860 to 3,400 Å over all temperatures, it is supposed that the temperature is constant at 10,000° K. By using this approximation it is believed that a maximum effectiveness of the ultraviolet radiation can be estimated.

6.58 Since the temperature of the ball of fire is always below about 7,500° K after the first minimum (see Fig. 6.6), it may be supposed that essentially all the ultraviolet radiation of interest is emitted before this point. The total thermal radiation represents approximately one-third of the total bomb energy (§ 6.2), and supposing 1 percent of this to be emitted before the minimum, the thermal radiation energy before the minimum is calculated to be 6.7×10^{10} calories. The amount falling upon 1 square centimeter at various distances, neglecting atmospheric absorption, is then readily calculated to be 0.5 calories per square centimeter at 1 kilometer, and 0.125 calories per square centimeter at 2 kilometers. This will be called the incident radiation energy. Only a fraction of the energy, estimated from the Planck equation and the absorption coefficient, as described above, is in the range of 1,860 to 3,400 Å; the values are given in the table below.

---

[11] The radiation emitted from the ball of fire extends below 1,860 Å, and this is also capable of producing skin burns. But since it is almost entirely absorbed in the atmosphere before reaching the earth (see § 6.17), it may be ignored.

[12] The actual range used in the calculations was 2,000 to 3,400 Å. This is justifiable, at appreciable distances from the bomb burst, because of absorption by air of the near ultraviolet radiations, as mentioned in § 6.30, footnote.

6.59 Further, not all the ultraviolet wave lengths are equally effective in producing erythema, etc., and an erythemal effectiveness factor, derived from actual experiments, can be estimated.[13] If this is multiplied by the energy fraction described above, the result is the over-all factor of effectiveness of the incident radiation energy given in the preceding paragraph. The product of the incident radiation energy and this over-all effectiveness factor represents the equivalent energy in terms of producing erythema.

6.60 Before these results can be turned to practical use, it is necessary to know the minimum amounts of energy in the critical region which will produce blistering, painful burn, erythema, and so on. These threshold energies vary from one individual to another, and so the general conclusions reached from the foregoing calculations, and recorded in Table 6.60, are given for the average individual, for 50 percent of individuals, and for the most sensitive individuals. The estimates have been made for two distances, namely, 1 and 2 kilometers from an atomic explosion, and for two different values of the visibility range, i. e., clarity of the atmosphere, 119 kilometers (perfectly clear) and 18 kilometers (clear).[14]

TABLE 6.60

ERYTHEMAL EFFECTS OF ULTRAVIOLET RADIATION FROM ATOMIC BOMB

Distance from Atomic Explosion	1 km.		2 km.	
Limit of Visibility (km.)	18	119	18	119
Incident Radiant Energy (cal./cm².)	0. 5	0. 5	0. 125	0. 125
Fraction in Range 1,860–3,400° A	0. 07	0. 12	0. 04	0. 11
Erythemal Effectiveness	0. 29	0. 31	0. 17	0. 21
Equivalent Energy (cal./cm².)	0. 010	0. 019	0. 001	0. 003
Effect on Individuals:				
Average	Vivid erythema	Painful burn	No effect	No effect
50 percent	Burn	Painful burn	No effect	Erythema
Most sensitive	Blistering	Blistering	Erythema	Vivid Erythema

[13] The most effective radiation in the near ultraviolet region is that of wave length about 2,970 Å; assuming this to have an effectiveness factor of 100, the values fall off rapidly for both longer and shorter wave lengths, e. g., the factor is down to 10 at 2,890 Å and at 3,100 Å. However, the erythemal factor increases again rapidly for wave lengths less than 2,000 Å.

[14] These visibility ranges correspond to mean attenuation coefficients (§ 6.30) of about zero and 0.22 kilometers⁻¹, respectively (see Fig. 6.31).

6.61 It would appear from Table 6.60 that on a clear day, only the most sensitive individuals exposed to ultraviolet radiation from an atomic bomb would develop erythema at a distance of 2 kilometers, i. e., about 6,600 feet. From Table 6.50 and from Japanese experience, however, it is probable that at this distance definite skin burns would have occurred due to thermal radiation. Consequently, unless the calculations are seriously in error,[15] it may be concluded that the ultraviolet range of the thermal radiation from an atomic bomb does not make the major contribution to skin injuries. If this is indeed the case, as appears probable, then infrared radiation is the main factor in causing the so-called flash burns due to the atomic bomb.

6.62 The question of whether it is the ultraviolet or the infrared region of the spectrum that is responsible for thermal radiation burns is a subject of more than mere scientific interest. If it is the infrared which is the most important, then there is a possibility that a person caught in the open by the explosion of an atomic bomb may have sufficient time to take cover, or other appropriate evasive action, and thus reduce the thermal radiation damage. This would be possible because most of the infrared radiation is emitted by the ball of fire in its later stages, following the second temperature maximum (Fig. 6.6), that is to say, from about 0.3 sec. to 3 sec. after the explosion. Thus, if protection could be found within 1 sec. of the explosion, the exposure to infrared radiation would be very roughly one-third of the total amount received at that distance. Under many circumstances this difference would be very significant.

Other Effects of Thermal Radiation

6.63 Apart from the actual ignition of combustible materials which resulted in fires being started, as will be described shortly, a number of other phenomena observed in Japan testified to the intense heat due to the absorption of thermal radiation. Fabrics (Fig. 6.63a), telephone poles (Fig. 6.63b), trees, and wooden posts, up to a radius of 9,500 feet from ground zero at Hiroshima and up to 11,000 feet in Nagasaki, if not destroyed by the general conflagration, were charred and blackened, but only on the side facing the center of the explosion. Where these were protected by buildings, walls, hills, etc., there was no evidence of thermal radiation burning.

---

[15] Because of absorption of the radiation in the near ultraviolet region in its passage through the atmosphere, it is probable that the influence of the ultraviolet has been overestimated, rather than underestimated, in these calculations.

Figure 6.63a.   Flash burns on upholstery of chairs exposed to bomb flash at window, 5,300 feet from ground zero.

6.64   An interesting case of shadowing of this kind, due to the fact that the radiation travels in straight lines, was recorded at Nagasaki.   The tops and upper parts of a row of wooden posts were heavily charred, but the charring was sharply limited by the shadow of a wall.   This wall was, however, completely demolished subsequently by the blast wave which must have arrived after the thermal radiation had caused the charring.[16]   By observing such shadows, cast by intervening objects where they shielded otherwise exposed surfaces, the center of the explosion was located with considerable accuracy (Figs. 6.64 a and b).   Further, in a number of cases these shadows also gave an indication of the height of burst, and occasionally a distinct penumbra was found from which it was possible to calculate the diameter of the ball of fire at the time the radiation intensity was at its maximum.

[16] The thermal radiation travels with the speed of light, but the velocity of the shock wave is much less, e. g., about 2 miles per second at a short distance from the explosion, ultimately dropping to the speed of sound, i. e., about one-fifth mile per second (see Chapter III).

Figure 6.63b.   Flash burns on wooden poles, 6,200 feet from ground zero.   The uncharred portions were protected from thermal radiation by a fence.

6.65   Among the striking effects of the thermal radiation was the roughening of the surface of polished granite where there was direct exposure.   This roughening was attributed to the unequal expansion of the constituent crystals of the stone, and it is estimated that a temperature of about 600° C. was necessary to produce the results observed.   From the depth of roughening and ultimate flaking of the granite surface, the depth to which this temperature was attained could be determined.   These observations were used to estimate the average ground temperatures immediately after the atomic explosion. The fact that granite was heated as high as at least 600° C., to an appreciable depth, is some indication of the high maximum temperatures that must have been reached.

6.66   Another remarkable effect was the bubbling or blistering of the tile which is widely used for roofing in Japan (Fig. 6.66).   This phenomenon was observed out to 4,000 feet from the explosion center.

The size of the bubbles and their extent increased with the proximity to ground zero, and also with the squareness with which the tile itself faced the explosion.   In a test, using undamaged tile of the same kind, at the United States Bureau of Standards, it was found that a similar blistered surface could be obtained by heating to

Figure 6.64a.   Flash marks produced by thermal radiation on asphalt of bridge. Where the railings served as a protection from the radiation, there were no marks.   The length and direction of the "shadows" indicate the point of the bomb explosion.

1,800° C. for a period of 4 seconds.   The effect so produced extended deeper into the tile than did that caused by the atomic bomb; from this result it was concluded that in the bomb explosion the tile was subjected to a temperature of more than 1,800° C. for less than 4 seconds.

6.67   A further interesting feature associated with the thermal

Figure 6.64b.   Paint on gas holder, 7,000 feet from ground zero, scorched by the thermal radiation, except where protected by the valve.

radiation was the behavior of light and dark fabrics.   As mentioned above, the former reflect a larger proportion of the radiation, and so they are a better protection against skin burns.   At the same time, they do not attain as high a temperature as do dark materials.   In one case, a shirt consisting of alternate narrow light and dark gray stripes had the dark stripes burned out, but the light stripes were undamaged (Fig. 6.67).   Similarly a piece of paper, which had been exposed about 1.5 miles from ground zero, had the characters, written in black ink, burned out, but the rest of the paper was not greatly affected.

D.   INCENDIARY EFFECTS

Atomic Bomb as Incendiary Weapon

6.68   The incendiary effects, that is, the effects due to fire, accompanying an atomic explosion, do not present any characteristic features.   In principle, the same result, as regards destruction by fire and blast, might be achieved by the use of conventional high-explosive and incendiary bombs.   It has been estimated, for example, that the physical damage to buildings, etc., equivalent to that at Hiroshima could be produced by approximately 325 tons of high explosive and about 1,000 tons of incendiary bombs.   It can be seen, however, that the atomic bomb is unique in the overwhelming nature of its destructiveness, and this is particularly true as far as incendiary effects are concerned.

Figure 6.66.   Blistered surface of roof tile near ground zero, about 2,000 feet from the point of the burst.   Left portion of the tile was shielded by an overlapping one.

6.69   Whereas the blast damage caused by any bomb, atomic or otherwise, is largely determined by its energy release, the same is not true for destruction due to fire.   Some evidence for this is the fact that at Hiroshima and Nagasaki similar blast effects were experienced in each case at equal distances from the center of the explosion.   On the other hand, the total area severely damaged by fire at Hiroshima, about 4.4 square miles, was about four times as great as in Nagasaki.   Probably the main reason for this difference lay in the nature of the terrain, Hiroshima being relatively flat while Nagasaki was hilly.   This reflected the distribution of combustible buildings and the opportunity for the spread of fire (cf. § 6.82).

6.70   It is generally true, for any incendiary weapon, that the ultimate results are greatly dependent on a variety of conditions. Some of these are related to the characteristics of the particular locality as, for example, the closeness of buildings, and their arrangement and combustibility, while others depend on meteorological conditions, such as air movements, moisture, etc. In considering the effects of the atomic bomb these factors must be borne in mind; it follows then that the types of generalizations which can be made in

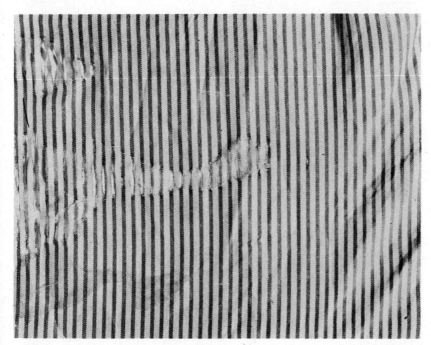

Figure 6.67. The light-colored portions of the material are intact, but some of the dark-colored stripes have been destroyed by the heat from the thermal radiation.

connection with blast effects (Chapter V) are not possible for damage caused by fire.

Origin and Spread of Fires in Japan

6.71 In view of the very high instantaneous surface temperatures produced by the thermal radiation from an atomic bomb, the question arises as to whether this may have been one of the primary factors responsible for the fire accompanying the explosions in Japan. Abnormal, enhanced intensities of radiation, due to reflection and focusing effects, might have caused fires to originate at certain points

Figure 6.71.   The top of a wood pole, about 6,700 feet from ground zero, was reported as being ignited by the thermal radiation.   (Note the unburned surroundings, the nearest burned building being 360 feet away.)

(Fig. 6.71). Definite evidence has been obtained from observers that the radiation caused thin, dark cotton cloth, such as the black-out curtains that were used in Japan, thin paper and dry-rotted wood to catch fire at distances up to 3,500 feet from ground zero. It was reported that a cedar-bark roof, at 5,000 feet from the center of the explosion, was seen to burst into flame, apparently spontaneously, but this has not been completely confirmed.

6.72 Interesting evidence of actual ignition of wood by the thermal radiation, apart from the charring mentioned earlier, was found about a mile from ground zero at Nagasaki. A light piece of wood, similar to the flat side of an orange crate, had its front surface charred, but, in addition, blackening was observed through cracks and nail holes, and around the edges adjoining the charred surface. The probable explanation is that the front surface of the wood had actually ignited, due to the heat from the thermal radiation, and the flames had spread through the cracks around the edges for several seconds before they were blown out by the wind of the blast.

6.73 It seems likely that much of the charring of the wood observed at Nagasaki and Hiroshima may have been accompanied by flame which was extinguished by the blast. At distances close enough to the explosion to cause actual ignition of wood, etc., the blast wind, coming within a few seconds, would generally be strong enough to blow out the flame. For this reason it would appear that relatively few of the numerous fires, which developed almost instantaneously after the atomic bombings of Japan out to distances of 4,000 to 5,000 feet from ground zero, that is, almost to the limit of severe blast damage, were due directly to thermal radiation from the bombs.

6.74 It is probable that most of the fires originated from secondary causes, such as upsetting of charcoal or wood stoves, which were common in Japanese homes, electrical short circuits, broken gas lines, and so on, which were a direct effect of the blast wave. In several cases, fires in industrial plants were started by the overturning of furnaces and boilers, and by the collapse of buildings on them.

6.75 Once the fires had started, there were several factors, for which the atomic bomb was responsible, that facilitated their spread,[17] apart from the important factors of weather, terrain, and the closeness and combustibility of buildings. By breaking glass windows, and blowing in or damaging fire shutters (Fig. 6.75), by stripping wall and roof sheathing, and collapsing walls and roofs, the blast made buildings of all types vulnerable to the spread of fire. Similarly, many non-

---

[17] It is of interest to mention that the fires did not always spread rapidly. It is reported that survivors were able to evacuate areas not far from ground zero as long as two hours after the explosion.

combustible buildings were left in a condition favorable to the internal spread of fires by damage to doors at stairways, elevators and in fire-wall openings, and by the rupture or collapse of floors and partitions. The spread of fire into fire-resistive structures was facilitated by burning brands from nearby buildings entering through broken windows and other openings.

6.76   Although there were firebreaks, both natural, e. g., rivers and open spaces, and artificial, e. g., roads, in Hiroshima and Nagasaki,

Figure 6.75.   Fire shutters in building, about 3,000 feet from ground zero, blown in or damaged by the blast.   Shutter at center probably blown outward by blast passing through building.

they were not very effective in preventing the fires from spreading, except at the perimeter of the initial burning area.   The reason for this was that fires started simultaneously on both sides of the fire-breaks, so that they could not serve their intended purpose.   In addition, combustible material was frequently strewn across the fire-breaks and open spaces, such as open yards and street areas, by the blast of the explosion, so they did not prevent the spread of fire. Nevertheless, there were a few instances where firebreaks assisted in preventing the burn-out of some fire-resistive buildings, and it is likely that if the firebreaks had been wider, say 100 feet or more, the number of buildings destroyed by fire would have been less.

6.77   It may be noted that, on the whole, it is considered that the destruction of buildings by the blast wave hindered rather than facilitated the development of the fires at Hiroshima and Nagasaki. Combustible frame buildings when blown down did not burn as rapidly as would have been the case had the same buildings been left standing. Further, the noncombustible debris produced by the blast frequently covered and prevented the burning of combustible material.

6.78   One of the important aspects of the atomic bomb attacks in Japan was that in the large area which suffered simultaneous blast damage the fire departments were completely overwhelmed (see Fig. 12.45).   It is true that the fire-fighting services and equipment were poor by American standards, but it is doubtful if much could have been achieved, under the circumstances, by more efficient fire departments.   At Hiroshima, for example, 70 percent of the fire-fighting equipment was crushed in the collapse of fire houses, and 80 percent of the personnel were unable to respond.   Even if men and machines had survived the blast, many fires would have been inaccessible because of the streets being blocked with debris.   For this reason, and also because of the fear of being trapped, a fire company from an area which had escaped destruction was unable to approach closer than 6,500 feet to ground zero at Nagasaki.   It was almost inevitable, therefore, that all buildings within this range would be destroyed.

6.79   Another contributory factor to the destruction by fire was the failure of the water supply in both Hiroshima and Nagasaki. The pumping stations were not largely affected, but serious damage was sustained by distributing pipes and mains, with a resulting leakage and drop in the available water pressure.   Most of the lines above ground were broken by collapsing buildings and by heat from the fires which melted the pipes.   At Nagasaki a large water main 3 feet below ground failed owing to uneven displacement of soil caused by oblique blast pressure, while at Hiroshima, a similar main was broken due to the distortion of a bridge upon which it was supported (see Fig. 5.68b).

FIRE STORM

6.80   About 20 minutes after the detonation of the atomic bomb at Hiroshima there developed the phenomenon known as *fire storm*. This consisted of a wind which blew toward the burning area of the city from all directions, reaching a maximum velocity of 30 to 40 miles per hour about 2 to 3 hours after the explosion, decreasing to light or moderate and variable in direction about 6 hours later.   The wind was accompanied by intermittent rain, light over the center of the city and heavier about 3,500 to 5,000 feet to the north and west. Because of the strong inward draft at ground level, the fire storm was a decisive factor in limiting the spread of the fire beyond the initial ignited area. It accounts for the fact that the radius of the burnt-out area was so uniform in Hiroshima and was not much greater than the range in which fires started soon after the explosion. However, virtually everything combustible within this region was destroyed.

6.81   It should be noted that the fire storm is by no means a special characteristic of the atomic bomb. Similar fire storms have been reported as accompanying large conflagrations in the United States, and especially after incendiary bomb attacks in both Germany and Japan during World War II. The high winds are produced largely by the updraft of the heated air over. an extensive burning area. They are thus the equivalent, on a very large scale, of the draft that sucks air up a chimney under which a fire is burning. The rain associated with the fire storm is apparently due to the condensation of moisture on the particles of carbon, etc., from the fire when they reach a cooler area.

6.82   The incidence of fire storms is dependent on the conditions existing at the time of the fire. Thus, there was no such definite storm over Nagasaki, although the velocity of the southwest wind, blowing between the hills, increased to 35 miles per hour when the conflagration had become well established, perhaps about 2 hours after the explosion. This wind tended to carry the fire up the valley in a direction where there was nothing to burn. Some 7 hours later, the wind had shifted to the east and its velocity had dropped to 10 to 15 miles per hour. These winds undoubtedly restricted the spread of fire in the respective directions from which they were blowing. The small number of dwellings exposed in the long narrow valley running through Nagasaki probably did not furnish sufficient fuel for the development of a fire storm as compared to the many buildings on the flat terrain at Hiroshima.

FLAME BURNS

6.83   In addition to the so-called flash burns, or thermal radiation burns, described above, many of the casualties from the atomic bomb explosions were due to flame burns. In buildings collapsed by the blast many persons, who might otherwise have survived their injuries, were trapped and burned. The burns suffered were of the kind which might accompany any fire and are not especially characteristic of an atomic explosion. It may be mentioned that burns of both types, flash and flame, were believed to be responsible for more than half of the fatal casualties and probably at least three-quarters of all the casualties at Hiroshima and Nagasaki. The magnitude of the problem, therefore, points to the necessity for making adequate preparations for dealing with large numbers of burned patients in the event of an emergency.

6.84   The subject of burns, as an aspect of the biological effects of an atomic explosion, will be examined more fully in Chapter XI.

CHAPTER VII[1]

INITIAL NUCLEAR RADIATIONS

A. INTRODUCTION

NATURE OF NUCLEAR RADIATIONS

7.1 As indicated in Chapter I, the explosion of an atomic bomb is accompanied by the emission of nuclear radiations, consisting of gamma rays, neutrons, beta particles (electrons), and a small proportion of alpha particles. The neutrons and some of the gamma rays are emitted in the actual fission process, that is to say, simultaneously with the explosion, while the remainder of the gamma radiation and the beta particles are liberated as the fission products decay. The alpha particles result from the normal radioactive decay of the plutonium 239 or uranium 235 which has not undergone fission.

7.2 Because of the nature of the phenomena associated with an atomic explosion taking place in the air, it is convenient, for practical purposes, to consider the nuclear radiations as divided into two categories, namely, initial and residual.[2] The line of demarcation is somewhat arbitrary, but it may be taken as about 1 minute after the explosion. The initial nuclear radiation, with which the present chapter will be concerned, consequently, refers to the radiations emitted within a minute of the detonation.

7.3 The range of alpha and beta particles is so small that they cannot penetrate to the surface of the earth. It is evident, therefore, that the initial radiations may be regarded as consisting only of gamma rays and neutrons produced during a period of one minute after the atomic explosion. Both of these forms of nuclear radiation have considerable penetrating power, so that they can reach the earth even when liberated at appreciable distances away. Further, both gamma rays and neutrons can produce harmful effects on living organisms (see Chapter XI).

7.4 The energy of the gamma rays present in the instantaneous or prompt nuclear radiation (§ 7.9) is about 3 percent of the total

---

[1] Material contributed by S. T. Cohen, M. S. Plesset, F. Reines, H. Scoville, Jr., R. C. Smith, B. R. Suydam.

[2] For an underwater or an underground burst, the initial nuclear radiations would probably be almost entirely absorbed by the water or the earth. Consequently, detonations of this type are not considered in the present chapter.

energy liberated by the bomb, but only a small proportion of this, perhaps 1 percent, succeeds in penetrating any great distance from the bomb. A somewhat similar amount is present in the gamma rays emitted by the fission products in the first minute after an atomic explosion. Nevertheless, in spite of the energy being considerably smaller than that appearing in the form of thermal radiation, the gamma radiation can cause an appreciable proportion of the atomic bomb casualties. On the other hand, nuclear radiations do not cause any incendiary effects.

7.5 Shielding from thermal radiation, at distances not too close to the explosion of the bomb, is a relatively simpler matter, but this is not true for gamma rays or neutrons. For example, at a distance of 3,000 feet from the explosion of a nominal atomic bomb, the initial nuclear radiation would probably prove fatal to 50 percent of human beings, even if protected by 12 inches of concrete, although a much lighter shield would be adequate against the thermal radiation. However, beyond about 7,000 feet, the nuclear radiations would be virtually harmless, without protective shielding, whereas exposure to the thermal radiation at this distance could produce serious skin burns in the same circumstances.

7.6 Because gamma rays and neutrons are so different in their properties, it is desirable to consider them separately. The subject of gamma rays will be considered in the section which follows, and neutrons will be discussed in the succeeding one.

B. GAMMA RAYS

Sources of Gamma Rays

7.7 In addition to the gamma rays which actually accompany the fission process, contributions to the initial nuclear radiation are made by other sources of gamma rays. Of the neutrons produced in fission, some serve to sustain the fission-chain reaction (§ 1.39), but others may be captured by nonfissionable nuclei. As explained in § 1.25, the resulting compound nucleus will be in an excited, i. e., high energy, state and it will generally radiate most of this excess energy in the form of one or more photons of gamma radiation. This is a reaction of the radiative capture type, often represented by the symbol (n, γ), implying that a neutron is taken up by a nucleus and gamma radiation is emitted. Thus, radiative capture of neutrons or, in other words, (n, γ) reactions will be a second source of gamma rays.

7.8 The neutrons produced in fission also act as a third source of these radiations. When a fast, i. e., highly energetic, neutron collides with an atomic nucleus, the former may transfer some of its energy to the latter, leaving it in an excited state. The excited nucleus may then return to its normal, or ground, state by the emission of one or more photons of gamma radiation.

7.9 The gamma radiations produced in fission, and by radiative capture and nuclear excitation all appear within a few millionths of a second of the explosion of the atomic bomb. For this reason, the radiation from the three sources described above is known as the *prompt gamma radiation.*

7.10 As already mentioned, many of the fission fragments and their decay products emit gamma rays in the course of their decay. The half lives of these radioactive isotopes range from a fraction of a second to many years. Nevertheless, since the decay commences the instant these unstable species are formed and since, in fact, the rate of decay is greatest at the beginning, there will be an appreciable liberation of gamma radiation during the first minute after the atomic explosion. In other words, the gamma rays emitted by the fission products make a significant contribution to the initial nuclear radiation. However, since the emission process is a continuing one, spread over a period of time that is long compared with that in which the prompt radiation is liberated, the resulting gamma rays are referred to as the *delayed gamma radiation.*

7.11 The total number of prompt gamma-ray photons released in fission is about equal to the number of delayed photons emitted by the radioactive decay of the fission fragments. However, the prompt and the delayed gamma rays are by no means of equal importance. The prompt gamma rays are, for the most part, emitted before the bomb has completely blown apart. They are therefore strongly absorbed by the dense bomb materials and very few of them reach the air outside the bomb. The delayed gamma rays, on the other hand, are mostly emitted at a later stage in the explosion, after the bomb materials have volatilized and expanded to form a tenuous gas. The delayed gamma rays thus suffer little or no absorption before reaching the air. The net result is that these gamma rays contribute about a hundred times as much as do the prompt gamma rays to the total dosage delivered at a distance from the atomic explosion.

7.12 There is another possible source of gamma rays which may be of some importance in the case of an explosion near the ground. Some of the neutrons emitted by the explosion will strike the ground and will interact with atomic nuclei of the soil; the resulting (n, γ) reactions and the excitation by fast neutrons will produce gamma rays. The magnitude of this effect will depend on the height of burst and on the chemical composition of the soil. It would probably be small for a bomb burst at an altitude above about 2,000 feet, and would not be of major importance at lower altitudes because of the relatively small number of neutrons.

INTERACTION OF GAMMA RAYS WITH MATTER

7.13 There are three important ways in which gamma rays interact with the matter through which they pass. When a gamma-ray photon makes an elastic collision, sometimes called a "billiard ball" collision, with an electron present in an atom, the photon transfers some of its energy to the electron. At the same time, the photon is deflected from its original path. This interaction, resulting in a scattering of the gamma rays, is known as the *Compton effect*. In passing through a nonabsorbing medium, a beam of gamma rays will lose energy, that is to say, it will decrease in intensity, as a result of Compton scattering, but the number of photons will remain unchanged.

7.14 The total Compton scattering per atom of the material with which the radiation interacts is proportional to the number of electrons in the atom, and hence to the atomic number (§1.9). It is consequently greater for an atom of a "heavy" element, i. e., one of high atomic weight, than for an atom of a "light" element of low atomic weight. The Compton scattering decreases, however, with increasing energy of the gamma radiation.

7.15 The second process whereby gamma rays can interact with matter is the *photoelectric effect*. A gamma photon, with energy somewhat greater than the binding energy of an electron in an atom, transfers all its energy to the electron which is consequently ejected from its atom. Some of the energy of the photon is used to detach the electron and the remainder appears as kinetic energy of the latter. Since the photon involved in the photoelectric effect loses all its energy, it ceases to exist. Thus, while in the Compton effect the gamma-ray photon remains after the interaction with an electron, although with diminished energy, the photoelectric effect results in the destruction of the photon. The magnitude of the photoelectric effect is proportional to the fifth power of the atomic number of the material through which the gamma rays pass, but it decreases rapidly with increasing energy of the photon.

7.16 Gamma radiation can interact with matter in a third manner, namely, that of *pair production*. When a gamma-ray photon with energy in excess of 1.02 Mev [3] passes near the nucleus of an atom, the photon can be annihilated in the strong electrical field with the formation of a pair of particles, consisting of a positive and a negative electron. By the Einstein law of the equivalence of mass and energy (§ 1.34), the energy equivalent of the total mass of the positive and negative electrons is 1.02 Mev, and this is the minimum energy necessary for the production of the electron pair. A gamma-ray photon with energy less than 1.02 Mev cannot cause pair production, but if the energy is greater than this value the process is possible. Any energy of the photon in excess of 1.02 Mev appears as kinetic energy of the electron pair. As in the case of the photoelectric effect, pair production results in the disappearance of the gamma-ray photon. The diminution in intensity of gamma radiation due to pair production, as a result of passage through matter, increases with the square of the atomic number of the element, and also with the energy of the photon in excess of 1.02 Mev.

7.17 The relative effectiveness of the three processes, described above, in decreasing the energy of gamma rays depends on the atomic number of the absorbing material and on the energy of the incident radiation. For energies below 1.02 Mev, the Compton and photoelectric effects occur exclusively, but the latter is of consequence only for the lowest energies and for elements of fairly high atomic number. The Compton scattering also decreases as the photon energy increases, but not so rapidly as does the photoelectric effect. In the intermediate energy range, where the latter effect is small but pair production is not yet possible, the Compton effect is dominant. With increasing photon energy, above 1.02 Mev, pair production becomes more and more important while the part played by the Compton scattering becomes increasingly less significant. The relative contributions of the various attenuating factors, determined as described below (§ 7.23), are shown for air ("light" elements) and for lead ("heavy" element) in Figs. 7.17a and 7.17b, respectively.

7.18 In each of the three processes by which a gamma-ray beam loses energy as it traverses matter, there is liberated an electron—in the case of pair production, two electrons—often moving with high speed. These energetic secondary electrons, as they are called, interact with other electrons present in various atoms, causing ionization of the latter and frequently disrupting chemical bonds. It is the decomposition of certain molecules in living organisms, resulting

---

[3] The symbol "Mev" represents 1 million electron-volts of energy, which is equivalent to 1.6×10^{-6} erg or 3.8×10^{-14} calorie. It is the energy acquired by a unit positive or negative charge when it is accelerated by a potential of 1 million volts. The Mev unit of energy is widely used by nuclear physicists. An electron-volt, represented by the symbol "ev", is a one-millionth part of an Mev.

from the breaking of chemical bonds, which alters the characteristics of vital parts of cells and causes physiological damage (Chapter XI). Incidentally, the ionization due to the electrons ejected or produced by gamma rays can be used for their detection (Chapter IX).

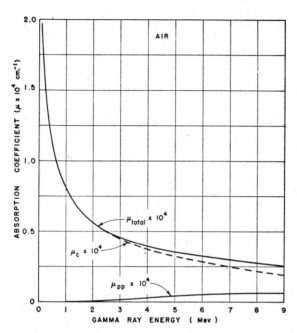

Figure 7.17a.   Absorption coefficient of air as function of gamma-ray energy.

CROSS SECTIONS AND ABSORPTION COEFFICIENT

7.19   It is the general practice in connection with nuclear and related processes to describe the probability of the occurrence of a particular reaction in terms of an area, called the *cross section* for the reaction.   The photoelectric effect and pair production represent, essentially, interaction between a gamma-ray photon and an atom or an atomic nucleus.   Consequently, the values of the reaction cross sections are given as those per atom of the material with which the radiation interacts.   The Compton effect on the other hand, involves a photon and an individual electron, so that there is a definite scattering cross section per electron.   However, if the result is multiplied by the number of electrons in the particular atom, i. e., by its atomic number, an effective atomic cross section is obtained.

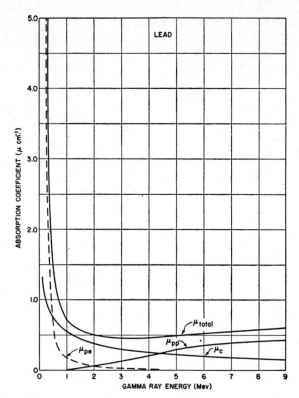

Figure 7.17b.   Absorption coefficient of lead as function of gamma-ray energy.

7.20   The values of the cross sections for the three processes under consideration can be calculated by means of quantum mechanics,[4] but for practical purposes it is more useful to express them in a somewhat different form.   Consider a narrow beam of monoenergetic gamma photons, i. e., of gamma rays of uniform wave length, incident on a slab of matter, in which there are N atoms per cc.   If σ_c, σ_{pe} and σ_{pp} represent the cross section *per atom* of the Compton, photoelectric and pair-production reactions, respectively, then in passing through a thickness dx cm. of this slab, the total probability of a photon interacting with an atom of matter is equal to $(\sigma_c + \sigma_{pe} + \sigma_{pp}) \, N \, dx$.   Let n be the gamma-ray photon flux, that is, the number of photons in the beam which cross 1 square centimeter in 1 second; the total number of interactions per second between the photons and atoms in traversing a distance dx over an area of 1 square centimeter, is then $n(\sigma_c + \sigma_{pe} + \sigma_{pp}) \, N \, dx$.

[4] See W. Heitler, "The Quantum Theory of Radiation," Second edition, Oxford University Press, 1944.

7.21   As the photoelectric effect and pair production involve destruction of photons, the latter are completely removed from the gamma-ray beam. It will be assumed, for the present, that the photons undergoing Compton scattering are also lost, a situation which, it will be seen later, applies in certain circumstances only. However, if this assumption is made, the quantity $n(\sigma_c + \sigma_{pe} + \sigma_{pp})N\,dx$ obtained above may be regarded as the decrease $(-dn)$ per second in the number of photons in the gamma-ray beam in its passage through a distance dx over 1 square centimeter of matter; that is to say,

$$-dn = n(\sigma_c + \sigma_{pe} + \sigma_{pp})N\,dx \tag{7.21.1}$$

or

$$\frac{dn}{n} = -(\sigma_c + \sigma_{pe} + \sigma_{pp})N\,dx. \tag{7.21.2}$$

Upon integration this gives

$$n(x) = n_0 e^{-(\sigma_c + \sigma_{pe} + \sigma_{pp})Nx} \tag{7.21.3}$$

as the relationship between the incident flux n_0 in the gamma-ray beam and the flux $n(x)$ after it has penetrated a depth x into matter. The quantity $(\sigma_c + \sigma_{pe} + \sigma_{pp})N$ in the exponent of equation (7.21.3) is generally represented by the symbol μ, called the *absorption coefficient* of the material for the particular homogeneous gamma rays under consideration. The photon flux may be replaced by the intensity I, to which it is proportional[5], and equation (7.21.3) then takes the familiar form of the exponential attenuation law, namely,

$$I = I_0 e^{-\mu x}, \tag{7.21.4}$$

where I_0 is the intensity of the beam of gamma rays falling on the medium of thickness x, and I is the intensity of the emergent beam.

7.22   Since the distance x is usually given in cm., the absorption coefficient is expressed in cm.$^{-1}$ units. The values as calculated for a number of common materials, namely, air, water, aluminum, iron, and lead, for gamma rays of several energies are recorded in Table 7.22. The figures for air refer to 1 atm. pressure and 0° C.

7.23   The data in Table 7.22 give the total absorption coefficients, for Compton scattering, photoelectric effect, and pair production. It is, of course, possible to divide this value into three separate parts,

---

[5] The intensity of an electromagnetic radiation, such as gamma rays, is strictly the amount of energy that flows in 1 sec. across unit area (1 sq. cm.) of a plane perpendicular to the propagation of the rays. Since each photon carries a definite amount of energy, the intensity or energy flux for homogeneous radiation, which is a measurable quantity, is proportional to the photon flux.

TABLE 7.22. ABSORPTION COEFFICIENTS (μ) FOR GAMMA RAYS

Gamma ray energy (Mev)	Absorption coefficients in cm.$^{-1}$				
	Air	H$_2$O	Al	Fe	Pb
0. 5	1. 11$\times$10^{-4}	0. 096	0. 23	0. 63	1. 5
1. 0	. 81	. 070	. 16	. 45	. 72
2. 0	. 57	. 049	. 12	. 33	. 50
3. 0	. 46	. 039	. 090	. 28	. 46
5. 0	. 35	. 030	. 075	. 24	. 48
10. 0	. 26	. 022	. 061	. 23	. 62

each being equal to the value of σN for the particular process. The separate partial absorption coefficients obtained in this manner for air and lead, taken as examples of extreme cases, are in fact the data which were plotted in Figs. 7.17a [6] and 7.17b. It is seen that for air, the Compton effect makes essentially the sole contribution to the absorption coefficient, at least for energies up to 3 or 4 Mev. This is generally true for materials consisting of light elements, e. g., animal tissues, water, etc.

7.24 The results given above show that the (total) absorption coefficients decrease, at first, with increasing energy of the gamma rays. This is due, as already mentioned, to the diminishing contributions of the Compton and photoelectric effects. At energies in excess of 1.02 Mev, pair production begins to play an increasingly significant part, so that at sufficiently high energies the absorption coefficient begins to increase, after passing through a minimum.[7] This is apparent in Fig. 7.17b and in the last column of Table 7.22 for lead. For elements of lower atomic weight, the increase does not set in until very high gamma-ray energies are attained, e. g., about 17 Mev for aluminum and 50 Mev for water.

7.25 As a very rough approximation, it may be stated that the absorption coefficient for gamma rays is proportional to the density of the material. In other words, the ordinary (or linear) absorption coefficient divided by the density, giving what is called the *mass absorption coefficient*, for gamma rays of a particular energy, is approximately independent of the nature of the absorbing material. This is especially true for light elements, i. e., those of low atomic weight, where the Compton effect makes the major contribution to the absorption coefficient.

---

[6] The photoelectric effect in air is so small that it cannot be shown in the figure.

[7] Pair production is accompanied by gamma radiation due to mutual annihilation of a positive and a negative electron. This effect is probably of small significance for the present discussion.

7.26   As seen in § 7.14, the Compton scattering per atom is proportional to the number of electrons in the atom, i. e., to the atomic number of the element.   Hence, the linear (Compton) absorption coefficient, which is equal to the $\sigma_c N$, is proportional to the product of the atomic number and the number (N) of atoms per cc.   This product for light elements varies approximately as the density, and hence the mass absorption coefficient, which is the linear absorption coefficient divided by the density, is roughly constant for many elements of low or moderate atomic weight, e. g., up to about 100. Since the density of water is unity, the mass absorption coefficient of a light element is about equal to the linear absorption coefficient of water as given in Table 7.22.   Alternatively, the linear absorption coefficient of a substance consisting of a light element or elements may be obtained upon multiplying the value for water by the density of the material.

7.27   Because the linear absorption coefficients for different elements do not vary in exactly the same manner with the gamma-ray energy, the rule given above has serious exceptions.   However, when no other information is available it may be used to give a rough indication of the absorption coefficient of any material, especially of low atomic weight.   For example, an average concrete has a density about the same as that of aluminum, and the mean of the atomic weights of its constituent elements is also close to the atomic weight of aluminum.   It would be anticipated, therefore, that the absorption coefficient of concrete for gamma rays should be much the same as for aluminum; direct measurements have confirmed this expectation.

7.28   If the mass absorption coefficients of different materials were actually constant, then it would appear that the extent of attenuation of gamma rays of given energy is determined solely by the mass of material through which they pass.   Thus, equal weights of concrete and of lead would be required to reduce the gamma ray intensity to the same extent.   But since the latter is more dense than the former, the lead shield would be proportionately thinner than that of concrete.

7.29   In order to test the exponential law of equation (7.21.4) and the absorption coefficients of Table 7.22 by direct experiment, it is necessary for the conditions to be such that none of the radiation scattered by the Compton effect reaches the receiver.   As stated in § 7.21, the results given above are based on the postulate that the scattered photons are lost from the gamma-ray beam.   Measurements made in such a manner as to satisfy this condition are said to represent *good geometry*.

Transmission Through Thick Media

7.30　It is true that the calculations based on good geometry are fundamental to the problem of protection from gamma radiation. Nevertheless, it must be realized that an individual exposed to radiation from an atomic explosion will actually receive a large proportion of the scattered gamma photons, as well as those which have survived, unchanged, passage through the atmosphere or through a shield. The conditions to be taken into account in a consideration of protection or shielding from gamma rays are those of *bad* (or *poor*) *geometry*. Not only does this complicate the situation, but there is a further difficulty. If the thickness of the material through which gamma rays pass is of the order of the mean free path of the photons,[8] the latter will, on the average, make more than one Compton collision with electrons. In other words, multiple scattering will occur, some energy being lost at each collision.

7.31　It should be noted that the problems of poor geometry and of multiple scattering are aspects of the Compton effect, while the photoelectric effect and pair production are influenced only indirectly. The complicating factors are thus of greatest significance in connection with the transmission of gamma rays of moderate energies through materials containing elements of low atomic weight, e. g., air, water, aluminum, and concrete, where the Compton effect is very important. For elements of high atomic weight, the influence of multiple scattering is not so great, but it cannot be ignored in considerations of shielding from the gamma rays emitted in an atomic explosion.

7.32　In the study of the attenuation of a monoenergetic beam of homogeneous gamma radiation incident upon a medium of given thickness, which is fundamental to the problem of shielding, it is convenient to consider two ranges of thickness. If the latter is small compared with the mean free path of the photons, the transmitted intensity is given, with sufficient accuracy, as the sum of the unscattered (good geometry) intensity and the intensity due to single scattering. For practical purposes connected with shielding from the gamma rays in the initial radiation from an atomic bomb, these conditions are not very important.

7.33　Much more significant is the case in which the thickness of the medium is of the same order as, or greater than, the mean free path of the photons. It is then necessary to take multiple scattering into account. One way in which this can be done is the following: For elements of low atomic weight and gamma rays of moderate

---

[8] As seen in § 6.12, footnote, this is equal to the reciprocal of the absorption coefficient.

energy, the photoelectric effect and pair production are negligible, and then it is possible to write

$$I = I_0 B(\epsilon_0, \mu_c x) e^{-\mu_c x}, \qquad (7.33.1)$$

where μ_c is the partial absorption coefficient due to Compton scattering. The factor $B(\epsilon_0, \mu_c x)$, which is a function of the energy ϵ_0 of the gamma-ray photon and of the product $\mu_c x$, takes into account the effect of multiple scattering. It should be noted that since the mean free path of the photon is $1/\mu$, the quantity $\mu_c x$ represents the number of mean free paths contained in the distance x traversed by the gamma rays.

7.34 The dependence of $B(\epsilon_0, \mu_c x)$ on $\mu_c x$ for an incident gamma energy of 1.25 Mev is shown in Fig. 7.34 for air at standard tempera-

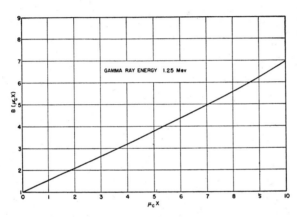

Figure 7.34. Dependence of multiple scattering function on thickness of air at S. T. P. for 1.25-Mev gamma rays.

ture and pressure (S. T. P.), i. e., 0° C. and 1 atm. pressure. For higher energies the B values are somewhat larger than shown in this figure. In the case of elements of low atomic weight, such as are being considered here, the function B appears to be almost independent of the nature of the element. In view of this fact and using the results in Fig. 7.34, it is found that a shield of concrete of 38 centimeters thickness would be required to reduce the intensity of gamma rays of 4.5 Mev to one-tenth of their initial value. This may be compared with 29 centimeters calculated from the ordinary exponential absorption equation (7.21.4), that is, using good geometry, so that multiple scattering is ignored. It is evident that much of the scattered radiation, which is neglected in good geometry treatment, actually penetrates the concrete.

7.35 In passing through shields containing heavy elements, gamma rays of moderate (and high) energies become attenuated by the photoelectric effect and pair production, as well as by scattering. The relationship between the incident and emergent intensities is given by an expression similar to equation (7.33.1) except that μ_c is now replaced by μ, the total absorption coefficient for the incident radiation. Further, it appears that for energies in the range of interest, that is, for about 0.5 to 5 Mev, the function B for a given element is dependent only, approximately, on x and is independent of the energy. Thus, the relationship may be written as

$$I = B(x) I_0 e^{-\mu x}, \qquad (7.35.1)$$

where $B(x)$, which takes multiple scattering into account, is a function of x, the thickness of the medium or shield.

7.36 Some calculated values of the multiple-scattering function $B(x)$ for lead, for various distances x, are quoted in Table 7.36. Because

TABLE 7.36

VALUES OF THE MULTIPLE-SCATTERING FUNCTION FOR LEAD

x	0	4	8	12	16 cm.
$B(x)$	1.0	1.4	1.9	2.5	3.1

of the decreasing importance of multiple scattering with elements of high atomic weight, as indicated earlier, $B(x)$ decreases with increasing atomic weight of the medium. From the data in Table 7.36, it can be shown that the thickness of lead required to reduce the intensity of 4.5-Mev gamma radiation to 0.1 of its original value is 5.8 centimeters, compared with 4.6 centimeters if multiple scattering is neglected. In general, in the region of interest for shielding from gamma rays in an atomic explosion the good geometry calculations, using equation (7.21.4), will give thicknesses which are 1 to 2 centimeters too low.

7.37 By using the various known absorption coefficients and the calculated B functions for different elements, it is possible to estimate the thicknesses of shields of various materials required to decrease the gamma radiation intensity to certain specific fractions of its incident intensity. In other words, the values of x can be calculated from equation (7.33.1) or (7.35.1), which correspond to specific values of the attenuation fraction I/I_0. The fractions chosen are 0.2, 0.1, 0.02, 0.01, and 0.001, and the approximate shielding thicknesses in inches

of water, concrete, iron, and lead are given in Table 7.37, for gamma
rays of 4.5-Mev and 0.7-Mev energy.[9]

TABLE 7.37

SHIELDING THICKNESSES FOR 4.5-MEV AND C.7-MEV GAMMA
RADIATION

Attenua-tion fraction	Thickness of shield in inches							
	4.5-Mev gamma				0.7-Mev gamma			
	Water	Concrete	Iron	Lead	Water	Concrete	Iron	Lead
0. 2	30	11	3. 8	1. 6	12	5. 1	1. 8	0. 7
. 1	40	15	5. 2	2. 3	16	6. 8	2. 4	1. 0
. 02	70	25	8. 3	3. 9	25	11	3. 9	1. 7
. 01	80	30	9. 5	4. 6	29	13	4. 5	2. 0
. 001	110	40	14	6. 7	41	19	6. 4	3. 1

TRANSMISSION FROM SOURCE

7.38   In the foregoing discussion, no account has been taken of the
source of the gamma rays or of its distance away.   All that has been
considered is the relationship between the intensity of the radiation
falling on a thickness of material, which acts as a shield by attenuating
the radiation, and the amount which penetrates the shield.   The
connection between the incident intensity I_0 and the properties of the
source, e. g., an atomic explosion, require two factors to be taken into
account; first, the inverse square law for the decrease of intensity with
distance, as used in Chapter VI, apart from absorption, and second,
the attenuation due to scattering and absorption in the atmosphere.
The latter aspect of the problem is, however, not essentially different
from that considered in connection with shielding, with the thickness
of the material greater than the mean free path of the photon.

7.39   If a point source of gamma rays emits n_0 photons per sec.,
each carrying a quantum ϵ_0 of energy, the intensity of radiation, i. e.,
the energy flux, at a distance D will be $n_0\epsilon_0/4\pi D^2$, apart from attenuation due to scattering and absorption.   Allowance for the latter
may now be made by using equation (7.33.1), so that the intensity of
the incident radiation falling on a shield at a distance D from the

---

[9] The values for these two energies are of special interest because the energy of some of the initial gamma
radiation is 4.5 Mev, while the residual radiation, to be considered in the next chapter, has a mean energy
of 0.7 Mev.

source, e. g., an atomic explosion, may be written as

$$I_0 = \frac{n_0 \epsilon_0}{4\pi D^2} B(\epsilon_0, \mu_c D) e^{-\mu_c D}. \qquad (7.39.1)$$

As before, the approximation has been made of neglecting the contributions of the photoelectric effect and of pair production in a medium, such as air, consisting of elements of low atomic weight.

7.40   Since μ_c and $B(\epsilon_0, \mu_c D)$ are known for air, it is possible to calculate I_0/n_0, that is, the energy received per photon emitted, at various distances from an atomic explosion, for gamma rays of specified energy ϵ_0.   However, since the numbers of photons of various energies emitted are not known, the results are of little practical value, although they might have some interest when further information becomes available.   For the present, the best procedure to adopt is to make use of actual measurements of radiation intensity, or of an equivalent quantity, as will be described below.

GAMMA RADIATION DOSAGE FROM ATOMIC BOMB

7.41   It was stated in § 7.18 that the physiological damage caused by gamma radiation is due to the ionization brought about by the high-energy electrons which are ejected or produced by the rays in their passage through matter.   For this reason, radiation dosage is measured in terms of a unit called the *roentgen*, symbol r, defined as the amount of gamma (or X) radiation which produces in 0.001293 gram of dry air, i. e., 1 cubic centimeter at 0°C. and 1 atm. pressure, electrically charged particles carrying a total of 1 electrostatic unit of charge of either sign.[10]   The conversion of gamma-ray energy values into roentgens is carried out somewhat in the following manner.   The energy absorbed per cubic centimeter of air at 0° C. and 1 atm. pressure due to the passage of gamma radiation is equal to the product of the cross section of the energy absorption per electron for the particular radiation, as derived from the Klein-Nishima formula,[11] the number of electrons per cubic centimeter of air at S. T. P., and the energy of the gamma radiation per square centimeter.   On the average, the production of 1 ion-pair (§9.2) in air requires 33.2 electron-volts so that the absorption of 1 Mev of gamma-ray energy produces 3.01×10^4 ion-pairs, which is equivalent to 1.44×10^{-5} roentgens, if it is absorbed in 1 cubic centimeter of air.   If the total energy absorption per cubic

---

[10] The measurement of radiation in terms of roentgens is described in Chapter IX; see also Appendix C.
[11] W. Heitler, *op. cit.*, pp. 149–157.

centimeter of air has been determined, by the method just described, the number of roentgens produced can be calculated.

7.42 The results obtained in this manner when combined with equation (7.39.1) might be used to determine the dosage in roentgens at a specified distance from an atomic bomb, provided the energy

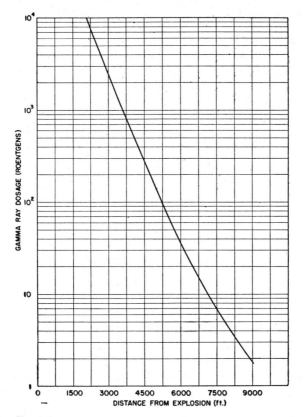

Figure 7.42. Total dosage of initial gamma radiation as function of distance from explosion.

distribution were known in terms of the respective numbers of photons emitted. As indicated above, this is not yet possible and so recourse must be had to calculations based on experimental results obtained at the time of an atomic explosion. The dosage, in roentgens, due to the initial gamma rays, at various distances from about 2,100 to 9,000 feet from the explosion of the nominal atomic bomb are given in Fig. 7.42.[12] Distances outside this range are of no interest, since at

[12] The dosage in roentgens can be expressed with fair accuracy by means of the expression $3.8 \times 10^{11} e^{-D/1026}/D^2$, where D is the distance from the explosion in feet.

less than 2,100 feet physical and thermal destruction are so serious in unprotected regions that radiological injury does not need consideration. At distances greater than 9,000 feet, the dosage is, in general, too small to be of serious consequence, unless it is repeated at short intervals.

7.43   It is usually accepted that a dose of 400 r of radiation received over the whole body in the course of a few minutes represents the median lethal dose which would be fatal to about 50 percent of human beings (see Chapter XI). From Fig. 7.42 it can be seen that the median lethal range of the gamma radiation from the nominal atomic bomb is about 4,200 feet. Thus a large proportion of human beings exposed to the initial gamma rays within 4,200 feet of an atomic explosion would die from radiation sickness. If part of the body were protected by a suitable shield, it is probable that a larger dose than 400 r would not prove fatal. However, it must be realized, in view of the great penetrating power of the gamma rays, that ordinary clothing can in no sense be regarded as protective.

7.44   The next matter for consideration is the shielding that would be necessary to reduce the gamma-ray intensity or dosage, which may be taken as being roughly proportional to one another, to amounts below the lethal value at various distances. In order to make reasonably accurate calculations, the gamma-ray spectrum, that is, the distribution of energies, from an atomic explosion should be known. However, this detailed information is not available, but an approximate estimate indicates that the average energy, at distances greater than about 3,000 feet from the explosion, is about 3 Mev, although the values for some components are as high as 4.5 Mev. In this event, the data in Table 7.37 may be used as a rough guide to calculate the thickness of shield that would be required to produce a particular degree of attenuation.

7.45   At the minimum distance of 2,100 feet from the explosion, for which Fig. 7.42 provides information, the dosage in an unprotected location would be 10,000 r. To reduce this to below the median lethal dose of 400 r would require something like 20 inches of concrete or about 3 inches of lead. The attenuation of gamma rays by tightly-packed soil is about 0.6 times that for concrete,[13] so that a layer of somewhat over 30 inches of soil would be equally effective. Underground shelters could thus provide adequate protection against the radiation hazard. An outside shelter of the type used in World War II as a protection against blast bombs, covered with about 20 inches

---

[13] The value varies somewhat with the nature and condition of the soil, but the factor 0.6 is probably a safe average.

of packed soil, would decrease the radiation dosage below the median lethal value at distances greater than about 3,000 feet from the explosion.[14] The thickness of concrete which would produce the same effect is roughly 12 inches, that of iron 4 inches, and that of lead about 2 inches. The thicknesses of concrete and iron which would be required to decrease the radiation dosages to 400 r, 100 r, and 25 r, respectively, at various distances from an atomic explosion, are indicated by the curves in Figs. 7.45a and 7.45b. The corresponding data for soil can be obtained upon multiplying the values for concrete by 1/0.6, i. e., by 1⅔.

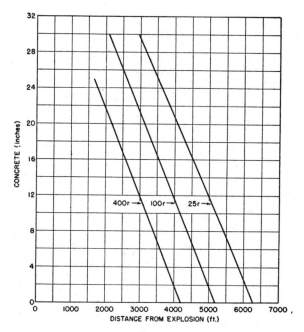

Figure 7.45a. Thicknesses of concrete required as function of distance from explosion to reduce initial gamma radiation to various amounts.

7.46 It was recorded above that an unprotected person within 4,200 feet of an atomic explosion would receive a median lethal dose of initial gamma rays from an atomic bomb. This statement is based, of course, on the supposition that the exposure lasts for the whole minute which was arbitrarily set as the period in which the "initial" radiation was emitted. It is of interest to inquire, therefore, into the time distribution of the radiation immediately following the explosion.

[14] For a height of burst of 2,000 feet, this would represent 2,250 feet or more from ground zero.

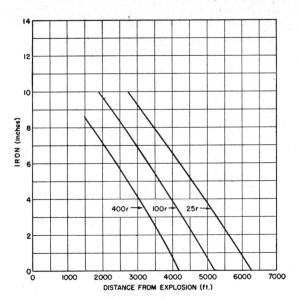

Figure 7.45b.   Thicknesses of iron required as function of distance from explosion
to reduce initial gamma radiation to various amounts.

Results based on actual observations are depicted in Fig. 7.46. The
recorded values depend to some extent on the distance from the atomic
explosion, and data in this figure apply to the distance at which the
mean lethal dose of 400 r would be received, i. e., 4,200 feet. It is
seen that at this distance about a half of the gamma-ray dosage is
received during the first second. Taking shelter quickly behind a
convenient building or in a slit trench, an act which is conceivable

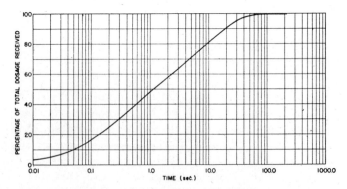

Figure 7.46.   Proportion of total dosage of initial gamma radiation received as
function of time after explosion.

within a second of seeing the bomb flash, might thus mean the difference between life and death to a human being at a point where the
unprotected dosage would be near the median lethal value.

7.47   The discussion thus far has been concerned with the nominal,
20 kiloton TNT energy equivalent, atomic bomb.   In concluding this
section on the initial gamma radiation, reference will be made to the
scaling laws applicable to bombs of various energy releases.   It is
probably sufficiently accurate to assume that the total gamma-ray
emission is proportional to the number of fissions, and hence to the
energy release.   The dosage in roentgens received at any given distance from the explosion is also approximately proportional to this
quantity, and hence to the TNT equivalent.   Consequently, for an
atomic bomb of W kilotons TNT energy equivalent, the ordinates in
Fig. 7.42 would all be multiplied by $W/20$.

-7.48   If the energy release of the bomb were doubled, for example,
from 20 to 40 kiloton TNT equivalent, the median lethal range, at
which the dosage is 400 r, would be increased from 4,200 feet to 4,750
feet.   This means that the lethal area of the initial gamma radiations
would be much less than doubled.   Consequently, the thickness of
shielding necessary to attenuate the radiation to less than the lethal
value at any point would not have to be increased greatly.   For a 40
kiloton equivalent bomb the dosage at 2,100 feet would be 20,000 r,
and about 25 inches of concrete would reduce it to 400 r, the median
lethal dose.   This may be compared with about 20 inches required at
the same distance for the nominal 20 kiloton TNT energy equivalent
bomb.

C.   NEUTRONS

Sources of Neutrons

7.49   The neutrons emitted in the fission process carry about 3 percent of the energy of the atomic explosion.   Of this amount, perhaps
less than 1 percent appears outside because of the loss of energy to the
components of the exploding bomb.   Consequently, the escaping
neutrons bear about 0.03 percent of the energy of the bomb, which is
of the same order as that of the prompt gamma rays (§ 7.4).   Like the
gamma rays, neutrons can penetrate considerable distances through
air, and since they are a physiological hazard, they are a significant
aspect of an atomic explosion.

7.50   More than 99 percent of the total number of neutrons accompanying the fission of uranium 235 or plutonium 239 are released
almost immediately, probably within 10^{-8} second of the explosion.

These are referred to as the *prompt neutrons*.   In addition, somewhat less than 1 percent, called the *delayed neutrons*, are emitted subsequently.   The latter are actually expelled from certain of the fission fragments, following beta decay.   The half-life periods of these fragments with respect to the emission of delayed neutrons range from about 0.5 second to nearly 1 minute.   Because of their relatively small number, the delayed neutrons are of little importance in the present connection, although they may play a highly significant part in the control of nuclear reactors.   Another source of neutrons from an atomic bomb are those produced by the action of gamma rays, i. e., by reactions of the (γ, n) type, on the atomic bomb materials, etc. But the number of such neutrons is very small and may also be ignored.

7.51   Although the prompt neutrons are actually all liberated within less than a millionth of a second of the explosion, as noted above, they are somewhat delayed in escaping from the environment of the exploded bomb.   It was thought at one time that these were actually the delayed neutrons referred to above, but this view has been shown to be incorrect.   From experimental observations, it appears that the number of neutrons emitted is greater than the expected delayed neutrons by a factor of twenty or more.   The neutrons leaving the bomb are thus mainly the prompt neutrons, the delay in their escape being due to interaction with the various atomic nuclei present in the exploded bomb.

7.52   In order to estimate the neutron hazard following an atomic explosion, it is necessary to know something of the energy spectrum; in other words, the distribution of energy values among the neutrons should be ascertained.   It has just been seen that the prompt neutrons are the most important, and their energies are fairly well known; hence it should be possible, in principle, to calculate the energy spectrum of the neutrons after penetrating the bomb materials.   However, since the latter are not completely dispersed when the neutrons are emitted, the neutron spectrum is dependent to a considerable extent on the detailed geometry of the bomb components at an extremely complex stage of the explosion.   Because of these and other circumstances, the calculation is virtually impossible and recourse must be had to experiment.

DIFFUSION OF NEUTRONS

7.53   Even if the detailed spectrum of the neutrons emitted from an exploding bomb were known, it would still be necessary, for the present purpose, to determine the energy distribution at the surface of the earth where the neutrons might be absorbed by human beings. In their passage through matter, neutrons undergo a process of diffusion which is quite different from the behavior of the other elementary particles or photons.[15] As a result, many neutrons which leave the environment of the bomb with high energies have their energies considerably reduced by the time they reach the surface of the earth, provided the burst takes place at an appreciable height.

7.54 Apart from collisions with nuclei in which the latter become excited, as described in §·7.8, and absorption or capture (§ 1.25), neutrons undergo *elastic scattering* when they collide with atomic nuclei. In collisions of this type, the incident neutron bounces off the target nucleus, like a billiard ball, and in doing so imparts some of its kinetic energy to the nucleus. As a result, the kinetic energy of the neutron is decreased; in other words, it is slowed down to some extent. As a neutron travels out through the air from its source, i. e., the atomic bomb, it makes elastic collisions with oxygen and nitrogen nuclei, losing energy at each collision. Consequently, the mean energy of the neutrons decreases with increasing distance from the source.

7.55 If the neutron is not captured, the slowing-down process continues until its energy is about the same as the mean kinetic energy of thermal motion of the molecules of the air. The neutron would then gain, on the average, just as much energy as it lost in each collision with a nucleus. In this condition, the neutrons are said to be thermalized. However, nitrogen nuclei, present in the air, readily capture neutrons of energy less than a few tenths of an electron-volt, compared with the mean thermal value of about 0.03 electron-volt at ordinary temperatures. Hence, neutrons reaching the earth from an atomic explosion are not thermalized, and very few have energies below 0.2 electron-volt.

7.56 Because of the difficulties of approaching the subject of the neutron energy distribution from a theoretical standpoint, it is better to use experimental results as far as possible. The methods of investigation consisted of exposing samples of sulfur and arsenic to the neutrons at various distances from the exploding bomb, and measuring the radioactivity induced in each case. This activity is a direct measure of the number of neutrons, in a given energy range, striking the exposed samples, and from its value it is possible to calculate the total number of neutrons emitted by the bomb in the specific energy range.

---

[15] The highly important subject of neutron diffusion theory is reviewed in "The Science and Engineering of Nuclear Power," vol. I, edited by C. Goodman, Addison-Wesley Press, Inc., Cambridge, Mass., 1947. A full treatment of neutron diffusion theory will be found in a book by G. Placzek and F. de Hoffmann, to be published in the National Nuclear Energy Series.

7.57   The element sulfur becomes radioactive when bombarded by fast neutrons of energy exceeding 3 Mev, and the induced activity is essentially independent of the neutron energy, provided it is larger than this value.   Thus, sulfur can be used to study neutrons of energy exceeding 3 Mev.   Arsenic, on the other hand, is activated by slow neutrons, i. e., neutrons of low energy of the order of 1 electron-volt or less, as well as by fast neutrons.   However, the activity induced by the slow neutrons can be recognized, so that arsenic can be used as a detector for slow neutrons.

7.58   Although the radial distribution of neutrons is a complex function of the distance from the source, i. e., the exploding bomb, an approximate expression may be used for appreciable distances, e. g., at the surface of the earth.   Let n be the number of neutrons in a particular energy region, i. e., high or low, impinging on 1 square centimeter of the sulfur or arsenic detector, respectively, at a distance D from the bomb, this number being estimated from the induced activity.   An apparent neutron source strength N, giving the apparent total number of neutrons of the given energy type emitted by the source, can then be defined by

$$\text{Neutrons per square centimeter } (n) = \frac{N}{4\pi D^2}\, e^{-D/\lambda}, \quad (7.58.1)^{[16]}$$

where λ is the apparent mean free path of the specified neutrons, i. e., the average distance these particular neutrons travel between successive collisions with nuclei in the air through which they pass.   The quantities D and λ in the exponent must be expressed in the same units of length; in the denominator D is in centimeters, since n is the number of neutrons per square centimeter.

7.59   By means of equation (7.58.1) and the measurements referred to above, the values in Table 7.59 have been calculated.   The "fast" neutrons are those detected by sulfur and the "slow" neutrons by arsenic.   These data, together with equation (7.58.1), make possible the calculation of the numbers of fast and slow neutrons reaching a given area at the earth's surface at various distances from the explosion.   Some of the results obtained in this manner are depicted in Fig. 7.59.

7.60   It is seen that about 10 times as many slow neutrons as fast neutrons are observed at large distances from the atomic bomb.   The fast neutrons are known to have energies in excess of 3 Mev, since

---

[16] It should be mentioned that equation (7.58.1) is applicable for slow neutrons, only because they arise through the slowing down of fast neutrons emitted by the bomb.

TABLE 7.59

APPARENT NEUTRON SPECTRUM FROM THE NOMINAL ATOMIC
BOMB

	Fast	Slow
Apparent neutron source strength (N)	3×10^{22}	$\sim 3 \times 10^{23}$
Apparent mean free path (λ)	630 ft.	~ 600 ft.

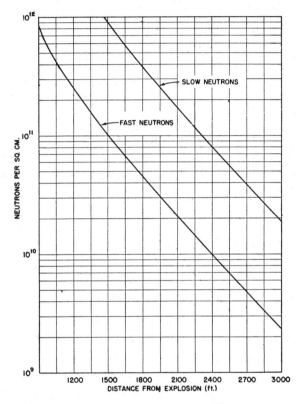

Figure 7.59.   Fast and slow neutrons delivered per square centimeter as function
of distance from explosion.

they induce activity in sulfur; the energy range of the slow neutrons
is somewhat uncertain, but it is probable that most of these neutrons
have energies around 0.2 electron-volt, this being the lower limit of
energy for neutrons which have traveled an appreciable distance in
air (§ 7.55).

7.61   The results quoted in Table 7.59 depend not only on the
energy release of the bomb, which was 20 kilotons TNT equivalent,

but also on its design, for the latter determines the spectrum of the neutrons leaving the region of the bomb (§ 7.52). Although they may be accepted for the purpose of calculation, in the absence of other data, it should be noted that they cover a limited region of energies, namely, greater than 3 Mev for the fast neutrons, and around 0.2 electron-volt for the slow neutrons. There is obviously a very large energy range from about 0.2 electron-volt to 3 Mev, for which no experimental information is available. The best that can be done to complete the spectrum is to make a very approximate guess. On the basis of the nature of the elastic-scattering process by which neutrons are slowed down, it is suspected that the number of neutrons with energies in the range from 0.2 electron-volt to 3 Mev is approximately the same as the number of slow neutrons.

LETHAL RANGE OF NEUTRONS

7.62   Taking the lethal number of slow neutrons as 5×10^{11} per square centimeter and of fast neutrons as 10^{11} per square centimeter, which are the values generally accepted, and using the data for N and λ in Table 7.59, it is estimated by means of equation (7.58.1), or from Fig. 7.59, that the lethal range of the neutrons from a nominal atomic bomb, as far as the fast and slow neutrons are concerned, would be about 1,800 feet. If, in addition, allowance is made for the neutrons of intermediate energy, between 0.2 electron-volt and 3 Mev, the distance would probably be increased to about 2,400 feet from the point of the explosion.

7.63   This result is admittedly approximate for, apart from the uncertainty relating to the distribution of neutron energies, many minor factors have been ignored. However, even if the estimated apparent neutron source strengths were too low by a factor of five, the lethal distance would be increased to only about 3,000 feet. The general conclusion to be drawn, therefore, is that neutrons from an atomic bomb would be lethal to unshielded persons at distances not greater than half a mile from ground zero. It should be noted that because of the presence of D in the negative exponent and of D^2 in the denominator of equation (7.58.1), the neutron intensity falls off very rapidly with increasing distance from the atomic burst.

7.64   As seen in § 7.43, the range for a median lethal dose of initial gamma rays, in the absence of shielding, is something like 4,200 feet from the exploding bomb. At this distance, it is reasonably certain that the neutron intensity will be well below the lethal range. In spite of the approximate nature of the estimate made above, it can be concluded that neutrons from an atomic bomb would not normally represent an additional hazard.

Possibility of Evasive Action

7.65   The initial radiations are emitted over an interval of time, taken as about a minute; it is of interest, therefore, to determine the length of the period during which neutrons reach the earth from an atomic explosion.   The velocity v of a neutron in centimeters per second is related to its energy E in Mev by the expression $v=1.26\times10^9\sqrt{E}$. Since a large proportion of the slow neutrons originate from fast neutrons which have been slowed down toward the end of their range, the rate at which most of these neutrons reach the earth's surface is determined essentially by the speed of the fast neutrons.   If their energy is taken to be 3 Mev, then they travel at a rate of about 2×10^9 centimeters per second.

7.66   If the neutrons moved in a straight line, they would cover the distance of 2,000 feet, i. e., the approximate lethal distance from the explosion, in less than one-thousandth part of a second.   It is true that some of the neutrons would be slowed down in the bomb and also in the air at an appreciable distance from the earth and consequently would arrive considerably later.   In addition, elastic collisions with air nuclei would cause the neutrons to travel in a tortuous path characteristic of a "random walk" (§ 6.14), so that they would be delayed still further.   It is estimated that even making allowance for these possibilities, all the neutrons from the bomb will reach a point 2,000 feet distant within less than a second.   It would appear, therefore, that most of the neutrons reaching the earth would do so within such a short period of time after the explosion that evasive action would not be possible.

Scaling Laws

7.67   The situation with respect to the scaling laws for neutrons is very uncertain because, as indicated above, the neutron spectrum depends in a complex way on the detailed construction and performance of the bomb.   However, as a rough approximation, it may be assumed that the number of neutrons in a particular energy range is essentially proportional to the energy yield of the bomb.   Thus, for a bomb of W kilotons TNT equivalent energy, the values of N for fast and slow neutrons would be obtained roughly by multiplying the results in Table 7.59 by $W/20$. The number n of neutrons per square centimeter at any distance D could then be obtained, to a moderate degree of approximation, by means of equation (7.58.1), using the λ values given. Alternatively, the ordinates in Fig. 7.59 may be multiplied by $W/20$.

7.68 Because of the exponential absorption factor $e^{-D/\lambda}$, and the relatively short mean free path, the lethal area increases fairly slowly with the energy of the bomb. For example, an increase in energy by a factor of two is associated with an increase of less than 400 feet in the lethal distance.

NEUTRON SHIELDING

7.69 The problem of shielding against neutrons is important in the operation of nuclear reactors, cyclotrons, etc., but in view of what has been stated above, it may not require too much attention in connection with an atomic explosion. Water or some other material containing hydrogen will slow down neutrons very effectively, and once being slowed down these neutrons will be fairly readily captured by hydrogen nuclei. This reaction is of the radiative capture type and the gamma radiation emitted has an energy of about 2.2 Mev. A gamma ray of this energy is quite penetrating and could do biological damage unless it were absorbed. As seen earlier in this chapter, water is not a very satisfactory shielding material for such radiation unless used in very thick layers. Borax dissolved in water acts as a good shield, since the boron nuclei capture the slow neutrons, but the process is not of the radiative capture type and no gamma rays are emitted.

7.70 In general, concrete may represent a fair compromise for neutron shielding. It contains a large amount of hydrogen, to slow down the neutrons, and, in addition, there are calcium, silicon, and oxygen atoms which absorb the gamma-ray photons that are produced when the neutrons are captured. However, unless used in considerable thicknesses, the main function of concrete is to slow down the fast neutrons and so make them less of a biological hazard. As seen in §7.62, the lethal number of fast neutrons is only one-fifth of the corresponding number of slow neutrons. At a distance of 2,400 feet from an atomic explosion, a thickness of 18 inches of concrete reduces the number of fast neutrons by a factor of about 10. The net effect is not large, since the fast neutrons are only a small proportion of the total, and there is some increase in the number of slow neutrons, but it is sufficient to provide some protection. Better results would be obtained by using a modified concrete made by adding a considerable proportion of an iron (oxide) ore, such as limonite or magnetite, to the cement. Small pieces of iron, such as steel punchings, may also be incorporated.

7.71   There is one difference in behavior between gamma rays and neutrons to which attention should be drawn. A gamma ray shield of proper thickness can have an opening away from the source of the radiation and still be quite effective, but with slow neutrons this will not be the case. Because of the extensive scattering undergone by slow neutrons from an atomic explosion before they reach the earth, their direction of motion will be quite random. They are, therefore, just as likely to impinge on the opening as on the bulk of the shield. Since a proper shield would be effective from radiations from all sides, this peculiarity of neutrons would not be very significant.

CHAPTER VIII [1]

RESIDUAL NUCLEAR RADIATIONS AND CONTAMINATION

A. INTRODUCTION

CAUSES OF RESIDUAL RADIATIONS

8.1.   The residual nuclear radiations, that is to say, those which are emitted after 1 minute from the instant of an atomic explosion, would arise mainly from the fission products, to a lesser extent from the uranium 235 or plutonium 239 which has escaped fission in the atomic explosion, and, in certain circumstances, from activity induced by neutrons in various elements present in the earth or in the sea.   Any of the radioactive material which is dispersed in and considerably diluted by the atmosphere may be ignored.   But that reaching the inhabited surface of the earth in appreciable amounts, for example, as a result of the fall-out (§ 2.29), a base surge (§ 2.45), or an underground explosion, may represent a serious physiological hazard.   In addition, there is the possibility which, although not highly probable, must nevertheless not be ignored, that radioactive material might be used deliberately, apart from an atomic explosion, for the purpose of making certain areas uninhabitable.

PERMISSIBLE RADIATION DOSAGE

8.2   Before proceeding with a more detailed discussion of the various sources of residual nuclear radiations and of their properties, further reference will be made to the matter of radiation dosage.   In the preceding chapter, interest was centered on the radiation emitted in a very short period of time.   The problem of dosage, sometimes called a "one-shot" dose, was then quite different from that arising in the case of the residual nuclear radiations which might persist for days, weeks or months.[2]   A human being receiving a total of 400 r of the initial nuclear radiation, that is, over a period of a minute or so, would have a 50 percent chance of survival, but, if the same amount of

---

[1] Material contributed by S. T. Cohen, L. R. Donaldson, E. S. Gilfillan, S. Glasstone, J. H. Hinds, B. Holzman, M. S. Plesset, H. Scoville, Jr., R. C. Smith, J. H. Webb.
[2] For the definition of the dosage unit, the roentgen (r), see § 7.41.

248

radiation was absorbed over a period of a month, the probability of death would be considerably less.

8.3   Although the susceptibility to radiation, as to other health hazards, varies from one individual to another, certain general conclusions concerning the tolerance doses have been reached.   These are based mainly on experience with X-rays, but there are good reasons for believing that nuclear radiations, such as beta and gamma rays, behave in a similar manner in that, in each case, the physiological damage is due to the ionization resulting, directly or indirectly, from the absorption of the radiation.

8.4   After examining all the available information, the U. S. Committee on X-rays and Radium Protection concluded in 1936 that the maximum human tolerance dose of X-rays or nuclear radiation, which could be taken up on successive days, was 0.1 r per day over the whole body.   In other words, it was thought that the whole body could absorb up to 0.1 r of radiation per working day for long periods without experiencing permanent harm.   This rate of absorption was accepted as the *tolerance dose* or *permissible dose* of nuclear radiation. However, in order to insure an adequate factor of safety for personnel who are exposed to radiations every working day for many years, the accepted permissible dose rate in the United States has now been reduced to 0.3 r per week.[3]

8.5   It should be understood that this safe dose applies to absorption over the whole body, and for chronic exposures, that is, repeated and protracted' exposures over long periods of time.   Small areas can be exposed to very much larger quantities of radiation with no more than local injury being experienced.   In addition, there is a difference between acute, that is, brief or occasional, exposure and the chronic exposure to which the tolerance limit applies.   Thus, a dose of 5,000 r can be used to treat a small skin cancer; this will leave a scar, but there will be no other permanent effect.   Even the whole body may absorb 50 r in one day without any apparent harm.   Somewhat larger single doses may have unpleasant consequences (Chapter XI), but will not prove fatal unless repeated on successive days.

8.6   The whole subject of radiation susceptibility is so indefinite that it is impossible to provide exact quantitative data on the amounts that may be tolerated under a wide variety of conditions.   It is hoped, however, that the information given above may prove useful as a rough guide to the safe dosage of radiation for an average human being.   Some individuals are undoubtedly more susceptible than

---

[3] Among X-ray technicians who are regularly exposed to radiations analogous to gamma rays, there is no authenticated case of injury where the exposure has been kept down to 0.1 r per day over extended periods.

others, but statistical averages must be considered for practical purposes.

B. SOURCES OF RESIDUAL RADIATION

FISSION PRODUCTS AND THEIR DECAY

8.7   The fission of uranium 235 or plutonium 239 results in the formation of at least 60 atomic fragments, representing isotopes of probably 34 different elements (§ 1.48). All of these isotopes are undoubtedly radioactive, decaying by the emission of beta particles (electrons), frequently accompanied by one or more photons of gamma radiation. The half lives (§ 1.18) of the radioisotopes may vary from a fraction of a second to many years, and the products of decay are usually also radioactive. The decay products may have longer or shorter half lives than their parents, depending on circumstances. As stated in § 1.52, each of the 60 or more primary fission fragments will undergo, on the average, three stages of beta decay, often accompanied by gamma radiation, before it is converted into a stable species.

8.8   It is evident that the fission products will constitute a complex mixture of radioactive substances. Further, the total activity of the products of an atomic explosion is very large. It has been calculated that at 1 minute after the detonation of a nominal atomic bomb, when the residual nuclear radiation has been postulated as beginning, the fission products will be emitting gamma radiation at the enormous rate of 2.1×10^{22} Mev of energy per second. Even after an hour, the rate of emission of gamma radiation will be nearly 1.6×10^{20} Mev per second, so that, although the gamma activity has decreased by a factor of about 130, it is still extremely large.

8.9   A method of expressing decay rates, which is widely used, is in terms of the unit called the *curie*. This is defined as a quantity of radioactive material undergoing 3.7×10^{10} disintegrations per second.[4] Because of the very high activities of the fission products, it is often more convenient to use the *megacurie* unit, which is equal to 10^6 curies, and corresponds to disintegrations at the rate of 3.7×10^{16} per second.

8.10   In considering the radioactivity of the fission products, the gamma radiation is of the greatest significance, since its penetrating power is very much larger than that of the beta particles. Consequently, it is more important to express activities in terms of the former. In Table 8.10 there are given the estimated total gamma activities of the fission products from a nominal atomic bomb, expressed in megacuries, at various times after the detonation.

---

[4] This figure was chosen because it is equal to the rate of disintegration of 1 gram of pure radium.

TABLE 8.10

TOTAL GAMMA ACTIVITY OF FISSION PRODUCTS IN MEGACURIES

Time	Activity	Time	Activity
1 minute	8.2×10^5	1 month	2.3
1 hour	6.0×10^3	1 year	.11
1 day	133	10 years	$.8 \times 10^{-2}$
1 week	13	100 years	$.6 \times 10^{-3}$

8.11   The rate of emission of gamma-ray energy at any of the times given in the table may be readily obtained by making use of the fact that the mean energy of the gamma rays from the fission products is 0.7 Mev. For example, at 1 hour after the explosion, when the gamma-ray activity is 6.0×10^3 megacuries, gamma photons are being expelled at the rate of $6.0 \times 10^3 \times 3.7 \times 10^{16}$, i. e., 2.2×10^{20}, per second. Taking the average energy per photon as 0.7 Mev, the rate of emission of gamma-ray energy is then $0.7 \times 2.2 \times 10^{20}$, i. e., 1.5×10^{20}, Mev per second. The rates at other times may be obtained in a similar manner.

8.12   The mixture of radioisotopes constituting the fission products is so complex that the total rate of disintegration does not follow the usual decay law applicable to a single species (§1.18). Nevertheless, it has been found experimentally that the over-all rate of gamma-ray emission, at any instant t second after the explosion of a nominal atomic bomb, can be represented to a fair degree of accuracy, by the relatively simple expression

$$\text{Rate of emission of gamma-ray photons} = 4.1 \times 10^{24} t^{-1.2} \text{ per second.}$$
$$(8.12.1)$$

Since the mean energy per photon is 0.7 Mev, it follows that

$$\text{Rate of emission of gamma-ray energy} = 2.9 \times 10^{24} t^{-1.2} \text{ Mev per second.}$$
$$(8.12.2)[5]$$

8.13   The rate of emission of beta particles from the fission products is roughly twice that of gamma-ray photons; hence, at a time t sec. after the detonation,

$$\text{Rate of emission of beta particles} = 8.2 \times 10^{24} \, t^{-1.2} \text{ per second,} \quad (8.13.1)$$

for the whole of the fission products produced in the explosion of a nominal atomic bomb. The average maximum energy of the beta particles expelled in fission is 1.3 Mev, but most of the particles have

---

[5] For references see K. Way and E. P. Wigner, "The Rate of Decay of Fission Products," *Phys. Rev.*, *73*, 1318 (1948).

smaller energies, so that the over-all mean is about one-third of this value (§ 8.43), namely, about 0.4 Mev.   Hence,

$$\text{Rate of emission of beta-particle energy} = 3.3 \times 10^{24} t^{-1.2} \text{ Mev per second.}$$
$$(8.13.1)$$

The total energy of the beta particles produced in fission is thus similar in magnitude to that of the gamma radiation.   However, because the beta particles do not penetrate to such great distances as do the gamma rays, the energy of the former would, as a general rule, only be of significance in border-line cases.

8.14   The equations given above represent the decay of the total activity of the whole of the fission products from a nominal atomic bomb, but relationships of the same type apply to the rate of decay of any quantity of fission product, provided there has been no separation, by chemical or other means, of the several elements present. Thus, the activity, expressed either as the number of gamma-ray photons or of beta particles, or as the corresponding energies, emitted per second at a time t sec. after the explosion, is given by

$$\text{Activity} = A_1 t^{-1.2}, \qquad (8.14.1)$$

where A_1 is the appropriate activity of the particular fission product specimen at 1 second after the explosion.   The time units need not be in seconds, for if A_1 is the activity in any chosen units at 1 minute or 1 hour after the detonation, then equation (8.14.1) will give the activity in the same units with t in minutes or hours, respectively.

8.15   For practical purposes it is useful to express the activity of a quantity of fission products in terms of the dosage rate in roentgens per unit time.   This dosage rate, whether due to gamma rays or to beta particles, or to both, will be proportional to the activity, i. e., to the rate of emission of the rays or particles or both, respectively. Consequently, the dosage rate in roentgens per unit time, due to any quantity of fission products, will be given by an expression analogous to equation (8.14.1); thus, the dosage rate at any time t can be represented by

$$\text{Roentgens per unit time} = I_1 t^{-1.2}, \qquad (8.15.1)$$

where I_1 is the dosage rate at unit time.   The quantity I_1 can refer to the dosage rate, due to fission products, in roentgens per unit time at any unit of time, e. g., second, minute, hour, etc., after the explosion; equation (8.15.1), with t in the same time units, will then give the dosage rate after the lapse of that time.   As indicated above, this result applies to gamma rays, to beta particles, or to both.

8.16   The same facts may be expressed conveniently in the form of a graph, as in Fig. 8.16, which is really a logarithmic plot of equation (8.14.1), the slope being −1.2.   It is supposed that the dosage rate is 1 r per hour at 1 hour after the atomic explosion; then the ordinates give the dosage rates at various other times, in hours.   If the dosage rate after 1 hour should be I_1 roentgen per hour, then Fig. 8.16 will

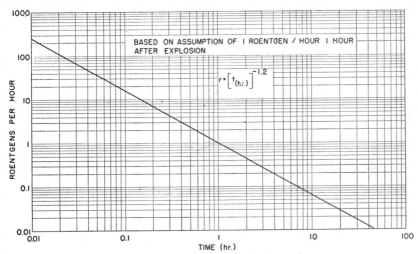

Figure 8.16.   Dosage rate as function of time, assuming 1 roentgen per hour at 1 hour after explosion.

still apply with the ordinates multiplied by I_1.   Incidentally, if the assumption is made that the dosage rate is 1 r per minute at 1 minute after the atomic explosion, then the same plot can be used except that the times will now be in minutes.

8.17   By a process of integration or summation, it is possible to determine from Fig. 8.16, or equation (8.14.1), the total dosage in roentgens that would be absorbed by continuous exposure for various periods of time to the radiation from the fission products.   Since the discussion in this chapter refers in particular to the residual radiation, the integrated dosage is calculated as from 1 minute after the explosion up to various times following the explosion.   The results, based on the assumption of a rate of 1 r per hour at 1 hour after the explosion, are plotted in Fig. 8.17.   If the dosage rate at 1 hour is I_1 roentgens per hour then, as before, the ordinates should be multiplied by I_1.   By subtracting the respective total dosages for two different times after the atomic explosion, the dosage received in the interval between these times is immediately obtained.

8.18 To illustrate the application of Figs. 8.16 and 8.17 suppose that after the lapse of 2 hours from the explosion, the measured dosage rate is found to be 1.5 r per hour. A line drawn through this point, parallel with that in Fig. 8.16, shows that at 1 hour the dosage rate must have been 3.4 r per hour. From Fig. 8.17 it is seen that a person who has remained in a region in which the dosage rate after 1 hour from the explosion is 1 r per hour will have received a total of 7.00 r of residual radiation within 2 hours from the atomic explo-

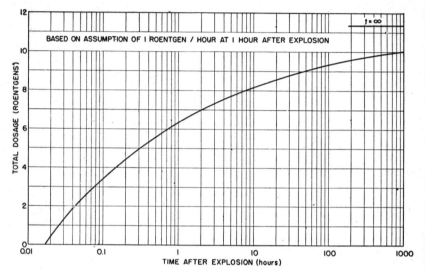

Figure 8.17. Total accumulated dosage from 1 minute after the explosion as function of time, assuming 1 roentgen per hour at 1 hour after explosion.

sion, 7.32 r within 3 hours, and so on. Hence, in the case under consideration the corresponding dosages will be 3.4 times as great, namely, 23.8 r after 2 hours and 24.9 r after 3 hours from the detonation. During the period from 2 hours to 3 hours after the explosion, the dosage received will be 1.1 r (see also § 10.22).

Neutron-Induced Activity

8.19 A second source of residual nuclear radiation which might be significant, especially in the event of a low burst, is due to radioactivity induced in material on the surface of the earth by the neutrons accompanying the fission process. It was mentioned in §1.25 that nearly all the known stable isotopes exhibit the radiative capture type of reaction with neutrons. A neutron is captured and at the same time a gamma-ray photon is expelled (§ 7.7). The gamma radiation accompanying the radiative capture reactions, even if the latter occur on the ground, is really part of the initial radiation, and will not be considered here. The matter of present interest is the fact that the product of the reaction is isotopic with the nuclear species which has captured the neutron and that it is frequently radioactive (§ 1.26).

8.20   It is seen, therefore, that neutrons from an atomic explosion which reach the earth's surface may interact with elements present there and produce radioisotopes. The latter, with but few exceptions, decay by the emission of negative beta particles, i. e., electrons, frequently accompanied by gamma radiation. Radioactivity, induced by the neutrons liberated in the fission process, may persist for some time, and so it can make a contribution to the residual radiation activity. As the neutron intensity at the earth's surface decreases rapidly with increasing distance from the bomb (§ 7.63), the induced activity would probably be significant only for relatively low air bursts, and then at distances not too great from ground zero. Underwater and underground explosions present special problems which will be referred to below.

8.21   The radiative capture reactions of neutrons with the atomic nuclei of oxygen, nitrogen, and hydrogen, the chief constituents of air and water, yield mainly stable, that is, nonradioactive, products. These elements, therefore, contribute little or nothing to the induced activity. Silicon, however, which is a major constituent of soil, has an isotope of mass number 30, constituting about 3 percent of the element, that can be converted by neutrons into the beta-active silicon 31. This isotope has a half life of less than 3 hours and its decay is apparently not accompanied by gamma radiation. Aluminum, another common constituent of soil, can form the isotope aluminum 28, but its half life of 2.4 minutes is so short that very little remains within an hour of the atomic explosion.

8.22   Perhaps the induced radioactivity which deserves most attention is that produced in sodium. Although this is present to the extent of about 0.2 percent in average soil, calculations indicate the possibility of the formation of appreciable amounts of radioactive sodium 24. This isotope has a half life of 14.8 hours; it emits beta particles, with average energy of about 0.5 Mev, and also, more important, gamma-ray photons of 1.4 and 2.8 Mev energy. The activity of the radiosodium would be superimposed on that of any fission products that might be present. The latter do not include sodium, but appreciable amounts of this element could be detected in the presence of fission products, by utilizing the difference in decay rates.

8.23 Apart from interaction with materials contained in the soil, the neutrons from an atomic bomb might be captured by other atomic nuclei, such as those contained in structural and other materials. Of these, probably zinc and copper and, to a lesser extent, iron are most liable to have radioactivity induced in them. Wood and clothing are unlikely to develop appreciable induced activity, but glass, subsequently shattered by the blast, might acquire radioactivity because of the presence of silicon and sodium.

8.24 In the event of an underground atomic explosion, a large proportion of the neutrons released would probably be captured by the elements present in the soil, leading to the formation of relatively large quantities of radiosodium, radiosilicon, etc. At the same time, the escape of a considerable fraction of the fission products would be restricted, so that the residual nuclear radiation would be very considerable in the immediate vicinity of the burst.

8.25 Since sea water contains some 3 percent of sodium chloride, the result of an atomic explosion at not too great a height above the surface of the sea or, particularly, of an underwater detonation, as at Bikini, is to produce notable amounts of radiosodium 24. In addition, a radioisotope of chlorine, mass number 38, is formed, with a much shorter half life, namely, 38.5 minutes. These active species represent somewhat of a hazard to marine life.

URANIUM AND PLUTONIUM

8.26 A third possible source of residual nuclear radiation is the uranium 235 or plutonium which may have escaped fission in the atomic bomb. These radioelements decay by the emission of alpha particles (§ 1.17). Because of their long half lives, 7×10^8 years for uranium 235 and 2.4×10^4 years for plutonium 239, the activity, measured in curies, is very small compared with that of the fission products. The amount of uranium 235 or of plutonium which undergoes fission in a nominal atomic bomb is 1 kilogram (§ 1.36), but since the efficiency is not 100 percent, the quantity of fissionable material required, much of which escapes fission, is larger.

8.27 The weight of the critical mass of the material in an atomic bomb has been stated to be between 1 and 100 kilograms.[6] The latter figure, based on an assumed efficiency of 1 percent, will be adopted for the present discussion, so that the mass of the fissionable

[6] H. D. Smyth, "Atomic Energy for Military Purposes," Government Printing Office, 1945.

material in the nominal atomic bomb will be taken to be 100 kilograms. From the known half lives, it can be stated that 100 kilograms of plutonium would have an alpha activity of 6,000 curies; the alpha activity of the same weight of pure uranium 235 would be only 0.2 curie. It is apparent from the data in Table 8.10 that, in terms of megacuries, the activity of the fissionable material would be exceeded by that of the fission products several years after the explosion.

8.28 It will be seen later (§ 8.46) that the alpha particles from radioactive sources, in general, are completely absorbed in an inch or two of air. This, together with the fact that they cannot penetrate ordinary clothing, indicates that uranium or plutonium deposited on the earth would not represent a serious external hazard.

8.29 Apart from the dangers due to these external radiations, the possibility that uranium or plutonium might enter the body must be considered. Breathing dust containing these elements would lead to their deposition in the lungs, where the emitted alpha particles might have serious consequences. Further, absorption of plutonium through contaminated food or water represents a special hazard. This element, like radium, tends to concentrate in bone, where the prolonged action of alpha particles from the plutonium may result in necrosis (see Chapter XI).

8.30 In view of statements which have been made with regard to the danger of plutonium poisoning following the detonation of an atomic bomb, the situation may be examined briefly. If the bomb explodes, the amount of plutonium which escapes fission will presumably be small, e. g., a maximum of 100 kilograms, and it will obviously be widely dispersed. It will probably rise with the atomic cloud and will constitute a small proportion of the fall-out. Except in special circumstances, it is doubtful if the amount of plutonium deposited in this manner would represent a great hazard.[7]

8.31 At the other extreme, there is the possibility that the bomb will fail to explode. In this case, the plutonium will remain in one spot and it is not likely to get into the air, food, or water. Perhaps the greatest chance of plutonium poisoning would arise from an atomic bomb which was a "fizzle" and broke apart before fission was appreciable (§ 1.44). The danger would presumably be localized and steps could be taken to avoid dispersion of the material which had escaped

---

[7] It has been calculated that in a locality where the dosage rate due to the gamma rays from fission products has the high value of 100 r per hour at 1 hour after the explosion, the plutonium, assuming a total mass of 100 kg., will be deposited at the rate of about 140 micrograms, i. e., 1.4×10^{-4} gram, per square meter. The strict laboratory tolerance dose for continued exposure, which allows a very considerable factor of safety, is taken to be 1 microgram per square meter, after all readily removable material has been scrubbed off.

fission. Incidentally, as in most circumstances following an atomic explosion, the concentrated fission products might constitute a more serious hazard than the plutonium.

ATTENUATION OF RESIDUAL RADIATIONS

8.32   The attenuation of the gamma radiation from fission products and from radioisotopes produced by the action of neutrons is the same as that considered in Chapter VII for the initial radiations. However, the mean energy of the gamma photons from the residual radiation, i. e., from fission products, which is approximately 0.7 Mev, is less than that for the radiation produced in the first minute after an atomic explosion. It can be seen from Table 7.22 that the absorption coefficients are appreciably larger for the gamma rays of low energy, so that the latter are more easily attenuated than are those of higher energy. This is also shown by the thicknesses of various materials required to produce specified attenuation fractions, as given in Table 7.37.

8.33   Calculations have been made of the dosage rate in roentgens per hour due to gamma rays of different energies, at various heights above the ground, on the assumption that there is a uniform contamination by radioactive material to the extent of one million curies, that is, 1 megacurie, per square mile; the results of these computations are shown in Fig. 8.33;[8] the curve for gamma radiation of 0.7 Mev energy is particularly applicable to fission products. It may be seen that at about 3 feet above the ground, the dosage rate is approximately 4 r per hour, which is equivalent to about 100 r per day, for a contamination of 1 megacurie per square mile due to fission products.

8.34   If the actual radiation density differed from 1 megacurie per square mile, the ordinates in the figure would have to be multiplied in proportion. It is of interest, in this connection, to examine the data in Table 8.10 for the total gamma activity of the fission products from the explosion of a nominal atomic bomb. An activity of 1 megacurie per square mile would be attained if at the end of 1 day these products were spread uniformly over 133 square miles. In a normal air burst, only a portion of the fission products would have descended by the end of 1 day (§ 8.67 et seq.), and the area covered would probably be greater than 133 square miles.

8.35   An extension of the problem of attenuation of gamma rays by the atmosphere is the question of the detection of a contaminated area by instruments contained in an airplane. For this purpose, the dosage rate, in roentgens per day, has been estimated at much greater

[8] This and the three succeeding figures are based on the calculations of M. S. Plesset and S. T. Cohen

heights above the ground than is the case for Fig. 8.33. In making
these calculations it is supposed that the dimensions of the contaminated ground area are large compared with the altitude of the
survey aircraft. In addition, the assumption is made, as before, that

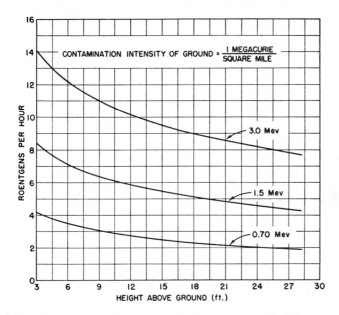

Figure 8.33. Dosage rates of gamma radiation near ground with contamination
intensity of 1 megacurie per square mile.

there is a uniform radioactive contamination of 1 megacurie per
square mile. The values recorded in Fig. 8.35 are for gamma radiation
of 0.7 Mev energy.

8.36 It should be noted that if the ground area is not uniformly
contaminated, as has been postulated above, an aerial survey for the
determination of the contamination density could be greatly in error.
If the survey altitude is large compared with the dimensions over
which the radiation density varies, the survey would give no indication of the actual variation on the ground.

8.37 The underwater detonation of an atomic bomb results in the
radioactive contamination of a large volume of water. It is of interest to obtain some indication of the dosage rate due to gamma
radiation in the water, and also at various heights above the water.
In Fig. 8.37a are given the results of calculations of the dosage rate
in the water, as a function of the gamma-ray energy, on the assump-

tion that there is a uniform radiation density of 1 curie per cubic yard. The dosage rates at various heights above the surface of the water for specified gamma energies are plotted in Fig. 8.37b, the radi-

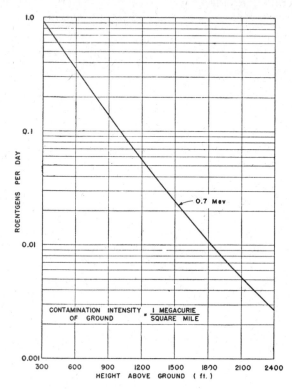

Figure 8.35.   Dosage rates of gamma radiation as function of height above ground with contamination intensity of 1 megacurie per square mile.

ation density being assumed to be the same as before. The dosage rates for other densities can be obtained by making proportionate changes in the ordinates.

Beta Radiation

8.38   In their passage through matter, beta particles, which are electrons moving with high speed, lose energy in two main ways; namely, by interaction with the electrons or with the nuclei of the material traversed. In the former case, which is more important, energy is lost by excitation, i. e., by raising an atomic electron to a higher energy level, or by ionization, i. e., by removal of an

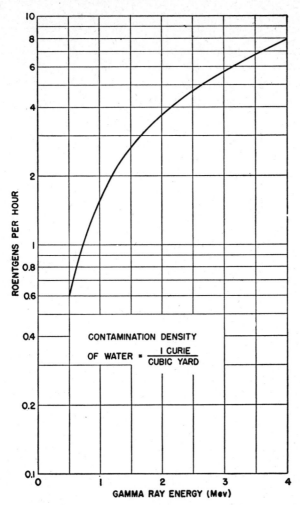

Figure 8.37a.   Dosage rates as function of gamma-ray energy within large volume of water with contamination density of 1 curie per cubic yard.

electron from an atom.   In the case of interaction with nuclei, the approach of a negative electron (beta particle) to an atomic nucleus results in some of the kinetic energy of the former being converted into electromagnetic radiation.   The effect becomes important only for high energies of the beta particle and with increasing atomic number of the medium.   This radiation, commonly known as *Bremsstrahlung* or, literally, braking radiation, is X-radiation.

8.39   It was stated in § 7.18 that the fast-moving electrons expelled by gamma rays in their interaction with matter cause ioniza-

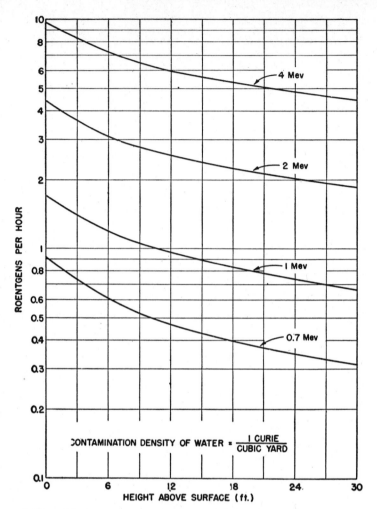

Figure 8.37b. Dosage rates as function of height above surface of water with contamination density of 1 curie per cubic yard for gamma rays of various energies.

tion, and this ionization is responsible for the harmful physiological effects of the radiation. As indicated above, beta particles produce ionization directly in their passage through matter; this is, of course, to be expected, since the particles are actually electrons of high energy. The effect on living organisms of beta particles is thus similar to that of gamma rays, and the dosage in. the former case, as in the latter case, can be expressed in roentgens.

8.40 By use of quantum mechanics, it is possible to calculate the loss of energy per centimeter of path in a given medium due to both causes mentioned in § 8.38.[9]   The results are shown graphically in Fig. 8.40, which gives the ranges of beta particles of various initial energies in air, water, and lead.   The range is here taken as the total distance a beta particle of specific energy would travel through a medium before it is virtually brought to rest.[10]   At this point, the

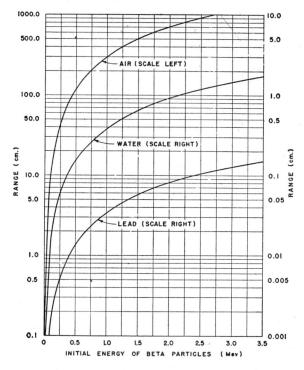

Figure 8.40.   Ranges of beta particles as function of energy in air, water, and lead.

beta particle ceases to be capable of producing ionization and hence is no longer a physiological hazard.   For example, a beta particle of 1 Mev energy would, according to Fig. 8.40, traverse a total distance of about 300 centimeters in air.   However, because the particle is continuously deflected, by the electrons and nuclei of the atoms of the medium, it follows a very tortuous path, and the *effective* distance it travels in a straight line is very much less.

---

[9] See W. Heitler, "Quantum Theory of Radiation," Second edition, Oxford University Press, 1944.

[10] When the velocity of an electron is reduced to a sufficient extent, it is usually captured by an atom or an ion.

8.41   Attention may be called here to a difference between the absorption of beta particles and gamma rays. The former can be stopped completely, so that they have a definite range in a given medium; the latter, however, suffer gradual attenuation, of an approximately exponential character, so that, theoretically, they are never entirely absorbed. However, with a sufficient thickness of material, the extent of attenuation of gamma rays can be made so large that the emergent intensity is negligible.

8.42   The range of a beta particle decreases greatly with the density and atomic weight of the medium, just as the absorption coefficient of gamma rays increases correspondingly (§ 7.25). In other words, the more dense a substance, the greater is its stopping power for beta particles as well as for gamma radiation. As a rough approximation, the stopping power of a medium for beta particles, i. e., the reciprocal of the range, may be taken as being proportional to the density. The total range of a 1-Mev beta particle in water, for example, is about 0.4 centimeter, compared with 300 centimeters in air.

8.43   In considering the range of beta particles from a given source, it is important to remember that the energies of the particles are not uniform, and so they do not really have a definite range. This is particularly the case for the beta particles originating from the fission products, but it is also true for the particles emitted by a single radioelement. Actually, there is a distribution of energies among the beta particles from a given source from zero to a definite maximum. It is this maximum energy, possessed by only a small proportion of the particles, which is recorded in the literature. The average energy of all the beta particles emitted by a given radioisotope is roughly one-third of the maximum energy for that substance.

8.44   Very few of the fission products give off beta particles with energies in excess of 2 Mev, and so the maximum possible range in water is about 1 centimeter, that is, less than half an inch. The range in wood is probably much the same, and it is even less in concrete. Human beings inside a house would thus be protected from beta radiation originating from outdoor contamination by fission products, etc., but they would not necessarily be safe from the accompanying gamma radiation. In a sense, therefore, the external beta-radiation hazard is not too significant, for, in general, if there is no danger from gamma radiation from fission products or from neutron-induced radioactivity, there will be no need for concern with regard to the beta particles. However, in borderline cases, the effect of the beta particles superimposed upon that of the gamma radiation might prove harmful to persons operating in areas contaminated with fission products.

8.45   It should be mentioned that beta particle emitters are caustic to the skin (§ 11.78), and so care must be taken to avoid direct contact with the surface of the body, by the use of protective clothing if necessary (§ 12.79).   Such clothing would also prevent the penetration of the external beta particles, although it would be ineffective against gamma rays.   Introduction of the source of the beta radiation into the system by inhalation, ingestion, or in other ways, must, of course, also be avoided.

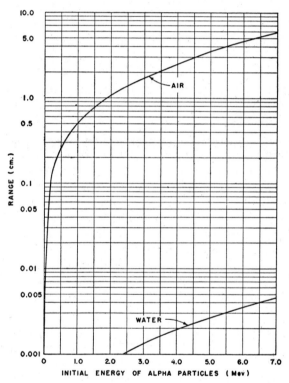

Figure 8.46.   Ranges of alpha particles as function of energy in air, and water

Alpha Particles

8.46   It has been already indicated that, as far as external effects are concerned, alpha particles are probably not a significant hazard. This is because they have such a short range in air, and even less in water, as seen in Fig. 8.46.   The range of the 5.1-Mev alpha particles from plutonium is less than 4 centimeters in air, and it is almost insignificant in water. It is doubtful whether alpha particles of radioactive origin can penetrate the unbroken skin, and they certainly will be stopped by ordinary clothing.

8.47 Of course, a source of alpha particles which is inhaled or taken into the system in any other way can have very serious consequences. The hazards due to ingestion or inhalation will be treated more fully in Chapter XI. Like beta particles and gamma rays, the harmful physiological effects of alpha particles are due to ionization, which causes disruption of molecules important to the living organism.

BACKGROUND RADIATION

8.48 In the introduction to this chapter, it was stated that human beings can tolerate a certain amount of radiation, received daily over long periods of time, without apparently suffering any harm. This means that if, after an atomic explosion, the radiation dosage in a particular area is reduced below the tolerance limit, that area will become entirely safe for habitation.

8.49 It is of interest to note in this connection that, even under normal circumstances, and before there was any thought of radioactivity, X-rays or atomic bomb, all living organisms were continually being exposed to radiation. This "background radiation" is due partly to the high-energy particles, known as cosmic rays, originating in outer space, and partly to radium and its disintegration products which are present in the earth and in the air. In addition, it is not generally realized, that the human body contains not insignificant amounts of radioisotopes of carbon and potassium. These radioactive species are also present in plants and in the soil.

8.50 It has been estimated that at sea level a human being absorbs, from all the aforementioned background sources, something like 0.003 r of radiation per week throughout his life. This is about one-hundredth part of the accepted, so-called, tolerance dose which is believed to be harmless (§ 8.4). At high altitudes, where the intensity of the cosmic rays may be increased many fold, e. g., a threefold increase at 15,000 feet, the total background radiation is appreciably higher.

8.51 In any event, it appears that during the average lifetime every individual receives from 10 to 15 r or more of radiation over the whole body, and this does not take into account additional amounts that may be absorbed as a result of X-ray or similar treatment. The same state of affairs has undoubtedly persisted during the whole period of man's existence on earth, although the total radiation absorbed in a lifetime has increased as the average life span has lengthened.

WORLD-WIDE CONTAMINATION BY RADIOACTIVITY

8.52   Fears have been expressed in some quarters concerning the danger of world-wide contamination by radioactivity resulting from atomic explosions.   That such fears are groundless can be shown by estimating the number of bombs which would have to be detonated to produce enough activity to cover the earth.   Such calculations may be made for external gamma radiation from the fission products, on the one hand, and for the internal hazard due to plutonium which has escaped fission, on the other hand.[11]

8.53   If the whole surface of the earth is to be contaminated, with a minimum number of bombs, they would have to be exploded within a short period of time.   Further, since contamination from fission products would be due essentially to the fall-out, sufficient time must be allowed for all the particles to settle out.   On the basis of these postulates, it has been calculated that in order to constitute a world-wide hazard, something like a million atomic bombs, of the nominal size, would have to be detonated, roughly one to each 200 square miles of the earth's surface.   This clearly represents a highly improbable situation.

8.54   An estimate of the possibility of world-wide contamination by plutonium is more difficult, because of the uncertainty concerning the proportion which escapes fission.   In order to take the extreme case it is supposed that the whole of the plutonium originally present in the bomb is uniformly distributed in the top centimeter of soil.   This plutonium may then be presumed to be absorbed by plants and thus find its way into the human body in the form of food.   Inhalation of dust represents another possibility which is taken into consideration. It appears from the calculations that for plutonium to constitute a world-wide hazard millions of atomic bombs would have to be exploded.

8.55   World-wide radioactive contamination would thus appear to be extremely unlikely, but local contamination due to a relatively small number of bombs might be a serious problem over a large area. The fact that the fall-out may be so widely dispersed means that radio-active particles will descend hundreds and even thousands of miles from the point of detonation.   Although they may not necessarily do any physiological harm, the particles may cause trouble.   An illustration is the case reported in § 8.73, where the radioactive dust from the Alamogordo explosion appeared in strawboard manufactured over a thousand miles away and, as a result, spoiled sensitive photographic film which was wrapped in this material.

---

[11] See Appendix E.

8.56   It is important at this point to distinguish clearly between world-wide and local contamination. To be a serious menace, the former would require, as seen above, the explosion of a very large number of bombs, but the explosion of a single bomb in appropriate circumstances might cause a hazard in a limited area. It is this latter aspect of the problem of residual nuclear radiation from atomic explosions of various types which will be considered in the following sections.

C. RADIOACTIVE CONTAMINATION DUE TO AIR BURST

CAUSES OF CONTAMINATION

8.57   In the case of an air burst of an atomic bomb, the radioactivity at the earth's surface would depend essentially on two factors, namely, neutron-induced activity and fall-out, since the direct deposition of fission products is negligible. There would also be contamination of the air by the radioactive cloud which would be a hazard to aircraft. As far as the induced activity is concerned, this would probably be somewhat localized in character and would be appreciable only near ground zero. There is a possibility, of course, that the radioactive material formed close to the position of burst may be carried over a fairly large area by the secondary winds created by the updraft of the rising cloud. A special case is that of an air burst over salt water because of the presence of relatively large amounts of sodium chloride (§ 8.25), and because of the fairly rapid diffusion of the activity in the water.

8.58   The relative importance of the sources of radioactive contamination following an air burst will depend on a variety of circumstances, for example, the nature of the terrain and the meteorological conditions. From a general point of view, however, the height of burst is perhaps of most significance, since this has a considerable influence on the more or less local contamination as well as on the fallout. For convenience, heights of burst may be described as high or low, and although it is not possible to make a sharp demarcation, it will be taken here to be about 500 ft. This figure is chosen because it is approximately the maximum radius of the ball of fire (§ 2.12), so that in an atomic explosion above this altitude the ball of fire will not touch the ground. Thus a high burst will imply a detonation at an altitude greater than 500 feet, and a low burst will refer to a lower level.

EFFECT OF HIGH AIR BURST

8.59   Typical examples of high burst atomic bombs were those exploded over Hiroshima and Nagasaki at altitudes of about 2,000 feet.   There seems little doubt that the height of the detonation was too great to permit an appreciable neutron flux at the earth's surface. Consequently, the amount of induced activity was small.   Since the ball of fire did not touch the earth, and most of the fission products were carried upward in the rapidly rising column of smoke, the extent of local contamination was small.   At Nagasaki, about 0.02 percent of the fission products were left on the ground within a radius of some 2,000 feet of ground zero; however, even a few minutes after the explosion, the area did not present a radiation hazard.

8.60   It was mentioned in Chapter II that the fall-out depends on debris of various kinds sucked up from the earth's surface after the atomic explosion.   It is believed that for a sufficiently high burst relatively little extraneous material would be taken into the cloud, and the fall-out would be negligible.   This is in general agreement with experience from the atomic explosions over Japan.   Since the fall-out is liable to be more significant for low bursts, it will be referred to again below.

8.61   If the air burst occurred at such an altitude that no appreciable debris was sucked into the cloud, the fission products would remain in a finely divided state for a long time, during which period they would be undergoing decay.   Eventually, the particles would descend to earth, but they would be so widely dispersed and their activity so much decreased that they could be ignored, as far as a danger to health was concerned.   Of course, special meteorological conditions, such as abnormal winds or perhaps rain clouds, might cause a large deposition of radioactive material in a particular area, but it is improbable that this would be at all general.

8.62   As already indicated, a not too high air burst over the sea would result in the formation of neutron-induced activity in the water, due mainly to sodium 24.   The evidence from the Bikini "Able" detonation, which took place several hundred feet above the level of the lagoon, indicates that almost all the fission products were carried upward in the atomic cloud.   Such activity as remained above the surface of the water, amounting to a maximum rate of 25 r per day at about 2 hours after the explosion, was due largely to gamma rays from the radioactive sodium.   This dosage rate, which decreases fairly rapidly because of the 14.8-hour half life of the sodium 24, would never result in a lethal dose.

8.63   The general conclusion to be drawn is that if an atomic bomb is detonated at a high altitude, so as to cause maximum blast damage in a city, the hazard due to radioactivity on the ground after the explosion is small.

EFFECT OF LOW AIR BURST

8.64   Atomic bombs were exploded experimentally at low altitudes at Alamogordo and at Eniwetok. Radioactive contamination of the ground was many times greater than for the high-altitude bursts, due to the fact that the ball of fire touched the earth's surface. The radioactivity near the center of the explosion resulted partly from condensation of fission products upon contact with the ground, and partly from radioactivity induced by neutrons. The approximate radiation dosage rates, in roentgens per hour, measured on the ground at Alamogordo, 1 hour after the detonation had taken place at a height of 100 feet, are given in Table 8.64 for various distances from ground zero.

TABLE 8.64

RADIATION DOSAGE RATE ON GROUND ONE HOUR AFTER
EXPLOSION

Distance from ground zero (feet)	Dosage rate (r. per hr.)
0	8, 000
300	5, 000
600	600
900	150
1, 200	30
1, 500	10
2, 250	5
3, 000	. 3
3, 750	. 07

8.65   It is apparent from these figures that after an air burst at low altitude an area, small compared with the damage area due to the bomb, near the explosion center would be uninhabitable because of the radiation hazard. Nevertheless, calculations show that a vehicle traveling at a moderately high speed could cross the contaminated ground about 15 minutes after the explosion without the occupants being greatly harmed. It would probably be 6 hours or more before it would be safe to walk across the area; but to stay for any length of time would, of course, be out of the question, unless proper shielding were available. The great amount of radioactive dust remaining in the air after a low-altitude explosion would require special precautions to prevent entry of the active material into the system.[12]

8.66   The disturbance of large quantities of earth and other material in the formation of a crater, which accompanies an air burst at low altitude, results in the deposition of contaminated debris at some distance away. In addition, much of the dust is carried aloft into the atomic cloud, but it eventually settles to the earth as the fall-out,

---

[12] Masks such as are used for chemical warfare protection are suitable for this purpose.

after picking up fission product particles (§ 2.23), to contaminate areas much further from the center of the explosion. After the Alamogordo test, for example, high concentrations of radioactivity were detected on the ground several miles north and east of the site of the explosion. The integrated dose was, however, not dangerous to human life.[13]

8.67 Most of the dust particles which are contaminated with fission products in a radioactive cloud rise to a considerable height before beginning to descend. The fall-out thus extends over an appreciable time after the explosion. According to Stokes's law, which is especially applicable to particles of from 5 to 300 microns, i. e., 5×10^{-4} to 3×10^{-2} centimeters, in diameter, the rate of fall of a particle in the air under the influence of gravity is equal to 0.35 $d^2 \rho$ feet per hour, where d is the diameter of the particle in microns and ρ is its density.

TABLE 8.67

TIMES FOR PARTICLES. TO FALL 40,000 FEET

Particle diameter (microns)	Time of fall (hours)	Particle diameter (microns)	Time of fall (hours)
840	0. 37	33	40
250	. 69	16	170
150	1. 95	8	680
75	7. 90	5	1, 700

In Table 8.67 are given the calculated times, based on this relationship, required for dust particles of various sizes to descend from 40,000 feet, this being taken as the height attained by the atomic cloud. The density of the particles is assumed to be the same as that of silica (sand). Particles with diameters less than 5 microns are seriously affected by Brownian movement and remain in the air for very long periods.

8.68 It has been found experimentally that the size distribution of any dirt raised by the wind is approximately the same regardless of the material. Consequently, it may be assumed, for purposes of calculation, that the size distribution of the particles in an atomic cloud is the same as observed at the Alamogordo "Trinity" test, which was similar to that for dust over the Sahara desert. Assuming this distribution of particle size to apply to the fall-out, it is possible to

[13] A number of cattle, about 10 to 15 miles from the "Trinity" explosion at Alamogordo, New Mexico, were inadvertently exposed to the radioactive dust from the fall-out. In the course of a few weeks, loss of hair and blisterlike lesions were apparent. The latter soon healed, however, and the hair, originally red in color, grew again, although it was white or gray in color. Continued observation of the animals has shown that the cows have produced normal calves, irrespective of whether they were mated with bulls which had or had not been exposed to the radioactive dust. There was, by the end of 1949, no evidence of any effects of the radiation, other than the graying of the hair.

calculate the proportions by weight of the fission products falling during certain intervals of time after an atomic explosion. Using the results in Table 8.67, and supposing the particles to be raised to

TABLE 8.68

PROPORTION OF ACTIVE MATERIAL DEPOSITED FROM ATOMIC CLOUD

Period (minutes)	Diameter of dust particles (microns)	Proportion deposited (percent)
First 22	840	3. 8
22-42	840-250	12. 6
42-117	250-150	14. 5
117-480	150- 75	18. 1

40,000 feet before they descend, the values in Table 8.68 have been obtained. These figures account for 49 percent of the activity present in the fall-out; the other 51 percent remains suspended for a very long time.

8.69   From the standpoint of radioactive contamination, the important factor is the surface area of the dust particles. The finely divided fission products deposit on the surface of these particles, and hence the proportion of the total radioactivity carried by dust particles of a particular size depends on the percentage of the total area associated with that size group. The results in the third column of Table 8.68 actually give the calculated percentages of the total area of the dust in various size ranges, and these are assumed to represent the proportions of the initial fission-product activity carried down, during various periods of time.

8.70   It should be noted that in deriving these results no allowance was made for the natural decay of the fission products during their ascent with the atomic cloud and their descent with the fall-out. However, because of this decay, the material deposited at increasing intervals from the time of burst will be less and less active. Thus, Table 8.68 indicates that in the period from 117 to 480 minutes after the atomic explosion, about 18 percent of the fission products will reach the earth's surface. But if allowance is made for the natural radioactive decay, it is probable that this would represent no more than about 0.1 percent of the original radioactivity of the atomic cloud.

8.71   While the particles are descending, they are subjected to the action of the prevalent winds and to diffusion, which tends to spread them out over a large area. It is evident that even for a wind velocity as low as 10 miles per hour, many of the particles of the fall-out would reach the earth at some distance from the explosion, in spite of changes of wind direction with time and altitude. Even the largest particles mentioned in the table, which are nearly 1 millimeter in diameter, would descend nearly 4 miles from their point of origin if the wind velocity remained constant at 10 miles per hour; many of the smaller particles would, of course, travel much further before descending.

8.72   Evidence for the great distances traveled by dust particles has been obtained in many instances, the outstanding example being the Krakatao eruption.[14]   After this disturbance the dust was detected thousands of miles away.   In fact, residual volcanic ash remained suspended in the atmosphere for approximately. three years.   Further, the brown coloration of the snow observed in New England in February 1936, was due to soil raised by a dust storm in Texas nearly 2 days earlier.

8.73   Of more direct interest is the fact that radioactive dust produced in the atomic bomb ("Trinity") test at Alamogordo, New Mexico, on July 16, 1945, was detected by its presence in strawboard produced at Vincennes, Indiana, on August 6, 1945.[15]   The source of the contamination was undoubtedly the water from the Wabash River, which drains a large area.   In spite of the fact that the activity was adsorbed by the straw from large amounts of water, used for washing, the total radioactivity was actually very small, and it would have undoubtedly escaped notice completely were it not for the fact that the strawboard was used for packing very sensitive X-ray films. Fogged spots were found on the film due to action of the radiations. It may be mentioned that at the "Trinity" test, the bomb was exploded on a tower about 100 feet above the ground, so that a large amount of debris was sucked into the atomic cloud (see Fig. 2.11).

8.74   Although the lateral transport of most of the particles in the fall-out will be due to the action of winds, a proportion will be dispersed by eddy diffusion.   It is expected that this factor is significant only in the lowest levels of the atmosphere, and then the roughness of the terrain may lead to an unequal deposition of particles.   If there is a very stable thermal stratification of the lowest layers of air, a greater concentration of activity may occur in a valley than at higher altitudes.   Even under conditions of turbulence, it is possible, as a result of eddy diffusion, for activity to be deposited in one area yet for it to be completely absent from neighboring areas.

8.75   The foregoing considerations tend to support the general conclusion that in most circumstances the fall-out from an air burst

---

[14] This eruption, of course, involved considerably larger amounts of energy, and much larger quantities of debris were raised, than for an atomic bomb explosion.

[15] J. H. Webb, *Phys. Rev.*, 76, 375 (1949).

will not be a serious radiological hazard. A special case might perhaps arise if the air were moist; in this event, the radioactive, metallic (fission product) oxides would attach themselves to the water droplets, which might subsequently fall as radioactive rain. In a warm front rainfall situation,[16] such as frequently occurs in temperate latitudes, the rain-bearing clouds may have a thickness of 20,000 feet. The radioactive particles, from an atomic bomb burst taking place a few hundred feet above the earth's surface, might ascend into the rain-bearing clouds. In a short time the atomic cloud within the rain-bearing cloud could possibly attain virtual equilibrium with the latter, and so become an integral part of the rain-producing system. The radioactive material might then be expected to deposit with the rain in a surface pattern dependent on the winds at the cloud level.

8.76   In the considered opinion of many who have made observations of atomic explosions, the fall-out in the case of a low air burst might be an inconvenience, but it would not, in general, represent a real danger. It would probably rarely be enough to prevent passage across an area, although it might necessitate suspension of operations for a few days within the area.

8.77   Special circumstances might, of course, arise, as indicated above, that would result in excessive contamination in certain localized regions. If there were a persistent wind in a particular direction, for example, a larger proportion of activity would probably be found in downwind areas. With the aid of a meteorological trajectory analysis,[17] it might even be possible to predict the location of these areas, provided sufficient data concerning wind directions and velocities were available.

Surface Explosion

8.78   The extreme case of an atomic explosion at low altitude would be represented by a burst taking place at the surface of the earth. Since there has been no detonation of this type it is possible only to speculate as to what the results might be. It is reasonably certain that the contamination due to neutron-induced activity in the vicinity of the explosion would be very high. Further, the probable formation of a large crater would, no doubt, be accompanied by considerable amounts of dust contaminated with fission products and with radioactive isotopes formed by neutron capture. This airborne activity,

---

[16] A warm front type of rainstorm is associated with thick-layered clouds extending over an area of hundreds or thousands of square miles. The rain is usually gentle but continues to fall steadily for some time.

[17] See Appendix F.

which would produce a significant fall-out, might constitute a serious hazard in areas directly downwind at some distance from the explosion.

8.79 It is to be expected that in the event of a surface burst, a larger proportion of the fission products would remain on or near the ground than in the case of an explosion taking place in the air. On the whole, therefore, it may perhaps be anticipated that a surface burst, although less destructive in other ways, would result in greater radioactive contamination, especially at not too large distances from ground zero, than the other types of detonation already considered.

RADIOACTIVE CLOUD

8.80 One further aspect of an atomic air burst may be mentioned, namely, the question of how much radiation to which a crew of an airplane flying through a radioactive cloud would be exposed. Some computations have been made, using certain simplifying conditions. The assumption is made that the cabin is hermetically sealed and the air intake is closed, so that none of the active fission products enter the airplane. In actual practice such internal contamination could not be avoided, so that the estimates will inevitably be too low. This is in agreement with the result of observations made during atomic explosions.

8.81 The case considered is that of an aircraft flying on a line through the center of a radioactive cloud, assumed to be spherical in shape. This line of flight gives the maximum cumulative radiation dosage. The additional postulates are that the motion of the atomic cloud in ascent and expansion is small compared with the speed of the aircraft; that the radioactivity of the cloud remains constant during its passage; and that the cloud has risen to an altitude where its density is essentially that of the atmosphere.

8.82 The results of the calculations, for an airplane flying at the rate of 300 miles per hour, assuming the radiation to consist only of gamma rays arising from the fission products, and that the dosage is due to external exposure, and not direct contact or inhalation of the fission products, are recorded in Table 8.82.[18] Because of the necessary simplification mentioned above, the values given are to be recognized as being very approximate. The altitude, in the first column, is that of the cloud center at various times after the explosion, given in the second column; the dosage, in roentgens, is almost entirely derived from inside the cloud, for the contribution from outside is only 5 r at 15,000 feet and is essentially negligible above 25,000 feet.

[18] Based on calculations made by M. S. Plesset and S. T. Cohen.

TABLE 8.82

ESTIMATED RADIATION DOSAGE OF AIRCRAFT AT 300 M. P. H. IN
RADIOACTIVE CLOUD

Altitude (feet)	Time after explosion (seconds)	Radius of cloud (feet)	Dosage (r)	Dosage rate (r per hr.)
15, 000	90	3, 100	550	140, 000
20, 000	140	3, 800	260	55, 000
25, 000	200	4, 500	130	24, 000
30,.000	300	5, 300	70	11, 000
35, 000	430	6, 100	40	5, 600
40, 000	600	7, 100	25	3, 000

8.83   The calculated dosage rates, in roentgens per hour, are plotted
in Fig. 8.83, as a function of the distance from the center of the cloud,
for various cloud heights. It should be emphasized that, as stated
above, the results are approximate; the actual accumulated dosage
rates will probably be higher.   It is seen that outside the cloud the
gamma-ray dosage falls off rapidly with increasing distance from the
center.   Further, with the lapse of time, i. e., for increasing height of
the cloud, the activity extends over increasing areas from the point
of burst.

D.   RADIOACTIVE CONTAMINATION FROM UNDERWATER BURST

CAUSES OF CONTAMINATION

8.84   For an underwater burst at moderate depths, the initial
gamma and neutron radiations can be ignored, since they are almost
completely absorbed in a few yards of water. Some radioactive
sodium 24 and chlorine 38 may be produced as a result of reaction
with neutrons, but it appears that most of the latter will be captured
by the hydrogen of the water to form the nonradioactive isotope
deuterium. The neutron-induced activity evidently makes a relatively
small contribution to the residual radiation, and this is largely due to
the fission products which do not escape as easily as they do in the
case of an air burst.

8.85   Of the types of atomic explosion the underwater burst at
Bikini, that is, the "Baker" test, produced by far the greatest degree
of radioactive contamination. It was estimated that almost all of
the fission-product activity either remained in the water immediately
following the detonation, or fell back into the lagoon in the form of
the radioactive base surge and rain (§ 2.45 et seq.). The extent and
degree of contamination following an underwater atomic explosion will

probably vary markedly with the conditions, such as the base surge, which in turn may well depend on the depth of the burst, the meteorological conditions, e. g., wind velocity and direction, rain clouds, etc., and the topography at the site of the detonation.

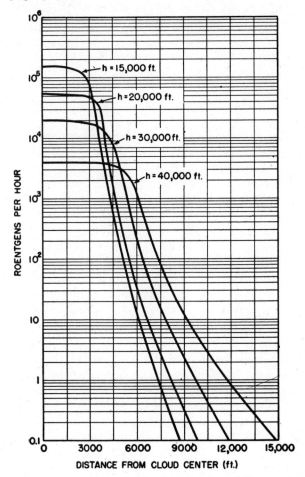

Figure 8.83.   Dosage rates in atomic cloud as function of distance from center at various heights.

Base Surge and Fall-Out

8.86   The phenomena, such as the formation of the plume, the base surge, and the mushroom (or cauliflower) shaped cloud, associated with an underwater atomic explosion were described in Chapters II and IV. The present discussion will be restricted, therefore, essentially to the radioactive contamination which can result from these effects. Partly because of the great weight of the water carried up in the plume, and partly because of the lower temperatures, the cloud does not ascend to such heights as in the case of an air burst. As a result, the fall-out, which is now in effect a radioactive rain, will commence to descend very soon after the explosion. At Bikini, for example, the first fall-out reached the surface of the sea at about a minute after the detonation. Consequently, instead of being dispersed, as it is for an air burst, a large proportion of the fission-product activity, aside from that remaining in the body of water, is precipitated in a short time within a radius of a few thousand yards of the point of detonation.

8.87 In the Bikini "Baker" test the base surge, consisting of a contaminated cloud or mist of small water droplets, which formed 10 to 12 seconds after the explosion and then moved rapidly outward, undoubtedly added markedly to the radioactivity deposited on ships in the lagoon. It is doubtful if any complete explanation of the base surge has yet been given, and, although several theories have been proposed, the subject is still a matter for controversy. One of the difficulties is, of course, that the phenomenon has been observed on one occasion only, and experimental tests of the various theories cannot be easily made. Although the development of the base surge into a cloud mass in the later stages may depend on the meteorological conditions, as indicated in § 4.80 *et seq.*, it is probable that the initial formation and its rapid outward movement are determined solely by the nature of the underwater burst.

8.88 There has been some discussion, too, of the influence of the depth of the water in which the explosion occurs, and it appears possible that relatively deep water, or water and mud, would be necessary to produce a base surge. However, there is no certainty regarding this matter, and so until there is definite proof, one way or another, it must be assumed that an underwater burst of an atomic bomb will result in the formation of the radioactively contaminated mist called the base surge.

8.89 The base surge consists of a cloud of water droplets of various sizes, moving outward with high speed from the point of the explosion. As the base surge passes over an area, the latter receives a particular radiation dosage for the short interval of time while the cloud is in transit. In addition, a certain amount of radioactive rain will fall from the base surge during this period, leading to deposition of contamination; however, this contributes a relatively small proportion of the total dosage.

8.90   Apart from the effect of the base surge, radioactive contamination will result from the rain produced by the fall-out.   There has been some difference of opinion concerning the relative contributions of the base surge and the fall-out to the total radiation dosage.   The question is of practical significance, since some protection of personnel from ordinary rainfall, as from the fall-out, is possible in the open. But since the base surge is a cloud which moves laterally, protection from its radiation is not so simple.   There is no doubt that at Bikini, the base surge was very significant, and it appears that, in general, both base surge and fall-out will contribute to the radiation dosage, the relative amounts depending on the depth of burst, depth of water, and other conditions.

8.91   From measurements made at the time of the Bikini "Baker" test, it has been possible to draw some general conclusions with regard to the integrated or total radiation dosage received at various distances from surface zero.   Actually, about 90 percent of this dosage was attained within 30 minutes of the explosion.   The results are represented in the form of radiation dosage contours in Figs. 8.91a,

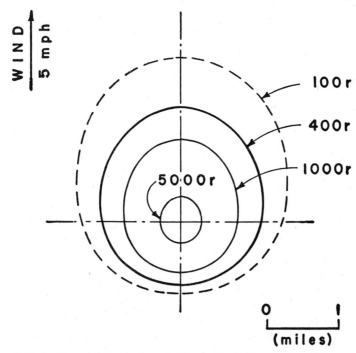

Figure 8.91a.   Contours for various integrated radiation dosages due to base surge from underwater burst.

b, and c. The dosage due to the base surge mist as it passes over and through an area is shown in Fig. 8.91a. The distortion from symmetry is due to the fact that a wind of about 5 miles per hour was blowing at and near the surface of the lagoon at the time of the detonation.   This results, of course, in the radioactive contamination extending much further downwind than in the upwind direction.[19]

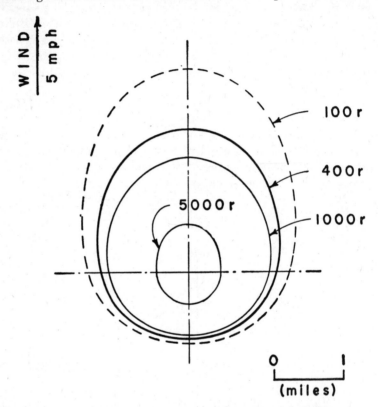

Figure 8.91b.   Contours for various integrated radiation dosages due to contamination from underwater burst.

8.92   The integrated dosage contours resulting from contamina-tion due to rain from both the base surge and the fall-out from the atomic cloud, are given in Fig. 8.91b, while Fig. 8.91c indicates the contours for total dosage, i. e., the sum of the base surge and con-tamination dosages.   It is probable that the data in Fig. 8.91b, and hence also in Fig. 8.91c, represent an underestimate, because a pro-portion of the contaminated water falling as rain ran off the decks of

---

[19] For the effect of wind on the area, etc., of the base surge, see § 4.79.

the ships and back into the lagoon, so that its activity was not included in the measured dosage.

8.93   It may be mentioned that the radioactive mist of the base surge is most hazardous within the first few minutes of its formation.

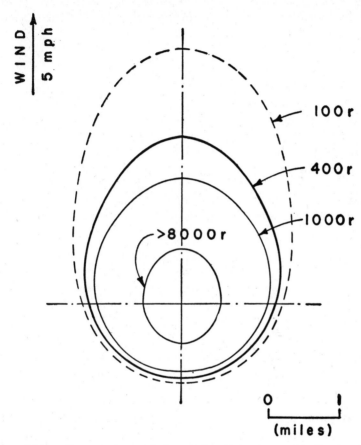

Figure 8.91c.   Contours for total dosage due to base surge and contamination from underwater burst.

Its activity decreases rapidly in the course of a short time due to the operation of three factors, namely, dilution by increase of volume as a result of mixing with air, raining out of the active material as the droplets increase in size, and natural radioactive decay.   Calculations which probably give a correct order of magnitude, at least, indicate that the dosage rate within the base surge decreases by a factor of about 400 in the interval between 1 and 4 minutes after the underwater burst. This rapid decrease indicates the advantage of protection from the base surge mist during the 3 or 4 minutes immediately following an atomic explosion. At Bikini, contamination of the interior of the ships, due to the base surge, was minimized by closing down the hatches and stopping the ventilating systems. Attention to this point, especially in the early stages, would obviously prove well worth while.

RADIOACTIVITY OF WATER

8.94 It was recorded earlier that in an underwater burst of an atomic bomb most of the radioactivity of the fission products ultimately appears in the water. Because of the large volume in which these substances are dispersed, the activity in the water is not as high as might be feared, except close to the explosion center and within a short time of the burst. As a result of diffusion of the active material, mixing with water from outside the contaminated area, and natural decay of the radioactivity, the dosage decreases with fair rapidity in a short time. In Table 8.94 are given the area and mean

TABLE 8.94

DIMENSIONS AND MAXIMUM DOSAGE RATE OF CONTAMINATED WATER IN BIKINI LAGOON

Time after explosion (hours)	Contaminated area (square miles)	Mean diameter (miles)	Maximum dosage rate (r per day)
4	16. 6	4. 6	75
38	18. 4	4. 8	10
62	48. 6	7. 9	5
86	61. 8	8. 9	1
100	70. 6	9. 5	. 6
130	107	11. 7	. 2
200	160	14. 3	. 01

diameter of the contaminated portion of the lagoon after the Bikini "Baker" test, together with maximum observed dosage rates at various times after the burst.

8.95. It is evident that, although a ship would not wish to remain in the contaminated area for any length of time soon after the explosion, passage across the water would not be a great hazard. It is to be understood, of course, that condensers and evaporators would have to be closed down while the ship is in contaminated waters. Further, because of the decrease in activity with time, it seems unlikely that an underwater burst of an atomic bomb would prevent operation of a harbor for any length of time, at least as far as contamination of the water is concerned. However, it should be borne in mind that the results in Table 8.94, although probably fairly representative, would be affected by the geophysical conditions of the harbor.

8.96 Another factor which contributed to the loss in activity of the water at Bikini was settling of the fission products to the bottom of the lagoon. To judge from samples of bottom material collected 7 and 16 days after the explosion, a considerable proportion of the active material must have been ultimately removed in this manner. The results indicate that the major deposition had occurred within a week and that it covered an area of over 60 square miles. On the assumption that the fission products had penetrated to a depth of 1 foot, it can be estimated that the total mass of the bottom material, in which the radioactivity was distributed, was about 1.4×10^8 tons. Consequently, even though the total initial activity of the fission products was high, about 2×10^6 curies measured a week after the explosion, its wide distribution at the bottom of the lagoon would mean that it did not represent a great hazard to marine life. Observations made several months after the explosion indicated, too, that there was no tendency for the contaminated material to spread.

8.97 It is of interest in this connection to calculate the amount of radiation due to the radioactive isotope of potassium, mass number 40, in sea water. This isotope is present to the extent of 0.012 percent in all forms of potassium, regardless of its source. It emits a beta particle, with a maximum energy of 1.3 Mev, and a gamma photon of 1.5-Mev energy. Because of its long half life, about 1.5×10^9 years, the activity is normally of little significance, although it makes an appreciable contribution to the total background radioactivity of the body (§ 8.49). Since sea water contains 0.4 gram of potassium per liter, the total weight of radiopotassium 40 in the Bikini lagoon is estimated to be 1.4×10^9 grams or 2.1×10^{31} atoms. From the known half life it can be calculated that there will be a total of about 4×10^{14} disintegrations per second, which is equivalent to 10^4 curies of activity due to the potassium 40 alone. In other words, the normal background activity of Bikini lagoon, before the atomic bomb explosion, was at least 10^4 curies. This is not very different from the fission product activity collected at the bottom about 18 months after the detonation.

8.98. There is a possibility that after an underwater burst of an atomic bomb, the radioactivity might be spread over a large area due to the action of marine life. It is well known that land plants absorb and so concentrate mineral elements from the soil and that these are further concentrated in animals feeding on the plants. Similar circumstances arise in water environments; the simple plants, i. e., phytoplankton and algae, absorb the nutritive salts from the water, and they are then accumulated in the larger aquatic forms, e. g., fish, which directly or indirectly consume the simple plants.

8.99   In water containing radioactive materials, the latter are concentrated by the fish in the same manner and for the same length of time as are the stable forms of the corresponding elements.   If the fish die, the radioactive isotopes are not lost, but they return to the water, as do the stable isotopes, to take part once again in the life cycle.   Because of the landlocked nature of the Bikini lagoon, there is evidently little or no outward migration of the larger aquatic organisms so that, as mentioned above, there is no appreciable tendency for the radioactivity to spread.   However, due to the behavior of the anadromous migratory fishes, e. g., salmon, shad, etc., which feed in the sea and then migrate upstream to die, or of birds that concentrate the minerals of the sea in guano, there might be some distribution of radioactivity in other cases following an underwater atomic explosion.   The extent of such dispersion and its effects would depend greatly on circumstances and appears difficult to estimate.

Radioactive Contamination of Land Areas

8.100   The underwater burst at Bikini took place far enough from shore to prevent any appreciable contamination of land areas.   Some radioactive rain fell at large distances from the explosion center (§ 2.36), but the activity was not serious.   The possibility must be considered, however, of an underwater atomic explosion so near to the shore that significant amounts of the fall-out and the base surge will reach the adjacent land areas, and possibly affect dock facilities, warehouses, etc.   As indicated earlier, because some of the radioactively contaminated water ran off the ships at Bikini, the values in Figs. 8.91b and 8.91c may represent an underestimate if applied to the shore.   However, there may be compensating factors in the deposition of active material on the roofs or protruding portions of buildings, and also because of the shielding effects of various structures.

8.101   A rough attempt to assess the contamination, in terms of radiation dosage rates, of adjacent land areas from the underwater burst of a nominal atomic bomb, at 1 hour after the explosion is made in Fig. 8.101.   The results are based on the assumption that the activity is due to fission products with a mean gamma-ray energy of 0.7 Mev (§ 8.11).   Four contour lines are shown, representing radiation dosage rates of 400, 50, 10, and almost zero roentgens per hour, respectively.   In the region outside the last contour line, the danger due to radioactivity may, in general, although probably not always, be ignored.   It should be noted that the results are based on the assump-

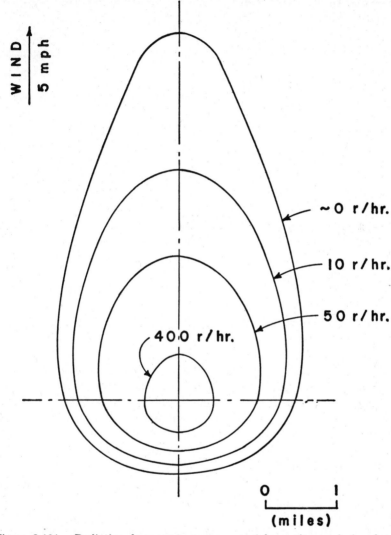

Figure 8.101.   Radiation dosage rate contours at 1 hour after explosion due to fission products from underwater burst.

tion that a 5-mile-per-hour wind is blowing, as was the case at Bikini. A difference in the wind velocity or a change in the direction or velocity within a short time after the explosion would, of course, alter the picture appreciably.

8.102   By combining the results of Fig. 8.101 with those in Figs. 8.16 and 8.17, some information can be obtained concerning the dosage rates and total dosage absorbed at various times after the explosion. The general method is the same as that indicated in § 8.18.

E. RADIATION CONTAMINATION FROM UNDERGROUND BURST

8.103   Although there are no data available for the effects of an underground burst of an atomic bomb, it is possible to make some qualitative statements concerning the extent of radioactive contamination. The latter will depend markedly on the depth at which the bomb is exploded, for this will determine the proportion of the fission products that will be trapped and the extent to which they will be mixed with dislodged dirt. The formation of a crater and the amount of debris thrown into the air are factors which will influence the extent of radioactive contamination in the immediate vicinity of the explosion and at a distance. In a fairly shallow underground explosion, where the underlying material is a thick bed of sand or mud, but not rock, a phenomenon similar to a base surge might be possible. It would presumably consist of very fine particles of dirt contaminated with fission products.

8.104   Extrapolation of results obtained in studies with ordinary high-explosive bombs [20] indicates that if a nominal atomic bomb was exploded at a depth of 50 feet, the diameter of the crater would be about 800 feet, and its depth 100 feet. The volume of such a crater would be 10^6 cubic yards, and its mass over half a million tons. If the fission product activity of the bomb uniformly contaminated the dirt from this crater, the activity an hour after the explosion would be about 6×10^3 curies per cubic yard. Probably a large part of this contaminated dirt would fall in the neighborhood of the crater and would constitute a serious hazard.

8.105   The crater itself would probably also be heavily contaminated, and supposing one-sixth of the activity of the fission products remained in the crater, the contamination density at 1 hour after the explosion would be 50,000 megacuries per square mile. Assuming a mean gamma-ray energy of 0.7 Mev, the dosage rate would be 5×10^5 r per hour at a point about 3 feet above the ground. Radiation intensities of this order of magnitude would not only make the crater area uninhabitable for a long time, but it would not be passable, to any degree of safety, even in a fast vehicle. The foregoing calculations do

[20] Appendix B.

not take into account activity induced by neutrons in the elements, notably silicon and sodium, present in the earth. These would undoubtedly make a substantial contribution to the radioactivity in the region of the crater.

8.106   The general consensus at the present time is that the area highly contaminated by an underground explosion would be less than in the case of an underwater burst. One reason is that the density of soil is greater than that of water and so a smaller mass would be thrown into the air to descend at a distance from the explosion. However, although the area covered may be less, the radiation intensity might be correspondingly greater at small distances from the bomb burst.

F.   RADIOLOGICAL WARFARE

Sources of Radiation

8.107   An extreme case of contamination by radioactive isotopes would arise if such substances were used deliberately as an offensive weapon. This possibility is generally referred to as *radiological warfare*, the term being used to describe the employment for military purposes of radioactive material with the object of contaminating persons, objects, or areas. The atomic bomb may be described as an indirect weapon of radiological warfare, for its main purpose is to cause physical destruction, the radioactive contamination being a secondary consideration. It is of interest to examine various aspects of the use of radioactivity as a weapon, apart from its occurrence as a result of fission in an atomic bomb.

8.108   Radioactive materials can be obtained in quantity in two ways. First, fission products are always formed in the nuclear reactors (or "piles") used for the production of plutonium for atomic bombs (§ 1.47) or for power. Considerable quantities of radioactive material could thus conceivably become available as a by-product of the manufacture of atomic bombs. The complex mixture of fission products could be used directly, or certain constituents might be extracted by chemical means.

8.109   Second, the irradiation of many stable elements by the intense neutron flux of a nuclear reactor leads to the formation of radioactive isotopes, as a result of radiative capture reactions (§ 1.25). It appears that for the same power level of a nuclear reactor, it is possible to produce larger quantities of radioactive material, in terms of activity, by neutron capture than by fission. In the latter case, the product is a complex mixture with varying rates of decay, but in the former case, a particular isotope, chosen as being suitable as a radiological warfare agent, could be made, if desired. However, it must be borne in mind that the formation of radioisotopes in a nuclear reactor, as a result of neutron capture, means that an equivalent amount of fissionable material, which can be used in a bomb, will be sacrificed.

8.110   It should be pointed out that, in any event, it would not be easy to produce large amounts of radioactive isotopes for radiological warfare. Under favorable conditions, a nuclear reactor operating for 100 days with a power output of a million watts would produce something of the order of a megacurie of activity. If this were spread out uniformly over a plane surface having an area of 1 square mile, the dosage rate 3 feet above the surface would be only 200 r per day for a 1.5-Mev gamma ray (Fig. 8.33). This rate would, of course, fall off with time, depending on the half life of the contaminating material.

8.111   As already seen, four types of nuclear radiation, namely, neutrons, alpha particles, beta particles, and gamma rays, produce harmful physiological effects. Apart from the atomic bomb, there does not appear to be any practical way of delivering and dispersing strong sources of neutrons, and so these need not be considered as possible radiological warfare agents. Because of their short range, alpha and beta particles would have little effect outside the body, but certain alpha and beta emitters when ingested can be lethal in relatively small quantities. A very high concentration of alpha-active or beta-active material would have to be placed over an area to insure that sufficient amounts entered the bodies of the inhabitants. Protection would be similar to that adopted against chemical warfare agents, and it seems unlikely that this form of radiological warfare would be worth while.

8.112   The caustic effect of beta-emitters on the skin (§ 11.78) might represent an important hazard, but this alone would hardly warrant employment of a pure beta-active substance as an offensive weapon. Nevertheless, it would represent an additional source of injury when a gamma-emitter is used.

8.113   On the whole it may be concluded that if radiological warfare is used as a weapon, it will be in the form of emitters of penetrating gamma radiation for which protective clothing and gas masks would be ineffective. With such substances it would be easier, than in the other cases, to achieve a level of radiation that would be lethal as the result of an appreciable exposure. However, it would appear to be a difficult matter to lay down such a concentration of gamma emitters over a large area as would cause serious injury from a short exposure.

Possible Advantages of Radiological Warfare

8.114 Since the physiological consequences of nuclear radiations are not apparent for some time after absorption, radiological warfare could be used to prevent the occupation of a particular area without causing immediate casualties and destruction. Contamination of a city, for example, might perhaps deny its use for habitation and close down its industries without causing the tremendous havoc produced by explosive and incendiary bombs. It is doubtful, however, apart from exceptionally highly contaminated areas, if such denial would be completely effective. By rotating the personnel, so that no individual received an excessive dose of radiation, the facilities of the city might be maintained, if on a reduced scale. In any event, the natural decay of the radioactivity means that the hazard would decrease with time, unless additional material was deposited at the same place.

8.115 Another aspect of radiological warfare which might be turned to advantage is its compactness. A few pounds of certain radioisotopes could produce millions of megacuries of activity. An example is provided by the fission products of an atomic bomb; here the initial activity of about two pounds of material is about a million megacuries. If this material could be spread uniformly over a limited area, it would cause serious harm. However, as may be seen from Table 8.10, the activity falls off rapidly with time, decreasing by a factor of nearly 10,000 by the end of the first day.

8.116 Perhaps the most important application of radiological warfare would be its psychological effect as a mystery weapon, analogous to the initial use of poison gas and of tanks in World War I. The obvious method to combat radiological warfare in this case is to understand and be prepared for it. Although nuclear radiations cannot be directly detected by the senses, there are available instruments which are very sensitive to such radiations (see Chapter IX). By the use of suitable devices their presence can be made apparent to the eyes and ears. It would then be necessary to take appropriate steps to evacuate the contaminated area, as described in Chapter XII.

Disadvantages of Radiological Warfare

8.117 The natural decay of radioactive material means that the contamination hazard is one which diminishes with time. This fact represents a disadvantage of radiological warfare in another sense: it is not possible to build up a stockpile of material for subsequent use, as can be done with other weapons, for there is a continuous loss of activity. Consequently, the active substances must be manufactured continuously in order to maintain the stockpile even when the weapon is not being used.

8.118   It might be thought that the difficulty of decay could be overcome by using radioisotopes of long life, but this is not very practical because the activity in curies of a given mass of radioisotope is inversely proportional to its half life, and to its atomic weight.   Relatively large quantities of material would have to be used, and it would be more difficult to achieve a high level of activity at any point on the ground.   Of course, if a radioactive isotope of long half life·could be used to produce considerable activity, it would mean that the area would remain contaminated for a longer time.

8.119   If gamma-ray emitters were to be used as radiological warfare agents, and these seem to be the only ones likely to be effective, the problem would arise of shielding personnel from the radiations during manufacture, storage, and delivery of the weapon.   The use of adequate shields, presumably of concrete, iron, or lead, would add greatly to the weight of the munition and would complicate the mechanism of dissemination on the target.   The uniform distribution of a relatively small amount of material over a large area would itself present a difficult problem, the solution of which might nullify the advantage of compactness.

8.120   Because its physiological effects would be delayed, radiological warfare could not be used as a tactical weapon, in the military sense of the term.   Operations could be continued in the contaminated area, if the occupying force was either willing to accept the risk of probable future losses, or if there were periodic replacement of personnel to avoid overexposure.

8.121   While it is impossible to predict, as in the case of chemical warfare, whether radiological warfare will be used or not, it is necessary to understand and be prepared for it.   Only in the event of being unprepared are the consequences likely to be as serious as the destruction caused by an atomic bomb.

CHAPTER IX[1]

MEASUREMENT OF NUCLEAR RADIATIONS

A. PROPERTIES AND EFFECTS OF RADIATIONS

IONIZING RADIATIONS

9.1 The subject of the measurement of nuclear radiations of different types is very extensive. Hence, the treatment given here will be restricted mainly to those aspects which have a bearing on the detection of radioactive contamination following an atomic explosion. In considering the measurement of nuclear radiations it is convenient to divide them into two categories, namely, electrically charged radiation and neutral radiation. The former consists of beta particles (electrons), alpha particles, and the fission fragments which initially carry relatively large electrical charges. The neutral nuclear radiations are gamma rays and neutrons; these are, in general, more penetrating than electrically charged radiations, and are consequently of greater importance from the present point of view. For clarity of discussion, however, the charged particles will be considered first.

9.2 In its passage through a gas, an electrically charged particle will occasionally approach close enough to an atom or molecule to exert an electrical force which is sufficient to remove an electron from the latter. The residue of the atom or molecule, after the removal of the electron, is a positively charged ion; the separate electron and the ion so formed constitute what is known as an *ion-pair*. Thus, electrically charged particles are ionizing particles, and as they traverse a gas they leave behind a number of ion-pairs in their path. For charged particles of the same mass, the particles carrying the higher charge will cause ionization to occur more rapidly. Further, for particles of the same energy, those of higher mass will be most effective in producing ionization; since they move more slowly, the forces of interaction resulting in ionization are operative for a longer time over a given distance.

9.3 The energy of interaction between an electrically charged particle and an electron of an atom or molecule may be insufficient to cause ionization of the latter, but sufficient energy may be trans-

[1] Material contributed by F. R. Shonka, H. L. Wyckoff.

ferred to raise it to a higher energy level, so that the atom or molecule is in an excited state (§ 8.38). Consequently, when an electrically charged particle travels through a gas, it loses energy principally by the processes of ionization and excitation of the atoms or molecules along its path. These two types of interaction can be used as the basis of methods for measurement of electrically charged radiation. In the first place, it is possible to determine the total charge of the ion-pairs produced, before they combine to form neutral atoms or molecules, and, in the second place, the characteristic radiation (fluorescence) emitted by the excited atom or molecule as it returns to its normal energy state may be studied.

9.4   Whereas electrically charged particles produce ionization and excitation directly, the neutral radiations, i. e., gamma rays and neutrons, do so indirectly. However, since the ultimate effects are essentially the same in all cases, no new principles are involved in connection with the measurements of the so-called neutral nuclear radiations. As seen in Chapter VIII, the interaction of gamma radiation with matter is accompanied by the ejection of electrons of high energy. The measurement of gamma rays is thus reduced to the study of the electrons they produce.

9.5   When a fast neutron collides with a hydrogen atom, which may be part of a compound, e. g., water or paraffin, it can transfer a considerable amount of energy to the atom, which is expelled as a positively charged hydrogen ion, or proton. The recoil proton so formed produces ionization in its path, thus permitting of its detection. Slow neutrons are captured by an isotope of boron with the formation of a lithium ion and an alpha particle, both of which are capable of producing ionization. Thus measurements of neutrons can be made by observing the effects produced by the electrically charged radiation resulting from their interaction with appropriate substances. Other methods for measuring neutrons have been used, but they need not be considered here, especially as the detection of neutrons is not likely to be of importance in connection with radioactive contamination due to an atomic bomb, or even with the deliberate use of radioisotopes as a weapon.

9.6   As implied above, the extent or density of ionization produced by ionizing radiation in its passage through a gas, will depend on its mass, energy, and the magnitude of its electrical charge. The nature of the gas is also important, for the energy required to produce an ion-pair differs from one gas to another. For air, for example, an electrically charged particle loses, on the average, about 33 electron-volts of energy for every ion-pair eventually produced (§ 7.41). This value varies somewhat with the identity and energy of the ionizing particle, but the figure of 33 may be adopted as a fair approximation.

9.7   The ionization density is usually expressed in terms of the *specific ionization*, i. e., the number of ion-pairs per centimeter of path.   The specific ionization of a beta particle in air at atmospheric pressure varies from about 30 to 300, according to the initial energy of the particle.   For alpha particles of radioactive origin, the ionization density is approximately 40,000 to 100,000 ion-pairs per centimeter of path.   Because the latter lose their energy more rapidly, in this way, alpha particles expelled from radioactive nuclei have a much shorter range than do beta particles of similar energy (see Chapter VIII).   A charged fission fragment has a specific ionization much higher than that of an alpha particle, but the ionization density decreases along the path as the fission fragments pick up electrons and so gradually lose their charge.

9.8   In the case of liquids and solids, processes somewhat more complicated but analogous to excitation and ionization take place. Therefore, if such substances are exposed to nuclear radiation, they may fluoresce, i. e., emit light, and they may be rendered conducting due to the separation of charges within them.   As in the case of gases, so also in liquids and solids, both properties, namely, fluorescence and conduction, may be utilized for detecting electrically charged radiation.

9.9   Some crystals have a relatively high fluorescence yield and, furthermore, the path lengths of electrically charged radiation in crystals are extremely short.   Both of these facts make it possible to focus the fluorescent radiation on a small, sensitive, light-detecting device such as a photomultiplier tube.   In this way crystals can be used as means for radiation detection.   An interesting property of some crystals is the fact that they do not return to their normal states immediately after interacting with the electrically charged radiation. The energy thus gained is, in a sense, trapped within the crystal and can be released at some later time by an external agent, for example, a light shining on the crystal.

9.10   Crystals, such as silver chloride, potassium iodide, diamond, calcium tungstate, sodium iodide, naphthalene, anthracene, and others, are now being used, mainly as research tools, for the study of radiation measurements.   Although they are not yet employed to any large extent in radiation protection survey work, a start has been made in this direction and important developments may be expected in the future.

9.11   In addition to the consequences of excitation and ionization mentioned above, there are other effects produced which may be utilized for the measurement of electrically charged radiations. Thus excitation and ionization may result in chemical changes, one of the most important being the formation of latent images in a photographic emulsion. Upon development of the plate or film, blackening or fogging is observed due to the indirect action of the electrically charged radiation. The discoveries of both X-rays and radioactivity were, in fact, made as a result of the effect of the radiations on photographic plates, and the method is still widely used in many aspects of radiation measurement.

9.12 It should be noted that the use of photographic emulsions for the quantitative measurement of nuclear radiations is based on the supposition that the amount of photochemical action depends only on the total energy absorbed and is independent of the rate of absorption. This postulate, known as the reciprocity law for photochemical reactions, has been verified experimentally for alpha and beta particles, and for gamma rays.

9.13 Another interesting possibility for the measurement of nuclear radiations, which is being investigated, is that the chemical effect produced by such radiations may result in color changes in certain substances. Simple detection devices might be developed if the principle could be utilized, but so far only limited success has been achieved in this direction.

B.   INSTRUMENTATION BASED ON IONIZATION OF GASES

Ionization Chambers

9.14 Consider two conducting electrodes, insulated from one another, placed in a closed vessel containing air. By connecting these electrodes to a battery, one may be charged positively and the other negatively. The potential between the electrodes is proportional to the charge on them, the two quantities being related by the capacity or capacitance of the system; this is defined as the charge required to produce a potential difference of 1 volt between the two electrodes. If the latter are well insulated, they will retain their charge even when the battery is disconnected. An arrangement of this kind represents, in principle, an *ionization chamber*.

9.15 Suppose, now, that the arrangement just described is exposed to radiation capable of producing ionization in the air. As they come into the electrical field between the charged electrodes, a force acts on the ions, with the result that those of positive sign will collect on the negative electrode, and vice versa. The charge collected in this way will partially discharge the electrodes, thus decreasing the potential between them. From the change in potential and the known capacitance of the system, the quantity of charge which has been collected by the electrodes can be determined. The charge collected will be independent of the actual potential between the electrodes, provided this is kept high enough to make sure that all the ions formed are actually collected. This quantity of charge is then a measure of the radiation dose which has entered the ionization chamber.

9.16 A familiar and simple form of ionization chamber is the gold-leaf electroscope. The containing vessel or case acts as one electrode and a central metal rod, insulated from the case, acts as the other; a gold leaf is attached near the end of the central electrode. A difference of potential is applied between the case and the insulated rod by means of a battery and as a result the gold leaf diverges from the rod. The deflection observed is a measure of the potential between the electrodes, the larger the potential the greater the deflection. If ions are formed in the vessel, due to exposure to radiation, electric charges of opposite signs are collected on the electrodes, the potential falls, and the deflection of the gold leaf decreases. In principle, it should be possible to calibrate the gold-leaf electroscope so that the charge collected, and hence the radiation dosage, can be estimated from the movement of the gold leaf.

9.17 For practical radiation measurement, various more refined types of ionization chamber are used. One form, the personnel pocket chamber (Fig. 9.17), widely used in the United States Atomic Energy Commission's installations for monitoring, that is, for determining the radiation exposure of personnel, is similar to a pocket fountain pen in size and shape. It consists of a central wire electrode insulated from a case, coated with graphite on the inside, which acts as the other electrode. The electrodes are charged up to a known potential, and the device is carried in the pocket during the working day. If there has been no exposure to ionizing radiation, and no leakage of charge, the potential will be unchanged. However, if exposure to radiation has occurred, the air in the chamber will have become ionized; the ions of opposite charges then travel to the two electrodes and reduce the potential between them. At the end of the day, the pocket chamber is placed in an electrometer for measuring the potential. From the difference between this and the initial value, the charge collected, and hence the radiation dosage, can be determined.

9.18 The pocket chamber is rugged and dependable, but suffers from the disadvantage that it must be taken to an electrometer to have the potential read.   In the self-reading pocket dosimeter (Fig. 9.18), which is similar in size and shape and is also an ionization chamber, a calibrated device is included, so that the dosage at any time can be indicated directly.   As before, a difference of potential is applied

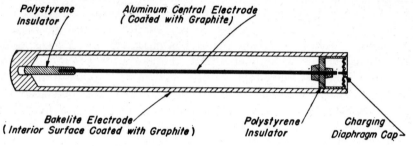

Figure 9.17.   Personnel pocket chamber.

INSTRUMENT—PERSONNEL TYPE

POCKET CHAMBER

Radiation Detected	Gamma
Full Scale Range	0.2 r, 10 r, 50 r, 100 r
Area of Acceptance or Volume of Chamber.	5 cc
Detector Stage	Ionization Chamber
Conversion Stage	Electroscope in separate charging and reading box
Recorder-Indicator Stage	Electrometer fiber projected on scale or image of fiber on reticle of microscope
Weight	1 ounce
Volume or Dimensions	0.5 x 5 inches
Description	Similar to pocket fountain pen
Battery Life	——
Chief Causes of Failure	Leakage across electrode insulator
Remarks	Extremely rugged and dependable

between the case, as one electrode, and a central wire; the latter has a metal-coated quartz fiber, which acts like the gold leaf of an electroscope, attached to it.   When the dosimeter is charged, the quartz fiber diverges from the wire, but if ions are collected, as a result of exposure to radiation, the deflection becomes less.   The position, at any time, of the quartz fiber on a calibrated scale, as observed through a small compound microscope fitted into one end of the chamber, gives the radiation dosage received up to that time.

9.19   The same principle is used on a larger scale in the quartz-fiber survey meter (Fig. 9.19); this is a rugged instrument used for

monitoring areas where radioactive contamination is likely to occur.
It has an ionization chamber of about 300 cubic centimeters volume,
and, in addition to the electrodes, quartz fiber, and microscope, it
has a timing device included.   The scale of the instrument is cali-

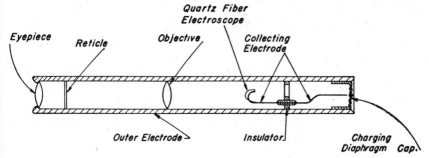

Figure 9.18.   Pocket dosimeter (self-reading).

INSTRUMENT—PERSONNEL TYPE

POCKET DOSIMETER SELF-READING

Radiation Detected_____	Gamma
Full Scale Ranges_____	0.2 r, 10 r, 50 r
Area of Acceptance or Volume of Chamber.	2.5 cc
Detector Stage_____	Ionization Chamber
Conversion Stage_____	Incorporated coated quartz fiber· electroscope
Recorder-Indicator Stage_____	Image of electroscope fiber on reticle of microscope
Weight_____	1 ounce
Volume or Dimensions_____	0.5 x 5 inches
Description_____	Similar to pocket fountain pen
Battery Life_____	——
Chief Causes of Failure_____	Leakage across electrode insulator
Remarks_____	Extremely rugged and dependable

brated so that, with the aid of the timer, the dosage rate, i. e., the dose
in roentgens received in unit time, is indicated directly.

9.20   The foregoing examples have been of electrostatic instruments
for the measurement of radiation.   However, if the charging battery
were left connected to the ionization chamber, as indicated diagrammatically in Fig 9.20a, the voltage between the electrodes would
remain constant, because the battery supplies charge at the same rate
at which the chamber is discharging due to ion collection.   The rate

of flow of charge in the battery circuit is called the *ionization current* and is a measure of the radiation dose rate. This ionization current is, in general, very small. For example, the maximum permissible

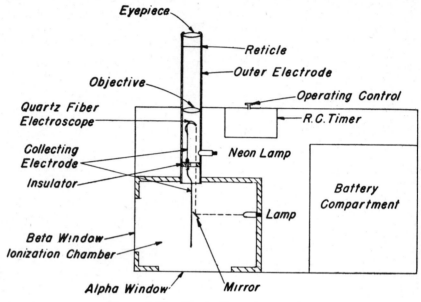

Figure 9.19.   Quartz-fiber survey meter.

INSTRUMENT—AREA SURVEY TYPE

QUARTZ-FIBER SURVEY METER

Radiation Detected_____	Beta and gamma
Full Scale Ranges_____	$\begin{cases}0\text{--}100 \text{ mr/hr}\\0\text{--}1 \text{ r/hr}\end{cases}$ gamma
Area of Acceptance or Volume of Chamber.	300 cc
Detector Stage_____	Ionization chamber
Conversion Stage_____	Quartz-fiber electroscope
Recorder-Indicator Stage_____	Rate of drift of electroscope fiber over reticle in microscope
Weight_____	5 pounds
Volume or Dimensions_____	4 x 7 x 6 inches
Description_____	Rectangular container with protruding microscope barrel
Battery Life_____	100 hrs. for artificial illumination
Chief Causes of Failure_____	——
Remarks_____	Rugged, keeps its calibration, hence used as secondary standard

radiation dose for an eight-hour working day would produce an average current of 1×10^{-11} amp. in a liter of air at atmospheric pressure. Such minute currents can, however, be readily measured with the aid of vacuum tube amplifiers. Some of these instruments frequently employ interchangeable absorbing screens on the chambers so that it is possible to distinguish between different types of radiations because of their different penetrating powers (Fig. 9.20b).

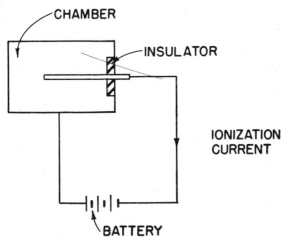

Figure 9.20a.   Diagrammatic representation of ionization chamber used to measure dosage rate.

9.21   An ionization chamber is one of the most flexible of the radiation measuring instruments. Its characteristics may be changed by varying any of the following factors: the material of the wall and the nature of the gas, the pressure of the gas, the size of the chamber, and the sensitivity of the conversion and output stages. The over-all sensitivity that can be obtained for a nonportable instrument is limited only by the statistical fluctuation of the background radiation.

9.22   Because of their high specific ionization, the alpha (and other heavily ionizing) particles produce appreciable pulses in the ionization current; this is the basis of the pulse-counting ionization chamber. The pulses can be electronically amplified to drive a mechanical register. In cases where fast counting is desired, the impulses are scaled down electronically, for example, counting only every tenth or hundredth pulse, thereby permitting counts to be taken at a rate far above the limiting counting speed of the mechanical register. Pulse chambers are very useful in the laboratory but do not lend themselves to portable instrument design, due to the necessary high amplification

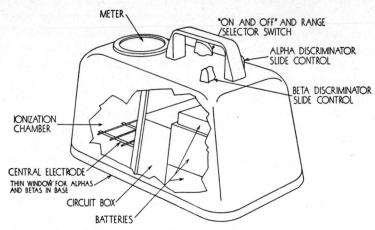

Figure 9.20b.   Ionization chamber instrument with absorbing screens.

INSTRUMENT—AREA SURVEY TYPE

ALPHA, BETA, GAMMA SURVEY METER

Radiation Detected	Alpha, beta, gamma
Full Scale Ranges	0–25 mr/hr for gamma (some instruments designed to read up to 500 r/hr) 0–40,000 d/m for alpha
Area of Acceptance or Volume of Chambers.	100 cc chamber with 100 sq. cm. window
Detector Stage	Ionization chamber
Conversion Stage	Electrometer amplifier
Recorder-Indicator Stage	Output current meter
Weight	9 pounds
Volume or Dimensions	5 x 6 x 12 inches
Description	Rectangular container with interchangeable filters on bottom side of ionization chamber
Battery Life	1,000 hours
Chief Cause of Failure	Usual D. C. amplifier difficulties, such as, insulation, drift, and fluctuations of battery voltage
Remarks	Very useful as general survey meter

of the electronic circuit.   It is important to note that in the form
described, the pulse-counting chamber counts the ionizing events and
does not measure the total ionization produced in the gas.

PROPORTIONAL-COUNTING CHAMBERS

9.23   In the various forms of ionization chamber relatively weak
collecting fields are used.   However, if the electric field is sufficiently

strong the electron from an ion-pair may acquire enough energy in a distance of a mean free path to ionize the atoms or molecules with which it collides; the electrons so formed produce still more ions and so on.   This process of multiplication of ionization is called gas amplification, and the ratio of the total number of ions produced to the number of ions formed by the original ionizing particle entering the chamber is called the *gas amplification factor*.   Gas amplification can be achieved either by increasing the strength of the electric field, by decreasing the energy required to cause ionization by a suitable choice of the chamber gas, or by decreasing the pressure of the gas.   Decreasing the pressure of the gas, of course, increases the length of the mean free path.

9.24   A method which is used for obtaining strong electric fields with moderate voltages is to employ two coaxial cylinders as the electrodes, the inner cylinder being an extremely fine wire.   The central wire is positively charged and strong fields exist in the neighborhood of this wire.   As a result of gas amplification the total charge collected may be many times greater than, although it is always proportional to, that due to the original ionization; hence, the name *proportional counter* is given to this device.   The usual amplification factor may be anywhere from 100 to 100,000.   This type of counter can be used for alpha particles alone (Fig. 9.24a) or for beta particles alone in the presence of gamma radiation.   A pulse of current is observed, chiefly due to the collection of the electrons by the central wire.   Owing to the high mobility of the electrons the pulses are of very short duration and the counter can be used for high counting rates.   Proportional counters with large "windows," i. e., the area through which the radiation is admitted into the chamber, can be built if a number of parallel wires are used.   Counters of such large sensitive areas are then convenient for measuring alpha-contamination on hands and clothing, the contaminated dust collected on filter paper (Fig. 9.24b), and the contamination on tables and other surfaces.

GEIGER-MÜLLER COUNTERS

9.25   In a proportional counter the gas amplification factor cannot be increased indefinitely, as a new phenomenon occurs in which the ion multiplication spreads along the entire sensitive area of the counter and a self-sustaining discharge takes place.   When used in this way the instrument is called a *Geiger-Müller counter* (or *tube*); the pulse size is independent of the number of electrons which initiated it, since even a single electron can trigger the discharge inside the tube.

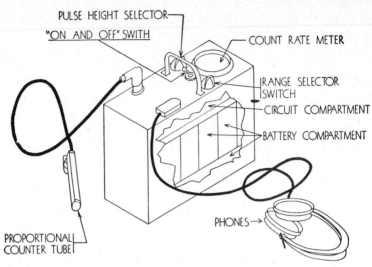

Figure 9.24a.   Proportional counter for alpha particles.

INSTRUMENT—AREA SURVEY TYPE

PORTABLE PROPORTIONAL COUNTER

Radiation Detected_____ Alpha only
Full Scale Ranges_____ $\begin{cases} 0\text{--}2{,}000 \text{ d/m} \\ 0\text{--}20{,}000 \text{ d/m} \end{cases}$
Area of Acceptance or Volume of   100 sq. cm.
  Chamber.
Detector Stage_____ 4-wire proportional counting chamber
Conversion Stage_____ Pulse amplifier of high sensitivity
Recorder-Indicator Stage_____ Counting rate on current output meter or
                                  earphones
Weight_____ 16 pounds
Volume or Dimensions_____ 5 x 8 x 12 inches
Description_____ Rectangular container with alpha window in
                                  bottom
Battery Life_____ 80 hours
Chief Causes of Failure_____ High-voltage leakage due to humidity
Remarks_____ Uses charged condenser for high voltage on
                                  counting chamber

Geiger-Müller counters therefore will count any radiation that will produce at least one ion-pair in the interior of the tube.   Beta rays which penetrate the walls of the tube will be counted with nearly 100 percent efficiency, whereas only those gamma rays that produce ionization within the tube or secondary photoelectrons from the tube's inner surface will be counted.   The efficiency for this radiation is usually less than 1 percent.

9.26   Before the counter can respond to another ionizing event it is necessary to quench the discharge.   This is done by using organic vapors inside the counter tube or by external electronic methods. The size of the pulse will depend on the design of the counter itself as well as on the external circuit.   These pulses can be of the order of many volts, so that they can‑produce audible sounds in earphones without any additional external amplification.   Geiger-Müller coun-ters are especially useful as light-weight, portable, sensitive, detecting

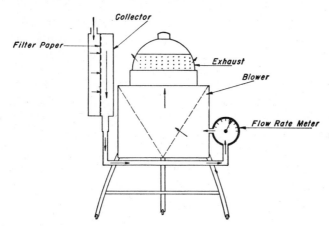

Figure 9.24b.   Air filtration unit.

INSTRUMENT—AREA SURVEY TYPE

FILTER UNIT

Radiation Detected	Alpha contamination on dust collected by drawing air through filter paper
Full Scale Ranges	——
Area of Acceptance or Volume of Chamber.	Size of filter paper 5.2 x 9.5 inches
Detector Stage	Filter paper analyzed for activity with portable or A. C. proportional counter
Conversion Stage	Filter paper analyzed for activity with portable or A. C. proportional counter
Recorder-Indicator Stage	Filter paper analyzed for activity with portable or A. C. proportional counter
Weight	35 pounds
Volume or Dimensions	12 x 12 x 20 inches
Description	Vacuum-cleaner type blower with flow rate meter and filter-paper holder
Battery Life	——
Chief Causes of Failure	——
Remarks	

instruments for survey work. In this case, also, it should be noted that Geiger-Müller counters respond to individual events and do not measure the amount of ionization produced by the radiation in the gas of the counter.

C. RADIATION MONITORING INSTRUMENTS

INTRODUCTION

9.27   Four methods of radiation detection and instrumentation are generally employed in radiation monitoring instruments; namely, the ionization chamber, the proportional-counting chamber, and the Geiger-Müller counter, which are based on ionization in gases, and the photographic process, based on the chemical effects of the radiation. As already stated, the chief residual radiations likely to be encountered from the atomic bomb and radiological warfare are gamma rays, beta particles, and alpha particles.   Consequently, the response of each of the four types of detectors to these radiations will be considered, in this order, since it represents their relative importance for the present purpose.

MEASUREMENT OF GAMMA RADIATION

9.28   Because of their great penetrating power, gamma rays are probably the easiest radiations to detect.   They are also the most important ones to measure accurately, as general external exposure to large dosages of them may have harmful physiological effects.   The unit used in the measurement of gamma ray dose is the roentgen, as has been already explained (§ 7.41).   The dosage rate is usually specified in terms of roentgens absorbed per unit time, e. g., r per minute or r per hour.[2]

9.29   In the ionization chamber, there is considerable latitude as to size, shape, wall material and thickness, and gas composition and pressure (§ 9.21); hence this detector can be designed to be sensitive to various radiation levels.   The highest sensitivity is not, however, consistent with portability.   The most important fact about the ionization chamber survey instrument is that it can usually be designed to read with sufficient precision for survey purposes in roentgens or in roentgens per hour for gamma rays over a wide range of energies. A properly designed ionization chamber survey meter will be suffi-

---

[2] A discussion of the roentgen, its measurement, and the response of the different types of detectors of gamma rays of various energies is given in Appendix C.

ciently independent of the gamma-ray energy in the range from 0.05 Mev to 3 Mev (Fig. 9.29).

9.30 The pocket chamber and the self-reading pocket dosimeter, described in § 9.17 and § 9.18, respectively, are forms of ionizing chambers, as stated earlier. They are thus especially useful for measuring the gamma radiation dosages acquired by personnel.

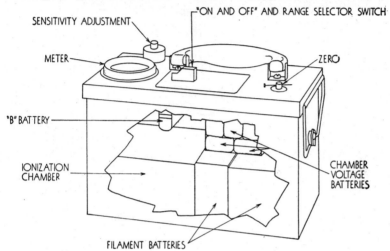

Figure 9.29. Ionization chamber for gamma (and beta) radiation.

INSTRUMENT—AREA SURVEY TYPE

Gamma Survey Meter

Radiation Detected	Gamma (some beta only)
Full Scale Ranges	Most units have 3 or 4 ranges Most sensitive range is 0–2.5 mr/hr Least sensitive is 0–5 r/hr (some instruments designed to read up to 250 r/hr)
Area of Acceptance or Volume of Chamber.	500–1,500 cc
Detector Stage	Ionization chamber
Conversion Stage	Electrometer amplifier
Recorder-Indicator Stage	Output current meter
Weight	5–20 pounds
Volume or Dimensions	Ranges in sizes from 4 x 5 x 9 inches to 7 x 10 x 14 inches
Description	Usually rectangular in shape
Battery Life	200–1,000 hours
Chief Causes of Failure	Usual D. C. amplifier difficulties, such as, insulation, drift, and fluctuations of battery voltage
Remarks	Most convenient instrument for measurement of gamma dosage rate

9.31   The proportional-counting chamber is very rarely, if ever, used as a gamma ray detector in any portable survey work.   How-

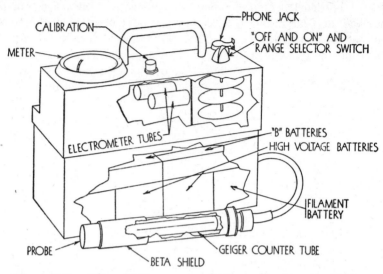

Figure 9.31.   Geiger-Müller counter for gamma (and beta) radiation.

INSTRUMENT—AREA SURVEY TYPE

PORTABLE DETECTOR

Radiation Detected	Beta and gamma
Full Scale Ranges	Usual ranges 0–1,500, 15,000, 150,000 cpm corresponding to 0–0.2, 2, and 20 mr/hr for Ra gamma
Area of Acceptance or Volume of Chamber.	Cylindrical, 2 cm dia. x 13 cm long. Wall thickness 30 mg/cm^2
Detector Stage	Geiger-Müller counter tube
Conversion Stage	Pulse amplifier of low sensitivity
Recorder-Indicator Stage	Counting rate on current output meter or earphones
Weight	4–15 pounds
Volume or Dimensions	5 x 6 x 10 inches
Description	Rectangular circuit and battery box with Geiger-Müller counter on probe. Counter tube had approximately 0.5g/cm^2 sliding filter
Battery Life	200–800 hours
Chief Causes of Failure	Breakage and life of Geiger-Müller tube
Remarks	Most convenient portable detector for beta and gamma radiation. Sometimes available as thin end-window counter for detecting alpha and soft beta.

ever, the Geiger-Müller counter is probably the most convenient portable instrument for gamma ray detection (Fig. 9.31). Except for a definite energy spectrum, it is not possible to calibrate it in terms of dosage rates. This is because it counts the ionizing events rather than the ionization produced in air, and because there is not a great deal of choice about the shape and wall material used. The Geiger-Müller counter can, however, be utilized to compare intensities of gamma ray beams of the same quality of radiation, and it can be calibrated in roentgens per hour for a particular gamma-ray energy distribution, such as the gamma rays from a standard radium sample or, possibly, from fission products. Due to energy dependence of the Geiger-Müller counter and the fact that its efficiency is at least a hundred times as great for some beta particles as it is for gamma rays, it is unwise to employ this instrument as a quantitative device for health monitoring survey work.

9.32 Photographic films are frequently used for measuring gamma ray dosage, and are especially valuable in the form of personnel badge meters for permanent records (Fig. 9.32). These film badges usually consist of a packet containing several dental size emulsions packaged in a thin material which is opaque to light but is readily penetrated by gamma rays. After development and drying, the density of the film is read on a densitometer in which the intensity of a small diffuse beam of light can be measured by a detector, such as a photoelectric cell. The intensities are read with and without the processed emulsion in the light beam, and the density of the blackening is defined as the logarithm of the ratio of these intensities, a correction having been made from an unexposed blank film.

9.33 Emulsions with known exposures, to serve as standards, and the unexposed blank emulsions are processed together with the badge-meter emulsions. Careful control of the techniques, temperature, and strength of the developing and fixing solutions used for the films is necessary if dependable exposure data are to be obtained. Care must also be taken of the films before development, since it is well known that they are sensitive to heat, light, moisture, pressure, etc. In the present state of the art, certain emulsions used with correcting filters can give roentgen dosages of gamma rays, reasonably independent of energy from about 0.05 to 2 Mev.

Measurement of Beta Particles

9.34 Since beta particles produce considerable ionization along their paths, measurements are usually made with ionization chambers

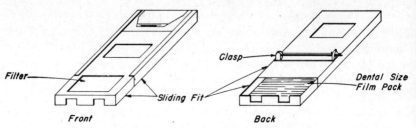

Figure 9.32.   Personnel film-badge meter.

INSTRUMENT—PERSONNEL TYPE

FILM BADGE

Radiation Detected_____ Beta and gamma
Full Scale Ranges_____ 0.05–10,000 r (in multiple film packet)
Area of Acceptance or Volume of {2 cm x 2 cm for gamma
  Chamber.   {1 cm x 2 cm for beta
Detector Stage_____ Photographic process
Conversion Stage_____ Development of latent image
Recorder-Indicator Stage_____ Density of emulsion read with densitometer
Weight_____ 1 ounce
Volume or Dimensions_____ 3.5 cm x 4.5 cm x 0.5 cm
Description_____ Rectangular container with clip
Battery Life_____ ——
Chief Causes of Failure_____ Limitations of photographic film as discussed
                                 in text
Remarks_____ Especially useful for permanent records of
                                 integrated dose

or with Geiger-Müller counters (Figs. 9.29 and 9.31). The proportional-counting chamber is not often used, however, since if it is made to respond to high-energy (hard) beta particles it will also respond to gamma rays, thus losing its chief advantage.

9.35   If a source of low-energy (soft) beta particles is in the gaseous form, and the gas is admitted into an ionization chamber, it is possible for all the energy of the beta particles to be absorbed within the chamber. The specific ionization along their paths will be roughly constant, and each beta particle will contribute an approximately equal amount to the total ionization. Under these conditions, it is possible to calibrate the ionization chamber to read in terms of the number of disintegrations as well as of the total ionization. High-energy (hard) beta particles are measured both by the rate of ionization they produce in the air of an ionization chamber and by the rate of disintegration of the sample, as observed with a Geiger-Müller counter.

9.36   The traces on a photographic emulsion due to beta particles will not usually show up as individual tracks, but will give a general blackening, the density of which will vary with the total number of these particles absorbed by the film.   Thus, film-badge meters of the type described for gamma radiation can be used for personnel monitoring for beta particles.

Measurement of Alpha Particles

9.37   The alpha particles, although very energetic, are, nevertheless, difficult to measure because of their short ranges.   The usefulness of alpha-sensitive instruments is principally for decontamination work, and the activity is specified in alpha disintegrations per unit time per unit area of surface, e. g., disintegrations per minute per square centimeter.

9.38   An ionization chamber can, however, measure the total ionization produced in the chamber and not merely the number of alpha disintegrations.   If a very thin window, such as nylon stretched to approximately 0.4 milligram per square centimeter, is used in an ionization chamber, the alpha particles will lose only a small fraction of their energy in entering the chamber.   Furthermore, if the chamber is shallow compared to the range of the alpha particles, the specific ionization along their paths within the chamber will be roughly constant, and each alpha particle will contribute about equally to the total ionization in the chamber.   Hence, as described above for beta particles, it is possible to calibrate the ionization chamber so as to give the total ionization in terms of the number of disintegrations without too much error (Fig. 9.38).

9.39   It must be remembered that any beta and gamma activity present will contribute somewhat to the reading.   However, in the presence of beta and gamma radiations, which do not produce extremely large ionization currents relative to that produced by the alpha particles, it is possible to estimate the contribution due to the alpha particles alone by taking readings with and without an absorbing screen in front of the window.   This screen must be just sufficient in thickness to absorb all of the alpha particles, but only a negligible proportion of the beta and gamma radiation.   After an atomic explosion, the beta and gamma activity greatly exceeds that due to alpha emitters; the latter would then make such a small contribution to the total ionization that the differential method just described would not be reliable.

9.40   The proportional-counting chamber (Fig. 9.24a), containing air at normal atmospheric pressure, can be adjusted so that it will re-

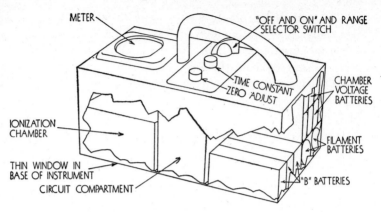

Figure 9.38.   Ionization chamber for alpha particles.

INSTRUMENT—AREA SURVEY TYPE

PORTABLE ALPHA SURVEY METER

Radiation Detected	Alpha
Full Scale Ranges	$\begin{cases} \text{0–5,000 d/m} \\ \text{0–50,000 d/m} \end{cases}$
Area of Acceptance or Volume of Chamber.	100 sq cm
Detector Stage	Ionization chamber
Conversion Stage	Electrometer amplifier
Recorder-Indicator Stage	Output current meter
Weight	8 pounds
Volume or Dimensions	5 x 6 x 9 inches
Description	Rectangular container with 0.4 mg/cm² nylon window on the bottom
Battery Life	900 hours
Chief Causes of Failure	Usual D. C. amplifier difficulties, such as, insulation, drift, and fluctuations of battery voltage
Remarks	Responds to beta and gamma. Discrimination possible by use of alpha absorbing screen.

spond only to heavily ionizing events. Thus alpha particles can be counted in the presence of beta and gamma radiation, and the calibration can be in terms of the number of alpha disintegrations. This intrument is capable of very high counting speeds. Its chief limitation is the leakage of the high voltage across the chamber insulators in humid weather.

9.41   The Geiger-Müller counter is seldom used for counting alpha particles since it requires a gas-tight, thin window of large area which is very fragile and difficult to make. As in the case of the ionization chamber, this counter would also respond to beta and gamma radiations.

9.42 If a suitable photographic emulsion absorbs an alpha particle, the result, after development, will be a dense track which is visible when viewed in a high-power microscope. Individual tracks of alpha particles are clearly resolved if a special, thick film is used. This method of measuring alpha contamination requires special techniques and is seldom used in survey work due, mainly, to the time required for the analysis of the film.

CHAPTER X

DECONTAMINATION [1]

A. INTRODUCTION

TREATMENT OF CONTAMINATED MATERIAL

10.1 It was seen in Chapter VIII that radioactive contamination may be caused by the fission products formed in the detonation of an atomic bomb, by neutron-induced activity in soil and water, and by the deliberate use of specific radioisotopes, apart from their association with the bomb, as radiological warfare agents. These sources would be largely responsible for external contamination. In addition, there is the possibility that plutonium which has escaped fission may act as a contaminant representing an internal hazard. It is now necessary to examine the problem of dealing with various objects which have become contaminated, in one way or another.

10.2 There are essentially three ways whereby the hazard associated with radioactive contamination may be minimized: first, to dispose completely of the material by deep burial in the ground or at sea; second, to keep it at a distance for a sufficient time to permit the radioactivity to decay to a reasonably safe level; and third, to attempt to remove the contaminant, that is, to decontaminate the material. These three procedures were used, in one way or another, in connection with radioactive contamination suffered by ships and their equipment after the Bikini "Baker" test.

10.3 The particular method that is adopted in any case will depend on circumstances. Large structures could not easily be disposed of, and decontamination could be attempted after the activity had decayed to some extent. With smaller structures, decontamination might prove too costly if the activity is high, so that burial is the most economical plan. If the radioactive contamination were not too great, however, decontamination could be attempted almost immediately. On the other hand, in certain instances, it might prove more advantageous simply to set the article aside for the activity to decay.

---

[1] Material contributed by E. S. Gilfillan, S. Glasstone, C. R. Schwob, W. E. Strope, W. H Sullivan.

10.4　At Bikini the U. S. S. *Independence*, a small aircraft carrier, received such a large radiation dosage that had there been any personnel on the hangar deck at the time they would have succumbed from external radiation, apart from the effects of blast. Yet 2 weeks after the detonation the dosage-rate was about 3 r per day, permitting short time access. About a year later, the average dosage rate was only 0.3 r per day, and 3 years after the original contamination the *Independence* was in use at the San Francisco Naval Shipyard, where she housed the experimental engineering group of the Naval Radiological Defense Laboratory. It was difficult at that time to find any areas on the ship where the radiation dosage would have exceeded the limit of 0.3 r per week adopted in installations of the Atomic Energy Commission (§ 8.4).

10.5　It should be noted that no decontamination of the *Independence* was attempted, primarily because the vessel was in a battered condition (see Fig. 5.79a), and it seemed unlikely that she could be returned to service as an aircraft carrier. However, some of the other vessels at Bikini were decontaminated and reclaimed much sooner. Two submarines, thus decontaminated (Fig. 10.5), were used soon afterward in the Naval Reserve, with no risk to the operating personnel. Most of the other target vessels were destroyed, not because decontamination was not feasible, but mainly because they were damaged in other ways and decontamination would not have been economical.

10.6　Except where radioactive solutions, such as were present after the underwater burst at Bikini, soak into porous materials, like rope, textiles, unpainted or unvarnished wood, etc., or where neutrons have penetrated and induced activity to some depth, the decontamination will be largely restricted to the surfaces of materials, objects, and structures. An outstanding exception would, of course, be the radioactive contamination of water supplies for drinking purposes. The problem of decontamination is thus, to a considerable degree, a problem of removing sufficient of the surface material to reduce the activity to the extent that it is no longer a hazard. The methods of surface removal may be divided into two main categories, namely, chemical and physical. In the first case, the contamination is eliminated by making use of chemical reagents which, if sufficiently mild, will have a minor effect on the underlying material. But in the second case, an appreciable thickness of the actual surface is removed.

10.7　It should be understood that the activity of a particular radioisotope is not changed in any way by chemical reaction. All the latter can do is to convert the active isotope into a soluble compound, so that it can be detached and washed off as a solution. Certain processes of decontamination, involving the use of detergents, represent a category intermediate between chemical and physical.

Figure 10.5.   Submarine U. S. S. *Skate*, damaged and radioactive after the Bikini "Able" explosion.

B.   NATURE OF RADIOACTIVE CONTAMINATION

IDENTIFICATION OF CONTAMINANTS

10.8   In order to devise suitable chemical decontamination procedures, it is necessary to know something of the nature of the radioactive material responsible for the contamination.   The composition of the fission products at various times after the atomic explosion is fairly well known, as will be seen below.   Consequently, if it is certain that the contamination is due to fission products, then appropriate chemical methods of treatment could be developed.   A

relatively simple test for the mixture of fission products is to determine the over-all rate of radioactive decay at various times after
the explosion, using a suitable instrument (Chapter IX). The plot
of the logarithm of the decay rate against the logarithm of the time
should give a straight line with a slope of approximately −1.2
(cf. Fig. 8.16).

10.9 Because the fission products are such a complex mixture,
it may be difficult to detect the presence of radioactive isotopes
resulting from the action of neutrons. It is probably justifiable
to state, however, that if the over-all decay rate satisfies the condition
given above, the neutron-induced activity may be neglected. In
the event that this is not the case, an attempt must be made to
identify the isotope responsible for the additional activity. This
may not be an easy matter, and the best approach is to look for the
most likely radioisotopes, for example, sodium 24.

10.10 If a fission-product mixture were employed as a radiological
warfare weapon, apart from the atomic bomb, the decontamination
problems would be much the same as might arise if the bomb were
used. However, if a specific radioisotope or a relatively simple mixture of such isotopes extracted from fission products were used for the
purpose, the nature of the elements would have to be determined.
In the simplest cases this might be done in two ways. First, assuming
the isotope is one which has been previously known, as is likely, and
its properties tabulated, measurements of its rate of decay, so as to
give its half life, and of the range of the particle emitted, which is
related to its energy, would probably be sufficient to identify the
radioisotope. Second, a chemical procedure, based on the fact that
a radioisotope has, for all practical purposes, the same chemical
properties as a stable isotope of the same element, might be employed.

10.11 The latter method involves the principles of *tracer chemistry*
which, although long known, has reached a high state of development
in recent years. It makes possible the identification of quantities of
radioisotopes so small that they would not be visible in the best
optical microscopes. Consequently, very small amounts of contaminated material could be subjected to analysis.

10.12 In outline, the process involves dissolving the material containing the radioisotope and then adding to the solution an appreciable
amount of the ordinary, stable form of the element of which it is suspected to be an isotope. For example, if a radioactive isotope of zinc
were suspected, a fair quantity of an ordinary zinc salt, such as zinc
sulfate, would be added to the solution. The zinc is then precipitated
by means of a suitable reagent, and if the precipitate contains all the
activity originally present, then it is reasonably certain that it is due

to a radioactive isotope of zinc. However, it is possible that an entirely different radioelement may be carried down with the zinc, by coprecipitation or by adsorption. This possibility may be eliminated by the addition of what is known as a "hold-back carrier," which will retain the extraneous element, or by precipitating the zinc with several different reagents.

10.13 If none of the activity is in the precipitate, but all remains in the solution, then it is definitely not zinc, and another element is tried. Should the precipitate carry part of the activity while part is retained by the solution, then zinc may be present in addition to another radioelement. On the other hand, it is possible that the zinc has merely carried down part of the activity of another element by adsorption, as indicated above, and appropriate experiments can be made to test the point. This is the way, in general, in which the very complex mixture of isotopes constituting the fission products was analyzed, and it can be applied to specific radioisotopes that might be used as radiological warfare weapons.

Fission Products as Contaminants

10.14 Since the nature of the fission products is known, while other contaminating materials are uncertain, and since contamination by fission products due to an atomic bomb seems the most likely contingency, these products will be considered further. Because of radioactive decay of one isotope into another (§ 1.52), the composition of the fission products, both as regards the radioisotopes and the actual elements present, is continuously changing. Altogether, a total of nearly 200 radioactive species of 34 different elements, with atomic numbers from 30 (zinc) through 63 (europium), have been found at various times after fission of uranium 235 by slow neutrons. The composition of the products of an atomic explosion is undoubtedly somewhat different, but probably not to a very significant extent.

10.15 From the standpoint of chemical decontamination, it is not so important to know the actual amount of any element present, but rather the fraction it contributes to the total activity. The complete removal of that element will then decrease the activity in the same proportion. In Table 10.15 are given the names of the elements which make the major contributions to the radioactivity of the fission products at various times after fission has occurred.[2]

---

[2] The data in Table 10.15 have been estimated from calculations of the percentages of the total disintegrations due to various elements at different times after fission (H. F. Hunter and N. E. Ballou, "Simultaneous Slow Neutron Fission of U 235 Atoms", Part I, Naval Radiological Defense Laboratory, ADC-65 (1949)). No account has been taken of the different energies of the beta particles and gamma rays (if any), but it is assumed that, on the average, the radioactive dosage rate, which is the important matter, will be approximately proportional to the disintegration rate.

TABLE 10.15

MOST RADIOACTIVE CONSTITUENTS OF PRODUCTS AT VARIOUS
TIMES AFTER FISSION

1 hour	1 day	1 week	1 month	6 months–1 year
Rare Earths*	Rare Earths	Rare Earths	Rare Earths	Rare Earths
Tellurium	Iodine	Iodine	Barium	Columbium
Barium	Zirconium	Tellurium	Zirconium	Zirconium
Iodine	Columbium	Barium	Strontium	Strontium
Rubidium	Xenon	Molybdenum	Ruthenium	Ruthenium
Krypton	Strontium	Xenon	Rhodium	Rhodium
Strontium	Molybdenum	Zirconium	Columbium	Barium
Xenon	Tellurium	Strontium	Iodine	
Molybdenum	Rhodium	Ruthenium	Xenon	

* Because of its chemical similarity, yttrium has been included with the rare-earth elements in every case.

Because of their similarity in chemical properties, the rare-earth elements and yttrium have been grouped together. The various elements are arranged in order of their decreasing contribution to the total activity.

10.16 It is an interesting and important fact that from an hour to a year, and probably longer, after fission has taken place, at least 30 percent of the fission-product activity is due to radioisotopes of the rare-earth elements and yttrium. The removal of these elements alone would thus reduce the degree of contamination by about a third or more. This has been achieved by the use of various substances which form soluble complex ions with the rare-earth elements (cf. § 10.51).

10.17 Any substance capable of forming complex ions in this manner is frequently referred to as a *complexing agent*. While salts of citric acid and other organic acids are perhaps the most important such agents in general use for decontamination purposes, it is possible that a concentrated solution of a chloride might prove to be a complexing agent for ruthenium and rhodium, and perhaps for some other important fission products.

10.18 Since one of the objects of decontamination is to prevent internal absorption of radioactive materials, brief mention may be made here of the hazards due to the ingestion of certain fission products. The subject will, however, be considered more fully in Chapter XI. Some elements, particularly iodine, strontium, barium, zirconium, and cerium, are strongly held in the body so that their consequences, when absorbed as radioisotopes, may be more serious than the amounts present would indicate. In addition, plutonium which has escaped fission, may represent an internal hazard, although, as indicated in § 8.30 the concentrations that are likely to be found after an atomic explosion are relatively small.

C. DECONTAMINATION PROCEDURES

THE TIME FACTOR

10.19 The problem of decontamination presents a number of complex aspects, especially with regard to the circumstances under which the process should be attempted and to what extent it should be carried out. It is probably true to state that, in general, given enough time and effort, any structure or equipment, unless it consists largely of porous materials, can be, at least partially, decontaminated. The question as to whether this will be worth while depends on (a) the importance of the structure or equipment, (b) the feasibility in the circumstances, and (c) the risk involved. If there will be an over-all saving of life or material, or a protection of health not otherwise possible, and if the time element makes immediate action necessary, then a decontamination operation is justifiable. The feasibility is dependent on the contamination and decontamination characteristics of the materials involved, and of the collection, transfer, and disposal of the radioactive residues. Finally, the risk factor is primarily determined by the radiation dosage that would be received while the decontamination is being performed.

10.20 An important aspect of the feasibility and risk factors of decontamination is how to carry out the process in a manner that will avoid exposing the operating personnel to excessive dosages of radiation. This will, in general, mean that any individual can be permitted to work in the contaminated area for a very short time, perhaps only a few minutes per week.

10.21 It was explained in Chapter VIII how Figs. 8.16 and 8.17 can be used to calculate the dosage received in a contaminated area during a specified interval of time provided the dosage rate at a known time following an atomic explosion has been measured. The procedure may, however, be simplified by means of Figs. 10.21a and b. In the former the dosage rate in roentgens per hour, measured at any time t hr. after the atomic explosion is the abscissa, while the corresponding dosage rate in the same area at 1 hour after the explosion is the ordinate; the various values of the time t are the parameters for the different lines. In Fig. 10.21b, the abscissa is the time after the

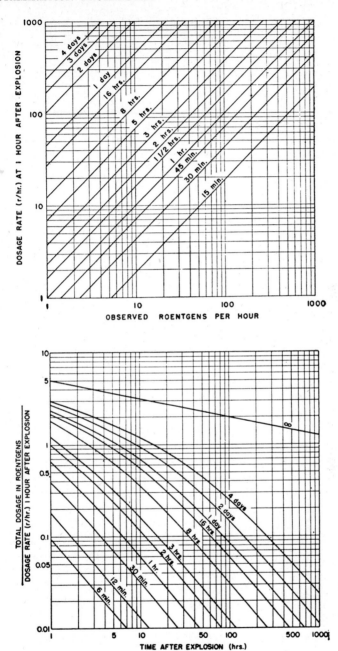

Figure 10.21a and b. Charts for determination of total radiation dosage in a contaminated area.

explosion when a person enters the area, and the ordinate is the total dosage received if he stays for various lengths of time, indicated by the parameters of the several curves, divided by the dosage rate at 1 hour after the explosion as determined above. It should be noted that the time of entry into the area to stay, i. e., the abscissa in Fig. 10.21b, may or may not be the same as the time t at which the measurement was made, i. e., the parameters of Fig. 10.21a.[3]

10.22   In order to illustrate the use of these figures, suppose that a measurement made in a given area at 30 minutes after an atomic explosion indicates that the dosage rate was then 70 r per hour. Taking the latter figure as the abscissa in Fig. 10.21a, and running up vertically to the line marked 30 minutes, the ordinate shows that the dosage rate at 1 hour would be about 30 r per hour. Suppose it is required to find the total dosage received by a person entering this area at 2 hours after the explosion and staying for 1 hour. From Fig. 10.21b, the abscissa of 2 hours and parameter 1 hour indicate a total dosage divided by the rate at 1 hour of 0.33 r. Since the actual rate at 1 hour is 30 r per hour, it is necessary to multiply 0.33 r by 30, giving the actual total dosage in the specified case as 9.9 r.

10.23   In connection with decontamination procedures, it would be helpful to know the amount of contamination one might expect at a specific time following the detonation. It is impossible, however, to make any predictions as to what condition will exist. It will depend upon many factors such as the type of burst (air, ground, underwater). Following an air burst, both residual and induced radiation will be minimal. Following a ground burst it will depend upon the character of the soil. At Eniwetok where the coral is saturated with sodium the induced radiation would be important. This would not be the case in other localities. Direction and velocities of wind are a factor—a high wind causing wider dissemination and thus reducing the concentration.

10.24   Thus an estimate of the situation will have to be made on the spot, and a working plan evolved to solve the problem. If the area is unimportant, radioactive decay may suffice. If it is necessary to occupy the area immediately, some plan of rotating individuals or removing contaminated material may be necessary. The permissible extent of exposure of personnel will depend upon the urgency of the situation.

10.25   In view of the fact that in the course of time the radioactivity of any contaminated body will decrease, according to the general rule

---

[3] When the time of measurement is the same as that at which a person enters the contaminated area to stay, the two sets of curves may be combined in one; this result is given in Fig. 12.77. However, Figs. 10.21a and b are of more general applicability.

given in equation (8.14), time may be regarded, in a sense, as a universal decontaminating agent. If the dosage rate at any time after the explosion has been determined, Fig. 10.21a may be used to calculate the dosage rate in the same area at any other time. To do this, the rate at 1 hour is first found, as described in § 10.22, and a horizontal line is drawn at this point in Fig. 10.21a. The dosage rate at any time is then given by the point where the parametric line for that time crosses this horizontal line. Thus if the dosage rate is 70 r per hour at 30 minutes after the detonation, it will be 30 r per hour at 1 hour after, 13 r per hour at 2 hours after, 7 r per hour at 3 hours after, etc.

EMERGENCY MEASURES

10.26 Except where a porous material has absorbed a radioactive liquid or where radioactive material has found its way into the water supply, contamination will be largely a surface phenomenon, as indicated earlier. The contaminant may be mechanically held on the surface or in pores or crevices, it may be imbedded to some extent by the force of the blast, or it may be adsorbed by physical or chemical forces as ions, atoms, molecules or larger aggregates. It is probable that following an atomic explosion, contamination may occur in one, two or more of these ways, and successful decontamination methods should be capable of dealing with all of them. However, as a general rule, a degree of decontamination adequate to the specific needs of a situation may be achieved by removing radioactive material held by only one or perhaps two of these mechanisms.

10.27 The actual process of decontaminating material and equipment can be resolved into two stages; first, immediate emergency measures, so as to permit continued operation, and second, final decontamination operations of a more thorough nature. Although the degree of decontamination achieved by the initial treatment may not be large, it will at least reduce the physiological hazard to an extent that will make possible, probably with changing personnel, operations which would otherwise have been impractical. A more complete decontamination can then be carried out, if necessary or desirable, at a later time.

10.28 The decontamination of personnel who have come into contact with radioactive material is, of course, a primary requirement. Normally, clothing will prevent access of the material to the skin. When contaminated, clothing should be removed and disposed of, by burial, for example, in such a manner as to prevent the spread of the radioactivity into uncontaminated areas, like the interiors of buildings.

10.29　Radioactive substances, especially beta emitters not accompanied by gamma radiation, when in close contact with the skin may represent a much greater hazard than would be indicated by an instrument held an inch or two away (§ 11.78). Consequently, attention must be paid to cleansing any exposed surfaces of the body. A very fair degree of decontamination of the exposed skin can be achieved by vigorous rubbing with soap and water, paying particular attention to the hair, nails, skin folds, and areas surrounding body openings, and with due care to avoid abrasion. Certain synthetic detergents, of which many are now on the market, e. g., soapless household cleansers, have been found to be especially effective in this connection.

10.30　If the soap and water treatment does not produce the desired decrease in activity, chemical agents, if available, may be used on the skin. Isotonic saline of pH 2, or depilatory or keratolytic agents, such as a mixture of barium sulfide and starch, will lead to the removal of material held tenaciously by the skin. A dilute solution of sodium bicarbonate is useful, especially on mucous membranes, because of its action as a complexing agent for some of the fission products.

10.31　In a dire emergency, any clean uncontaminated material at hand, such as paper, straw, grass, leaves or sand, will remove activity from the skin if applied vigorously. However, care must be taken not to tear the skin, or to drive the loosened material into wounds, body openings or skin folds.

10.32　For the emergency decontamination of inanimate objects, almost any procedure would be helpful. Household cleaning and scouring compounds, grease removers, detergents, paint cleaners, dry cleaning solvents, gasoline, etc., will all help to remove radioactive particles from surfaces. In carrying out these processes, care must be taken not to distribute the radioactivity. The cloths or other materials used should be buried and not burned, unless special incinerators, which prevent escape of the active material, are available.

10.33　Exposed surfaces, especially in cities, are usually covered with "industrial film" of grease and dirt. It has been observed, in many instances, that radioactive contamination attaches itself primarily to this film, and that its removal consequently affects considerable decontamination. Special cleaning methods for the removal of industrial film have been developed; an example is the use of live steam, into which is fed a concentrated solution of a detergent, for cleaning airplanes. In the absence of contrary indications, removal of the industrial film, if present, may be the first step in decontamination. Besides producing some decrease in the radioactivity, the removal of the film will facilitate the action of the various agents used for more thorough decontamination.

10.34 In every attempt at decontamination, preliminary or final, the safety of personnel is an essential consideration. The immediate emergency measures must consequently be delayed, as stated above, until the activity has decayed sufficiently to permit operation without excessive risk. Those directly employed in the decontaminating work should wear suitable protective clothing, of rubber if necessary, and should be provided with rubber boots and gloves. If spray or dust is produced in the operation goggles, and masks must be worn (cf. § 12.79 *et seq.*).

10.35 Shielding, whether by distance, terrain, walls, structures, etc., must be used as advantageously as possible. For example, the decontamination of a building or a ship should be started from a suitable position in the interior, where the activity will probably be less than on the outside. In this connection it is recommended that installations of strategic importance, in a situation where contamination is a possibility, should be provided with hosing down equipment controllable from the interior.

10.36 It is not possible to give a general rule concerning the areas from which decontamination should be initiated. In some cases it would be advantageous to start in a region where the activity is low, for this will not only make the operation less hazardous but will allow time for decay of the more highly contaminated portions. On the other hand, in certain circumstances, it might be advisable first to carry out a quick, even if preliminary, decontamination of an area of high contamination in order to permit freedom of movement.

Surface Removal

10.37 The problems of thorough decontamination are so involved and so novel that a great deal of work will be necessary before the most effective procedures are developed. The information given here, based on limited experience, is the best available at the present time. But improved methods for the treatment of materials, structures, etc., which have become contaminated with radioactivity, will undoubtedly be developed in due course. At present, although certain general principles are apparent, it seems impossible to make predictions concerning the efficiency of a particular decontamination procedure in any given circumstances. It would be necessary, therefore, in actual practice, to use a succession of methods until the desired degree of decontamination is achieved.

10.38   For nonabsorptive substances, removal of the entire surface of the material is an obvious means of securing decontamination. While it cannot be applied to all surfaces, it is highly successful whenever it is feasible, except perhaps where capture of neutrons has induced activity at some distance below the surface.   In this, as in all decontamination procedures, it is necessary to exercise rigid control over the radioactive residues.   They must not be allowed to recontaminate newly exposed or adjacent surfaces, nor must they be permitted to become an inhalation or ingestion hazard in the form of dust.   During an operation, these requirements can be met by wetting down the surfaces with water or with solutions of certain chemicals which dissolve the solid particles, as mentioned below.

10.39 · Physical methods of surface removal are often difficult because they involve much labor and sometimes special equipment. Methods employing abrasion are perhaps the most effective; wet sandblasting, for example, was used successfully in decontaminating large areas of the Bikini target vessels (Fig. 10.39).   The techniques

Figure 10.39.   Wet sandblasting for removal of radioactive contamination. (Note protective clothing worn by the operator.)

involved here are a part of normal ship maintenance, and the equipment and trained personnel are generally available at military and industrial establishments. The wet sandblasting method can also be employed for the decontamination of unprotected concrete. This procedure leaves large volumes of sand and water, containing the active material, and although their disposal may present a problem, the fact that the contaminant is thereby considerably diluted is some compensation.

10.40 Abrasives less radical than sand, and which effect removal of only a thin surface layer, have also been used. Soft materials like sawdust and other substances of a similar nature, have been suggested for the decontamination of delicate articles, such as instruments or bearing surfaces, that would be injured by sand. Similarly, scrubbing may be used for the removal of a thin outer layer. Steel wool, wire brushes, floor polishers, or various buffing or polishing machines, can be adapted to decontamination by surface removal in various circumstances.

10.41 Chemical means can also be applied to remove the surface, and with it the contaminating radioactivity. The action is rapid and certain, and in some instances it is the only practical method. The use of highly corrosive or other dangerous chemicals, although they might be effective, should be avoided if possible. The substances employed must be capable of being stored without danger, available in large quantities, and preferably of small bulk. Because of these requirements, primary consideration must be given to the use of aqueous solutions. Organic solvents are usually inflammable or toxic, or both, but most water-soluble chemicals can be stored easily, and dissolved quickly when desired. The heat evolved when some materials, such as caustic soda, are dissolved is often advantageous in that it hastens chemical action. Further, standard fire-fighting equipment, pumps, transport and mixing devices are particularly adapted to the handling of aqueous solutions.

10.42 Decontamination by chemical means usually results in the transfer of the activity to fairly large volumes of liquid, thereby presenting a disposal problem. Mere wetting of the surface by the solution of the chemical reagent is nearly as efficient as flooding for decontamination. If wetting only is used, the waste material can be confined and is controllable, but it will have a relatively high activity. On the other hand, with the flooding method the resulting solution is more dilute and the radioactivity is dispersed in a larger volume. Both procedures have advantages and disadvantages, and the particular method used must be determined by the circumstances.

10.43 Chemical methods of surface removal can be designed for each specific type of surface. For example, alkalis have been found to be effective in removing contaminated layers of paint. In special cases, drastic treatments using acids, caustic alkalis, and other corrosive agents have proved successful in removing surfaces, but they are liable to be destructive, since they erode and pit the base material while removing the surface. Mild chemical means of surface removal, such as by the use of complexing agents, which will be mentioned below, have been employed in certain cases, for example, for paint containing titanium.

10.44 A combination of physical and chemical treatments is represented by live steam as a decontaminating agent, especially in conjunction with a detergent, as mentioned in § 10.33. It has been found particularly valuable for cleaning up highly contaminated areas in laboratories and plants. It appears to be especially efficient for painted surfaces, the action being based on the partial destruction of the paint by hydrolysis. In addition, loose or mechanically held contamination is swept away, and the surface suffers some disintegration because of the sudden increase of temperature. It is probable that the combination of live steam with a detergent may prove useful in decontaminating many types of surfaces and objects.

10.45 Heat by itself acts in a manner similar to live steam. The contact of a blow-torch flame with a contaminated paint surface for a fraction of a second produces a marked reduction in activity. This method of decontamination should not be attempted unless adequate ventilation is available for removal of the radioactive fumes.

Removal of Lightly Held Material

10.46 In the examination of the naval vessels which had become contaminated with radioactivity at Bikini, it was observed that much of the activity was associated with dust, corroded areas, etc., which could be removed without difficulty. In some circumstances, up to 90 percent of the radioactivity remaining on ship surfaces three years after being contaminated was removable by vacuum sweeping or brushing.

10.47 In the event of contamination due to radioactively contaminated water, following an underwater burst of an atomic bomb, water under high pressure can be used for removing loosely held contaminants (Fig. 10.47). However, there is some evidence that radioactive dusts, such as might be produced from an underground burst or dry fall-out or might be used in radiological warfare, tend to become attached to surfaces as a result of treatment with water or an aqueous solution. In such instances, dry physical methods, e. g., vacuum cleaning, brushing, application of adhesive, etc., are pre-

Figure 10.47. Preliminary decontamination of U. S. S. *New York* after the "Baker" test at Bikini; the decks are being washed down with sea water by a Navy fireboat.

ferred as an initial step to prevent spread or strong attachment of the contamination.

10.48 Adhesives of various kinds have been found practical for removing loose dust and mechanically held contamination. An adhesive coating is applied to the contaminated surface, and is then stripped off; some of the radioactive material will be retained by the coating when it is removed. Sprayed strippable coatings, which can penetrate pores and crevices, are useful for decontaminating moderately rough surfaces. For smooth surfaces, adhesive tapes of different kinds have proved successful. Several types of putty have been tried, but the results have not been satisfactory.

10.49 In dealing with loosely held contamination, the obvious use of soap and water cannot be neglected. As indicated previously, not only will soap and other detergents remove dirt, dust, grease, etc., which has become radioactively contaminated, but it is safe for most surfaces, nonhazardous, and does not call for particular experience in its application. As will be seen later, detergents and wetting agents have other valuable properties in decontamination.

REMOVAL OF TIGHTLY HELD MATERIALS

10.50 When the extent of decontamination resulting from the removal of lightly held radioactive material is not sufficient, further treatment will be necessary. Surface removal, as described above, may be employed, but the procedures are necessarily harsh and unsuitable for delicate equipment; further, after decontamination, the surface must frequently be renewed to provide protection against corrosion. The roughened surface is also liable to be more susceptible to subsequent contamination. The use of chemical methods can frequently avoid these disadvantages. By means of a solution of a chemical reagent, it may be possible to transfer the radioactivity to a liquid phase which is then washed off. In this connection three general principles have been employed; they are formation of soluble complexes, ion exchange, and solubilization.

10.51 Substances which have a greater affinity for the decontaminating element than for the surface, and which form water-soluble compounds with it, are suitable complexing or sequestering agents. Much research has been conducted with the object of finding compounds or ions which form complexes with the fission products and with the fissionable material constituting the atomic explosive. Sodium citrate solutions were used with some success in the clean-up operations after the Bikini tests, but other substances, such as the sodium salts of ethylenediamine-tetracetic acid, aminotriacetic acid, and pyrophosphoric acid, have been found to be more satisfactory and generally cheaper. It is of interest to mention that, contrary to theoretical expectation, strongly acidified citric acid solutions were more effective than neutral citrate in removing radioactive contamination. Apparently, the hydrochloric acid present dissolved rust and scale in which the contaminants tended to concentrate, and which were consequently difficult to decontaminate. Much research still remains to be done before a reliable complexing agent or a simple mixture of such agents can be recommended for general use.

10.52 The partial removal of radioactive ions from surfaces is rendered possible by application of the principle of chemical equilibrium. The undesirable ions of a radioisotope may exchange with ions of nonradioactive isotopes of the same element applied in solution. The exchange will result in a decrease in the number of radioactive ions on the surface, even though the total number of ions, radioactive and stable, may actually increase. For decontamination due to fission products from an atomic explosion, this procedure would require, theoretically, 34 elements in a variety of valence forms. Some of these are prohibitively rare, while others, namely, technetium (atomic number 43) and promethium (atomic number 61), do not exist in nonradioactive forms. Possibly certain common ions of high valence, such as aluminum, iron, or cerium, may prove useful in this connection. Unfortunately, the exchange reactions are very slow, and laboratory results obtained so far have not been too encouraging.

10.53 Insoluble contaminants, such as oxides, basic salts, etc., may not furnish enough ions to permit rapid complexing or exchange action. However, some of these will respond to the action of wetting agents and detergents. The peptizing properties of these substances allows the particles of insoluble material to be washed away as a suspension. The use of a detergent in any decontamination procedure is beneficial because, in addition to the so-called solubilizing effect just mentioned, it promotes more complete and rapid wetting of the surface, as well as facilitating, as noted earlier, removal of dust, dirt, etc., carrying radioactive material.

10.54 In considering the problem of decontamination, there is one fundamental point which must not be forgotten. Decontamination procedures do not neutralize the radioactivity; they merely transfer the active material from one place to another. Consequently, before undertaking decontamination it is necessary to arrange for the proper disposal of the material removed, to a location where it does not represent a hazard. The method to be used must be determined by the circumstances existing at the time.

City and Domestic Decontamination

10.55 In the event of serious radioactive contamination of a large part of a city, steps would have to be taken to make it habitable within a reasonable time. The most important matter in this connection would appear to be the removal or coverage of loose material which might form dust that would be inhaled or ingested with food. For paved streets flushing, perhaps with the aid of detergents, street cleaning or vacuum sweeping, if feasible, might be the first steps. If the contaminant is on the surface or has not penetrated too deeply, concrete, stone and brick buildings would perhaps have to be wet-sandblasted and reroofed. Painted wooden structures might be decontaminated by some of the methods given earlier in this chapter, but stucco buildings might have to be removed. The same could well apply to roofs, which would collect considerable amounts of radioactive material, but could not be easily decontaminated.

10.56   Soils have a fairly high specific surface and also have well-defined base exchange properties; as a result they will tend to concentrate radioactive material. This is fortunate, in a sense, because in the washing down of contaminated streets, buildings, etc., much of the water will be transferred to the surrounding soil, if special drainage facilities are not available. Because of the properties mentioned above, the radioactivity will remain in the uppermost few inches. The only scheme that seems to be practical for dealing with such topsoil, as well as that from parks and lawns in the contaminated city, is to remove it or to cover it with at least a foot of fresh soil. This could perhaps be done by turning the soil over, so that the lower uncontaminated soil covered that which had become contaminated. In any operations with such soil, standard wetting-down procedures would be required to minimize the hazard due to radioactive dust.

10.57   Badly contaminated clothing, as well as rugs, curtains, and upholstered furniture would have to be discarded and buried or burned in proper incinerators perhaps designed to prevent the escape of radioactive smoke. If the contamination is not too serious, laundering may be effective in reducing the activity sufficiently to permit reuse. In most cases, it is probable that interior walls and floors of houses and buildings, if still surviving after an atomic explosion, could be decontaminated by thorough washing. They could then be repainted, papered, or varnished according to circumstances.

Decontamination of Food and Water

10.58   Properly covered foods should undergo little or no contamination. The same will be true of canned goods or any materials in impervious, dustproof wrappings. There appears to be no feasible means for salvaging unprotected food, either in the home, the store or in the fields, which has become radioactively contaminated.

10.59   The contamination of water supplies might arise in several ways, such as fall-out particles dropping into a river or reservoir, accumulation of radioactivity from fall-out particles deposited on the watershed, explosion of an atomic bomb in or near a reservoir, or the deliberate use of radioisotopes in radiological warfare. If the degree of contamination is not too severe, then it is probable that, as a result of the operation of several factors, e. g., dilution by flow, natural decay, adsorption, etc., the water will not usually be rendered unfit for consumption, except perhaps for a limited time immediately following the contamination.

10.60   In surface waters, radioactive contaminants will tend to be adsorbed by the suspended and colloidal matter that is invariably present.   This matter will partly settle or be adsorbed by the walls and bottom of the reservoir.   In urban water systems radioactive material escaping adsorption in the reservoir itself may be picked up by the surfaces of the distribution system which usually consist of highly adsorbent brick or rusted iron.   When, in addition, the purification process includes coagulation, sedimentation and filtration stages, it is expected that very little radioactive material will normally reach the consumer.

10.61   Because of the adsorptive properties of soil, referred to above, underground sources of water are generally safe from contamination.   For the same reason, moderately deep wells, even under contaminated ground, can be used as sources of drinking water, provided surface drainage of contaminated material is prevented.

10.62   If a reservoir or river is seriously contaminated, and the water is not subjected to coagulation or filtration, as described above, the water may be unfit for consumption for several days.   However, because of dilution and natural decay of the radioactivity, the degree of contamination will decrease with time.   It would be necessary, in cases of this kind, to subject the water to careful examination for radioactivity and to withhold the supply until it is reasonably safe for human consumption.   It should be remembered in this connection that since the water is taken internally, alpha and beta activity, as well as gamma activity, is important.

10.63   In some cities water is taken directly from a river and merely chlorinated before being supplied for domestic consumption.   If no alternative source of water is available in case of emergency, consideration should be given to the provision of cationic and anionic exchange columns or beds to be used if the regular supply should become contaminated.   Home water softeners might serve the same purpose. In hospitals and on ships sufficient water for emergency purposes could be obtained by distillation.   It was found at Bikini, for example, that contaminated water when distilled was perfectly safe for drinking purposes; the radioactive material remained behind in the residual scale and brine.   It should be emphasized, however, that mere boiling of water contaminated with radioactivity is of no value.

10.64   The suggestion has been made that algae and zoogleal bacteria, such as are used in the activated sludge process for purification of sewage, which absorb and concentrate mineral elements directly from water (cf. § 8.98), could be employed to remove radioactive contamination from reservoirs.   In order to be effective, the conditions would have to be such as to cause profuse growth of the organisms.   Once the activity is incorporated into the latter, the water could be drawn off, and the bacteria, etc., removed by mechanical filtration or by sludge beds and allowed to decay.   Whether this procedure will prove practical on a large scale is not yet known, although preliminary experiments indicate some success in the removal of plutonium from contaminated water.

10.65   The accepted safe tolerance level for water containing fission products is 4×10^{-6} microcurie/cc.   Assuming the mean gamma-ray energy to be 0.7 Mev (§ 8.11), it can be shown by means of Fig. 8.37b that the dosage rate measured just above the surface of a body of water contaminated to this extent would be nearly 4×10^{-6} r per hour. This activity in curies is appreciably lower than that of some radioactive mineral waters which are consumed in quantity without obvious deleterious consequences.   It would appear, therefore, that in an emergency, water with many times the accepted tolerance limit could be used for drinking in limited amounts.   Because of the rapid decay of the fission products with time, the activity of the water and the corresponding hazard, if any, would soon decrease.[4]

SPECIAL PROTECTIVE METHODS

10.66   The ideal defense against radioactive contamination is to use, wherever possible, surfaces which are either resistant to such contamination or from which the active material can be readily removed.   It has been found, for example, that surfaces coated with certain plastic paints are relatively easily decontaminated.   Attempts are being made to classify materials according to their contamination and decontamination characteristics, but it will be some time before a clear understanding of the subject can be obtained.   In a general way, however, it can be stated that an ideal surface for the purpose in mind should have its specific surface area, i. e., area per unit mass, porosity, and chemical and surface activity as small as possible.   There are indications at present that certain materials, such as polyethylene,

---

[4] The presence in a reservoir of appreciable amounts of plutonium, with its long half life and tendency to concentrate in the body (§ 11.93), would present a special problem.   For the accepted tolerance level of plutonium in water, see § 12.72.

have these desirable properties, and these substances could be used to form thin surface layers on various articles or equipment.

10.67 Structural materials, e. g., concrete, brick, and soft woods, present a special problem, since decontamination of porous substances is virtually impossible. At the present time, it appears that well-maintained paint or other sealer is the only means of protection against radioactive contamination. This matter should be borne in mind, especially in connection with new construction near bodies of water where an underwater explosion is a possibility. In designing structures, efforts should be made to eliminate inaccessible spaces, sharp concavities, and poor drainage.

10.68 Another possibility in connection with protection against radioactive contamination, which has been found successful in laboratories handling high levels of activity, is to use strippable coatings. A removable protection of this kind, consisting of adhesive tape or special sprayed or brushed coatings of a plastic material, is affixed directly to the surface to be protected. In the event of radioactive contamination, the plastic surface is stripped off and replaced with a new one.

10.69 Where the foregoing procedures are not possible, vital equipment may be kept under cover, by means of tarpaulins or other movable protection. Emergency access ways to installations should be protected in some manner, for experience at Bikini has shown that a simple shelter can be very effective in decreasing the extent of radioactive contamination.

CHAPTER XI [1]

EFFECTS ON PERSONNEL

A. TYPES OF INJURIES

INTRODUCTION

11.1 The injurious effects to personnel resulting from an atomic explosion may be divided into three categories: these are, blast injuries, burns, and nuclear radiation injuries. Although it was estimated in Chapter VI that at least 50 percent of the fatal casualties due to the atomic bombings of Japan were caused by burns of one kind or another, it is virtually impossible to determine the relative importance of the various factors. Many people who were injured by blast were also burned, and this undoubtedly was also the fate of others who would have ultimately succumbed to the effects of radiation. Within about 2,500 feet of the center of the explosion, it is probable that blast, burns, and radiation could separately have been lethal in many cases. It should be pointed out, however, that not everyone within the 2,500 feet radius from the center of burst was killed. Among those who survived the immediate results of the explosions at Hiroshima and Nagasaki, a number died later from what was ascribed to radiation sickness; these were believed to represent from 5 to 15 percent of the total number of fatal casualties.[2]

11.2 In spite of the fact that no definite information can be obtained from Japanese experience concerning the relative contributions of the three causes of injury, some general conclusions can be drawn with regard to the type of burst. In the case of a high air burst, such as at Hiroshima and Nagasaki, most of the casualties will be due to burns and blast effects. There will be a small proportion of radiation injuries resulting from exposure to the initial nuclear radiations, but the effect of contamination by residual radiation will be negligible.

11.3 An explosion at low altitude or at ground level would produce somewhat fewer casualties from blast or burns, but a small area would be highly contaminated with radioactive material. If proper precautions are taken, the casualties due to this residual radiation should be a very small fraction of the total.

---

[1] Material contributed by J. P. Cooney, R. D. Evans, A. C. Fabergé, G. M. Lyon, Shields Warren.
[2] A number of persons who were within 2,500 feet of the atomic explosions in Japan survived because they were sheltered in one way or another (cf. § 11.71).

11.4 After a shallow underwater burst the number of casualties from blast and burns will also be diminished. However, some casualties might arise from exposure to the radiation from fission products and, to a lesser extent, material which has escaped fission, spread over an appreciable area by the base surge and the fall-out (§ 8.64 *et seq.*). During the first two months or more the primary danger would be due to the gamma rays, in particular, and the beta particles from fission products. Subsequently, the ingestion of plutonium might in exceptional circumstances become a hazard. In the event of serious contamination of this kind, it would be necessary to evacuate the population from the affected areas, until they could be adequately decontaminated, as described in Chapter X.

Blast Injuries: Direct and Indirect

11.5 Two types of blast injuries, namely, direct and indirect, may be considered. Direct blast injuries result from the positive pressure phase of the shock wave acting on the body so as to cause injury of the lungs, stomach, intestines and eardrums, and internal hemorrhage. Such injuries occurred in World War II after large-scale air raids with conventional high-explosive bombs. At Nagasaki and Hiroshima, however, the direct blast effect was not a significant primary cause of fatality, since those near enough to the explosion to suffer injury in this manner were burned or crushed to death. A pressure of about 35 pounds per square inch or more is required to cause direct harm to a human being, and the peak pressure of the shock wave from a nominal atomic bomb would attain such values only at distances of 1,000 feet or less from ground zero, assuming a height of burst of 2,000 feet.

11.6 More important than the primary blast injuries in the Japanese bombings were the indirect or secondary effects due to collapsing buildings, and to timber and other debris flung about by the blast wave. Persons were injured by flying objects, crushed or buried under buildings, and thrown against fixed structures. Glass fragments penetrated up to an inch beneath the skin, and the light summer clothing worn at the time offered little protection. Unless proper precautions are taken, as described in Chapter XII, glass thus represents a considerable hazard.

11.7 The nature of the indirect injuries from blast varied from complete crushing, severe fractures, and serious lacerations with hemorrhage, to minor scratches, bruises, and contusions. Patients were treated for lacerations received up to 10,600 feet from ground zero in Hiroshima, and out to 12,200 feet in Nagasaki. Shock, both physiological and traumatic, i. e., due to bodily injury, was a serious complication in many cases. It may be mentioned, too, that many burns were also, in a sense, an indirect effect of the blast.

11.8 The number of blast casualties of various kinds that might be expected from an atomic explosion will evidently be related to the type of building construction, and also to the height of the burst. However, on the whole, the indirect blast injuries due to the atomic bomb are similar to those caused by conventional bombs. The only important difference is the much greater number and variety of such injuries produced in a short interval of time in the former case. This fact is well illustrated by the figures in Table 11.8 [3] where the casualties

TABLE 11.8

COMPARISON OF CASUALTIES FOR ATOMIC AND CONVENTIONAL BOMBS

	Hiroshima	Nagasaki	Tokyo	Average of 93 attacks
Weapon	Atomic bomb	Atomic bomb	1,667 tons TNT and incendiary	1,129 tons TNT and incendiary
Population per square mile	35, 000	65, 000	130, 000	—
Square miles destroyed	4. 7	1. 8	15. 8	1. 8
Killed and missing	70, 000	36, 000	83, 000	1, 850
Injured	70, 000	40, 000	102, 000	1, 830
Mortality per square mile destroyed	15, 000	20, 000	5, 200	1, 000
Casualties per square mile destroyed	30, 000	42, 000	11, 800	2, 000

produced by the atomic bombs at Hiroshima and Nagasaki are compared with those in the attack on Tokyo with conventional bombs on March 9, 1945, and with the average results of 93 attacks on other Japanese cities with similar weapons. The high mortality and casualty rates per square mile destroyed by the atomic bomb are very apparent.

FLAME AND FLASH BURNS

11.9 As stated in Chapter VI, two types of burns were observed at Hiroshima and Nagasaki; these were generally differentiated as (a) fire or flame burns, and (b) flash burns due to thermal radiation.

[3] "The Effects of Atomic Bombs at Hiroshima and Nagasaki," U. S. Strategic Bombing Survey (1946).

When the area of the body not protected by clothing, e. g., the face and hands, was small, the latter were characterized by more or less sharp limitation of area, which suggested the appelation "profile burns" (§ 6.54); flame burns on the other hand, covered large portions of the body that were originally protected from thermal radiation. It may be noted, however, that where large parts of the body were exposed to the thermal radiation, the flash burns also covered considerable areas. Because of the numerous and extensive fires that developed after the atomic explosion, it is not surprising that the total number of casualties, fatal and otherwise, due to flame burns, was very large. The evidence indicates that burns of one kind or another occurred as far out as 14,000 feet at Nagasaki and 12,000 feet at Hiroshima.

11.10 Since flame burns due to an atomic explosion, apart from their frequency, do not present any features different from those caused by other conflagrations, they need not be considered in detail. A brief description will, however, be given of some of the major characteristics of flash burns.[4] In addition to being restricted in area to exposed parts of the body, the majority of flash burns show a much smaller depth of penetration of the skin. This is to be expected in view of the fact that the thermal radiation which is responsible is absorbed in such a very short time, during the first 3 seconds following the explosion. A very high surface temperature is thus produced in a small time interval. Within the depths to which the thermal radiations penetrate, the tissues appeared to be completely destroyed; in a radius of 3,600 feet from ground zero blackening indicated that actual charring had occurred.

11.11 According to the Japanese reports, marked redness of those portions of the skin exposed to thermal radiation from the atomic bomb appeared almost immediately, with progressive darkening and blistering taking place over a period of a few hours. As with flame burns, the subsequent development depended on the degree (or depth) of the burn. Uninfected first degree burns that were not irritated healed promptly without, apparently, any unusual features. However, it was noted, in many cases, that after healing, there were marked overgrowths of scar tissue, i. e., keloid formation. It was suggested, at one time, that this might have been due to nuclear radiations, e. g., gamma rays, but this view is not now accepted. The degree of the keloid formation was undoubtedly influenced by secondary infections, that complicated healing of the burns, and by mal-

---

[4] Because of their importance in relation to the effects of an atomic explosion, a comprehensive study of flash burns is being sponsored by the U. S. Atomic Energy Commission.

nutrition, but more important is the known tendency for keloid formation to occur among the Japanese, as a racial characteristic. Thus, many spectacular keloids were formed after the healing of burns produced in the fire raids on Tokyo.

11.12   The margins of healed flash burns were usually sharply defined and were often accentuated by a narrow zone of pigment loss in the adjacent skin.   The edge of the scar, however, showed a denser pigmentation that tended to fade to a lighter color toward the center. This pigmentation is not necessarily an effect peculiar to thermal radiation, since other factors, such as ultraviolet light and certain chemicals, e. g., mustard gas, which stimulate the pigment layer of the skin produce similar results.

11.13   A form of thermal radiation or flash burn, sometimes distinguished as a contact burn, was caused by dark-colored clothing materials becoming hot and so burning the skin with which they were in contact.   This accounts for the fact, mentioned in § 6.55, that where burns occurred through clothing, the regions involved were those where the clothes were tightly drawn over the skin, e. g., the shoulders, elbows, waist, etc.

11.14   Hair exposed to thermal radiation from the atomic explosions in Japan was sometimes burned off or singed.   Occasionally the sweat glands and hair follicles were injured or destroyed in this manner. There is no doubt that sometimes the effects were due to the thermal, and not to the nuclear, radiations for where a cap provided a protective medium for the head, the area of hair loss was restricted by the cap. If gamma rays had been responsible, the cap would, of course, have offered no protection.

Treatment of Burns

11.15   For practical purposes of diagnosis and treatment, it is not necessary to distinguish among burns caused by thermal radiation, by flame, or by contact.   Although there are differences with respect to extent of body surface involved, depth of the injury to the skin, and general reactions of the individual to burns of different types, the indicated treatment for burns due to an atomic explosion appears to be the same as for those encountered in large-scale incendiary raids and in civil disasters.   The unique feature of the atomic bomb burns is the great number of casualties produced in a very brief period of time, the variety of burns encountered, and the wide range of severity, depending on the distance from the explosion.

11.16   A great deal was learned during World War II concerning the treatment of burns, but the subject is still under investigation and has not yet become stabilized.   It may be recommended, therefore, that until there is more general agreement, the medical men in each community should employ the treatment for severe burns which they have found most efficacious.

OPHTHALMIC EFFECTS

11.17   The effect of thermal radiation on the eyes was surprisingly small; even those who looked directly at the explosions at Hiroshima and Nagasaki, from some distance, of course, reported only temporary loss of vision.   In one case a patient was so blinded by the flash that he was unable to distinguish light from dark for two days, but eventually his recovery was complete.

11.18   Temporary blindness of this type may be due to two known causes.   First, the intense light results in the complete utilization of the visual purple of the retina.   Blindness will then persist until such time, usually not more than half an hour, as sufficient of this substance is once more produced to permit vision.   Second, temporary blindness may be due to the focusing of thermal, particularly infrared, radiation on the retina by the lens of the eye.   An example of this type of injury is the so-called "eclipse blindness" experienced from gazing directly at the sun.

11.19   One reason why there were relatively few persons in Japan who suffered from burns of the eyeballs due to thermal radiation from the atomic bombs is that the structure of the eye is more resistant to heat than is the average skin.   Further, in locations relatively near to the explosion, where the radiation was most intense, the recessed position of the eyes provided protection from the rays.   In addition, the blink reflex of the eye acted as an effective protective mechanism; the thermal radiation is emitted during a period of about 3 seconds and this is quite appreciable compared with the time required to blink.

B. NUCLEAR RADIATION EFFECTS

RADIATION INJURY AND RADIATION SICKNESS

11.20   The injurious effects of radiation from an atomic bomb represent an aspect of an atomic explosion which is completely absent from conventional bomb bursts.   For this reason the subject of radiation sickness will be discussed at some length in this book.   It should be clearly understood, however, that the extended treatment is not meant to imply that radiation is the most important source of casualties in an atomic explosion. This was certainly not the case in Japan, where, as stated earlier, a maximum of 15 percent of the fatalities were attributed to radiation, compared with over 50 percent due to burns. While nuclear radiation may definitely be a hazard, the extent of which will depend on the type of atomic explosion (§ 11.2 *et seq.*), it is by no means to be regarded as being of dominating significance.

11.21 It has long been known that excessive exposure to any radiation, for example, X-rays, alpha and beta particles, gamma rays, and neutrons,[5] capable of producing ionization in living tissues, can cause injury to the organism. After the discovery of X-rays and radioactivity toward the end of the nineteenth century, serious and sometimes fatal exposure to the radiations were sustained by radiologists, before the dangers were fully realized. With the passage of time, however, means for providing protection were developed and serious overexposure became less frequent, although occasional accidents have occurred with personnel operating radiographic equipment, powerful X-ray machines in industrial laboratories, cyclotrons, etc., or working with radioactive materials.

11.22 As a general rule, the exposures in these cases were limited to certain parts of the body, and the effects were referred to as *radiation injuries*. These included local destruction of tissue, loss of hair, and temporary sterility. In a very few instances there had been accidental exposure of large parts of the body to an overdose of radiation, and this led to systemic, rather than or in addition to a localized effect. This systemic disease is called *radiation sickness*.

11.23 Before the bombings of Hiroshima and Nagasaki, radiation sickness was a rare occurrence, but in these attacks exceptionally large numbers of individuals were exposed to gamma rays of varying intensity. There were consequently available for analysis a wide variety of forms and severities of the illness in a large group of people who had absorbed radiation dosages covering a considerable range, from insignificant quantities to amounts which proved fatal. A complicating factor was the difficulty of differentiating casualties according to direct and contributory causes, for many victims of radiation also suffered burns or mechanical injuries, or both. Nevertheless, certain general conclusions have been drawn with regard to the effects

---

[5] Neutrons produce very little or no ionization directly. However, as the result of collisions with hydrogen nuclei contained in the water or other constituent of tissue, fast neutrons produce recoil protons which cause ionization in their paths (cf. § 9.5). Slow neutrons can suffer radiative capture (§ 7.7) by hydrogen nuclei accompanied by the emission of gamma rays of about 2.2 Mev energy. The latter are capable of causing ionization in the usual way.

of nuclear radiation on the human organism; these will be discussed later in this chapter.

11.24 It has been established that all radiations capable of producing ionization directly, e. g., alpha and beta particles, or indirectly, e. g., X-rays, gamma rays, and neutrons, can cause radiation injury or radiation sickness of the same general types.[6] However, although the effects are qualitatively similar, the various radiations differ in their quantitative behavior. Thus, for the same amount of energy absorbed in tissue, an alpha particle is from 10 to 20 times, a slow neutron about 5 times, and a fast neutron about 10 times as effective biologically as a beta particle, while the latter has been found to be approximately equivalent to a gamma-ray photon. By making use of these relationships, it is possible to express radiation dosages in terms of the roentgen, although, as defined (§ 7.41), this unit is strictly applicable only to X-rays and gamma rays.

RADIATION DOSAGES

11.25 The effects of radiation on living organisms depend not only on the total amount absorbed, but also on the rate of absorption, on whether it is chronic or acute, and on the area of the body exposed (cf. § 8.5). Some radiation phenomena, such as genetic effects (§ 11.96 *et seq.*), are apparently independent of the rate of delivery of the radiation, and depend only on the total dosage. In some cases it has been claimed that the effectiveness of the radiation has been increased upon decreasing the rate of delivery; this has been attributed to an increase in the sensitivity of the tissue as a result of continued irradiation.

11.26 In the majority of instances, however, the biological effect of a given dose of radiation decreases as the rate of exposure decreases; thus, to cite an extreme case, 600 r would certainly be fatal if absorbed by the whole body in one day, but it would probably have no noticeable consequences if spread over 30 years. The most reasonable explanation of this fact is that if the dosage rate, i. e., the amount of radiation taken per day, is very small, the damaged tissues have a chance to recover. If the intensity or rate of delivery of the radiation is increased, recovery cannot keep up with the damage, and an increased effectiveness is to be expected. It is apparently the recovery factor which makes it possible for human beings to accept limited

---

[6] It will be understood that the term "radiation" as used in the present and succeeding sections of this chapter refers to any radiation which causes ionization directly or indirectly. Thermal radiation is, of course, not included, since it cannot produce ionization.

doses of radiation, at least 0.3 r per week (§ 8.4), for long periods of time without any apparent harmful consequences.

11.27 The foregoing considerations account for the necessity for distinguishing between acute exposure, i. e., occasional large doses, and chronic exposure, i. e., continued exposure to small doses, of radiation. As far as the effects of the atomic bomb are concerned, the situation is simplified by the fact that the initial nuclear radiations are emitted for a short period, taken as about a minute or so, so that exposure to these radiations may be regarded as being of the acute type. On the other hand, the residual radiations, due to fission products, etc., would represent a chronic hazard, either as internal or external radiation.

11.28 Because large acute doses have been accepted by human beings only as a result of accidents of one kind or another, it is not possible to state definitely that a particular amount of radiation will have certain consequences. Nevertheless, from experiments with animals, whose sensitivity to radiation relative to that of human beings has been studied, certain general conclusions have been drawn. These cannot be exact, in any event, since there are marked variations among individuals insofar as sensitivity to radiation is concerned. The results given in Table 11.28 may therefore be regarded as an approxi-

TABLE 11.28

PROBABLE EARLY EFFECTS OF ACUTE RADIATION DOSES OVER WHOLE BODY

Acute dose	Probable effect
0–25 r	No obvious injury.
25–50	Possible blood changes but no serious injury.
50–100	Blood-cell changes, some injury, no disability.
100–200	Injury, possible disability.
200–400	Injury and disability certain, death possible.
400	Fatal to 50 percent.
600 or more	Fatal.

mate indication of the early effects on human beings of various acute doses of radiation, assuming exposure of the whole body.[7] Somewhat larger doses may be accepted, with an equivalent likelihood of injury, if the exposure is protracted over several days or weeks, or if it is limited to a portion of the body. For these extended or split-up exposures, however, it is not possible to give any satisfactory rules for estimating the risk factors.

---

[7] The possible delayed effects of radiation are being studied in Japan as part of a long-range program of the Atomic Bomb Casualty Commission of the U. S. National Research Council, sponsored by the Atomic Energy Commission. Apart from cases of cataracts (§ 11.71), nothing significant has been observed 4 years after the atomic explosions.

11.29   Because of the variations among individuals, it appears that an acute dose exceeding 200 r may prove fatal to a human being, the probability increasing with the dosage.   The general variation of the survival rate with dosage for rabbits and rats is represented in Fig. 11.29, and from the results the corresponding curve, shown dotted, for human beings has been inferred.   It would appear that an acute dose of 200 r would prove fatal to about 5 percent of those exposed, while an almost equal proportion would be expected to survive a dose of 600 r.

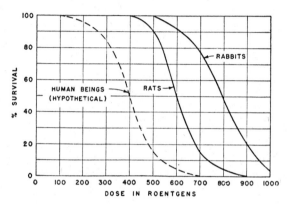

Figure 11.29.   Percentage survival as function of acute radiation dosage.

11.30   Most of the victims of the initial nuclear radiations from the atomic bombings of Japan were exposed over a large part of their bodies, since clothes are no protection against gamma rays.   From the observations made, much information has been obtained concerning the symptoms and development of radiation sickness of different degrees of severity.   For convenience, the description given here will refer to three main degrees of exposure within a short period of time.[8] They are: (*a*) lethal dose, i. e., about 600 r or more, which is fatal in nearly all cases within 2 weeks of exposure; (*b*) median lethal dose, i. e., about 400 r, resulting in death to 50 percent of the patients from 2 to 12 weeks after exposure; and (*c*) moderate dose, i. e., from 100 to 300 r, which is generally not fatal.

11.31   It may be mentioned that in Japan deaths from radiation, in those protected from blast and burns, began about a week after exposure and reached a peak in 3 to 4 weeks; these were probably the

---

[8] There are, of course, no sharp lines of demarcation between the three postulated types of exposure; the distinction, which is one of degree only (cf. Fig. 11.29), is made here for the sake of convenience in description.

individuals who had received doses of more than about 400 r. Subsequently, the death rate declined, and became very small after about 8 weeks.

C. CLINICAL SYNDROME OF RADIATION SICKNESS (ACUTE RADIATION SYNDROME)

LETHAL DOSE

11.32   In the most severe exposures, probably several thousand roentgens, death may occur within a few hours, but there are few reliable observations on the course of the radiation sickness in these circumstances.   In cases of lethal, but not extreme, exposures, individuals were found to exhibit varying degrees of shock, possibly within a few hours.   This was accompanied, or followed shortly, by nausea and vomiting, and then by diarrhoea, during the first day or two after exposure; subsequently, there was a development of fever. The diarrhoea was frequent and severe in character, being watery at first and tending to become bloody later.

11.33   The sooner the foregoing symptoms developed, the sooner was death likely to supervene.   Although there was no pain in the first few days, patients experienced a feeling of discomfort or uneasiness (malaise), accompanied by marked depression and bodily fatigue. The early stages of the severe radiation sickness may or may not be followed by a so-called latent period of 2 or 3 days, during which the patient is free from symptoms, although profound changes are taking place in the body.   This period, if it occurs, is succeeded by reappearance of the same symptoms and active illness, accompanied by delirium or coma, in many cases, terminating in death usually within 2 weeks.

11.34   Among other symptoms which have been observed are secondary infection and a tendency to spontaneous internal bleeding toward the end of the first week.   At the same time, swelling and inflammation of the throat is not uncommon.   Loss of hair, mainly from the head, may occur by the end of the second week.   Examination after death revealed a decrease in size, and degenerative changes, in the testes and ovaries; ulceration of the tonsils and of the mucous membrane of the large intestine were noted in some cases.   The development of the illness was accompanied by a characteristic increase of the body temperature; generally between the fifth and seventh days, sometimes as early as the third day, after exposure, there was a steplike rise usually continuing until the day of death.   There were also some striking changes in the blood of the patient, to which reference will be made below.

Median Lethal Dose

11.35 The initial symptoms, namely, nausea, vomiting, loss of appetite, and malaise, of a person who has received a median lethal dose of radiation over the whole body will be the same as for a lethal dose; however, they will, in general, develop somewhat later and be less severe.   After the first day or two the symptoms disappear and several days to two weeks may elapse ("latent period") in which the patient feels relatively well.   This is followed by a recurrence of the illness, with the symptoms, including fever, severe diarrhoea, and the steplike rise of temperature, the same as for the lethal dose, as described above.

11 36   Commencing between 14 and 21 days after exposure, there is a marked tendency to bleed; blood spots under the skin, called petechiae, are common and are a manifestation of this tendency. Bleeding may occur into any organ or group of tissues, and from any mucous membrane.   Particularly common are spontaneous bleeding in the mouth, and from and into the lining of the intestinal tract. There may be blood in the urine from bleeding into the substance of the kidney or into the urinary tract leading from the kidney.   The hemorrhagic tendency apparently depends on injuries produced in tissues and cells, e. g., thrombocytes, involved in the very complicated blood-clotting mechanisms, and on capillary damage.

11.37   Other symptoms observed were loss of hair, and ulceration about the lips.   These ulcers extended from the mouth through the entire gastro-intestinal tract in the terminal stage of the sickness.   A contributory factor to ulcer formation was the loss of white blood cells, which allowed bacteria to multiply, so that an overwhelming infection ensued.   Susceptibility to secondary bacterial infection was, in fact, one of the most serious complicating factors.

11.38   In the cases where the symptoms were most extreme, there was severe emaciation with fever and delirium, resulting in death within from 2 to 12 weeks after exposure.   Those patients who survived for 3 or 4 months, and did not succumb to tuberculosis, lung diseases or other complications, gradually recovered.   Whether the recovery was complete or whether after-effects will appear in the course of time is not known (§ 11.28, footnote).

MODERATE DOSE

11.39　Moderate doses of from 100 to 300 r total-body radiation received within a brief period of time are generally not fatal. Exposures of this kind were common in Hiroshima and Nagasaki, particularly among those persons who were some distance from the atomic explosions.

11.40　The illness resulting from moderate dosages of radiation presents much the same picture as in the case of more severe exposure, except that the onset is less abrupt and the symptoms are less marked. There may be a so-called latent period, up to 2 weeks or more, following exposure during which the subject has no disabling illness and can proceed with his regular occupation. The usual symptoms, such as loss of appetite, malaise, loss of hair, diarrhoea, and tendency to bleed, then appear, but they are not very severe. The changes in the character of the blood, which is typical of radiation sickness, are found, but neither their severity nor their persistence is as marked as with patients receiving larger doses of radiation. If there are no complications, due to injuries or infections, there will be recovery in nearly all cases, with hair growth recommencing after about two months.

11.41　It may be noted that recovery may be hindered by changes in the intestinal tract that greatly hamper the assimilation of food, thus producing serious malnutrition. The intractability of the diarrhoea may also be important in this connection. With these factors to be considered, it is consequently not usually possible to predict a definite course of convalescence. In general, however, the more severe the early stages of the radiation sickness, the longer and more difficult will be the process of recovery.

11.42　Single exposures of from 25 to 100 r over the whole body may produce mild and somewhat indefinite symptoms, or there may be nothing more than the characteristic blood-cell changes (§ 11.44 *et seq.*) to a minor extent. Disabling illness is not common, and exposed individuals should be able to proceed with their usual duties.

11.43　A simplified summary of the clinical symptoms of radiation sickness, obtained from data collected in Japan, is given in Table 11.43.[9]

---

[9] Adapted from "The Atomic Bombings of Hiroshima and Nagasaki," The Manhattan Engineer District, 1946, p. 32.

TABLE 11.43

SUMMARY OF CLINICAL SYMPTOMS OF RADIATION SICKNESS

Time after exposure	Lethal dose (600 r)	Median lethal dose (400 r)	Moderate dose (300–100 r)
	Nausea and vomiting after 1–2 hours.	Nausea and vomiting after 1–2 hours.	
First week	No definite symptoms.		
	Diarrhoea. Vomiting. Inflammation of mouth and throat.	No definite symptoms.	
Second week	Fever. Rapid emaciation. Death. (Mortality probably 100 percent.)		No definite symptoms.
		Beginning epilation.	
		Loss of appetite and general malaise.	
Third week		Fever.	Epilation.
			Loss of appetite and general malaise.
		Severe inflammation of mouth and throat.	Sore throat.
			Pallor.
Fourth week			Petechiae.
		Pallor. Petechiae, diarrhoea, and nosebleeds.	Diarrhoea.
			Moderate emaciation.
		Rapid emaciation. Death. (Mortality probably 50 percent.)	(Recovery likely unless complicated by poor previous health or superimposed injuries or infections.)

DIAGNOSIS OF RADIATION SICKNESS

11.44   Of the biological consequences to exposure of the whole body to a large single dose of radiation, perhaps the most characteristic are the changes which take place in the blood.   Soon after exposure there is a drop in the number of lymphocytes, i. e., those white blood cells (leukocytes) which are formed in portions of the lymphatic tissues of the body, such as lymph nodes and spleen.   In some instances an increase in the total white blood cell count was reported in Japan following the atomic explosions; this was apparently due to a gain in the number of granulocytes, i. e., the white blood cells formed mainly in the bone marrow.   But such an increase was soon followed, within a few hours, by a sharp decrease (Fig. 11.44a).   As a result, there was, after the first day, a rapid decrease in the total white blood cell count which continued for about 5 or 6 days (Fig. 11.44b).   The total number

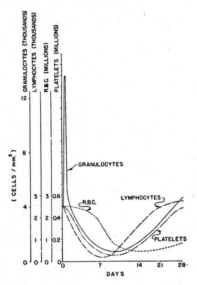

Figure 11.44a.   Variation in blood   Figure 11.44b.   Variation of total
cell counts with time in radiation   white blood cells with time in
sickness.   radiation sickness.

of white blood cells had then decreased from the normal value of from 4,000 to 10,000 per cubic millimeter to something like 1,000 to 3,000 per cubic millimeter.   In severe cases, the white blood count dropped to 300 or less before death.

11.45   After about a week the lymphocytes had reached their low point, and then their number began to increase, in patients who were in process of recovery.   By the end of the third week, the lymphocytes may show considerable gain, while the number of granulocytes is also growing.   During this period the erythrocytes, i. e., the red blood cells, indicated by R. B. C. in Fig. 11.44a, formed normally in the bone marrow, may show a decline, especially where the radiation dosage has been high.

11.46   The main function of the leukocytes in the blood is to defend the body against infection and to remove injured tissue.   Most bacterial infections, whether localized or generalized, stimulate an outpouring of the white blood cells. These cells then restrict the infection and overcome it. The failure of the bone marrow and of the lymphoid tissues to produce granulocytes and lymphocytes, respectively, as a result of the action of radiation, means that an important defense mechanism of the body is rendered inoperative, and there is an increased susceptibility to infection, as mentioned above.

11.47 Although there are changes in the red blood cell count and in other factors of the blood, it is the net decrease in the total number of white cells soon after the exposure which is always observed in radiation sickness, particularly in severe cases. If the number of cells falls much below 2,000 per cubic millimeter, the chances of recovery are not good, and if it is less than 500 per cubic millimeter, the consequences are almost certain to be fatal. At present the white blood cell count is considered to be the most valuable and direct single index of radiation sickness. It can thus be used for establishing a diagnosis and in following the course of the illness.

11.48 It is important to note, however, that by itself the number of white blood cells cannot be taken as presumptive evidence of overexposure to radiation. Various other diseases and infections, unrelated to radiation, can cause similar blood-cell changes. If it is suspected that a group of individuals have been exposed to radiation, from an atomic bomb, for example, and they all show a similar reduction in the white blood cells, then it is probable they will suffer from radiation sickness. Evidence from other symptoms must nevertheless be obtained before the diagnosis can be regarded as conclusive. The situation could be confused if there were an epidemic of some virus infection, such as acute influenza, at the time of the bomb explosion, for the white blood cell count would then be low in any event. On the whole, however, the combination of such circumstances may be discounted.

11.49 It should be emphasized that the white blood cell count can be used as an indication of radiation sickness only when the exposure has been at least moderately severe. Because of the occurrence of daily variations, of unobserved low-grade infections, and of differences in counting techniques, the count for an individual may be appreciably lower than his previously established normal without exposure to radiation. Consequently, the observed decrease in the white blood cell count must be appreciable if any importance is to be attached to it as a means of diagnosis.

Treatment of Radiation Sickness

11.50   While little of a specific nature can be done in the treatment of radiation sickness where the acute dose is 600 r or more, there is a possibility that where the dose is smaller, particularly 400 r or less, many lives can be saved with proper treatment.   Immediate hospitalization, so as to insure complete rest, and avoidance of chills and fatigue, is an essential first step.   Whole blood transfusion should be given, as required, until the bone marrow has had time to regenerate and produce blood cells.   Adequate nourishment could be provided by intravenous feeding to supply the necessary sugars, proteins, vitamins, etc.   Infection may be controlled by the use of penicillin and other antibiotics.   The whole subject of radiation sickness is being given intensive study, and important advances in its treatment may be expected.

D.   PATHOLOGY OF RADIATION SICKNESS

Cellular Sensitivity

11.51   The discussion presented above has been largely concerned with over-all symptoms of radiation sickness; even the changes in the blood are, to a great extent, indirectly due to the effect of the radiation on the bone marrow, etc.   It is of interest, therefore, to consider briefly the pathological changes produced by radiation in some individual organs and tissues.   The damage caused by radiation undoubtedly originates in the individual cells; some of the effects which have been observed by microscopic examination of cells are chromosome breaks, clumping of the chromatin, changes in cell division, increased granularity of the cytoplasm, swelling of the nucleus or of the entire cell, and complete disintegration of the cell. In addition, changes in the viscosity of the protoplasm and in the permeability of the cell membranes have been noted.

11.52   Different types of cells show remarkable variations in their response to radiation.   It has been stated that primitive, that is, less highly specialized, cells, such as white blood corpuscles and reproductive cells, are more sensitive than are more highly specialized tissues, e. g., brain cells, nerve cells.   However, although this rule applies in certain instances, it is not generally reliable.   The giant ameba, for example, which is a primitive cell, is very resistant to radiation, while the highly specialized, ciliated epithelial cells of the bronchus of mammals have a high sensitivity. In general, it is the nucleus of the cell which reacts to radiation, whereas the cytoplasm is not so sensitive. Hence, a large cell with much cytoplasm, such as the giant ameba, is not greatly affected by radiation, but a small cell containing a large percentage of nuclear material will be sensitive. Rapidly multiplying or actively reproducing cells are on the whole more radiosensitive than are those in a more quiescent state.

11.53 Of the more common tissues, the radiosensitivity decreases in the following order: lymphoid tissue and bone marrow; epithelial cells (testes and ovaries, salivary glands, skin and mucous membrane); endothelial cells of blood vessels and peritoneum; connective tissue cells; muscle cells, bone cells; and nerve cells. The behavior of some of these tissues under the influence of radiation is outlined below.

Lymphoid Tissue

11.54 The lymphoid tissue is the tissue characteristic of lymph glands, tonsils, adenoids, spleen, and certain areas of the intestinal lining. Lymph glands, found in various parts of the body, are rounded masses of lymphoid tissue; they are not true glands, but a network of connective tissue fixed in the meshes of which are small, round lymphoid cells having relatively large, round, deeply-staining nuclei. These cells, when mature, are carried off by the lymph fluid, flowing through the gland, and become the lymphocyte constituent of the white blood cells. As indicated in the preceding paragraph, the lymphoid tissue is the most radiosensitive of all tissues.

11.55 Lymphoid cells are injured or killed when the tissue is exposed to radiation. Microscopic examination shows degenerative changes characteristic of cell death; the nuclei may stain deeper and be fragmented, and there may be vacuoles in the cytoplasm. The degeneration of lymphoid tissue, including the formation of cells of abnormal types, was an outstanding phenomenon in the victims of the atomic bombs in Japan and in the animals exposed at Bikini.

11.56 Damage to lymphoid cells accounts for the decrease in the number of lymphocytes in the blood, for the radiation not only damages the lymphocyte-producing tissue, but it also kills or injures the cells within the blood. It appears to be established with some certainty that if no drop is detectable in the total number of lymphocytes within 72 hours of exposure to radiation, the dose has been too small to cause serious illness. It is of interest to note that if recovery from radiation sickness is to take place, the lymphocytes are the first cells to shows signs of regeneration, as indicated by an increase of their number in the blood.

11.57   Lymphoid tissue injured by radiation tends to become edematous, that is, to swell due to the accumulation of serous fluid. This characteristic, related to throat tissues, contributed to the severe sore throats experienced at Hiroshima and Nagasaki. The swellings became severely ulcerated and infected, so that breathing and swallowing was difficult. Wasting of the lymph glands, as well as of the tonsils and lymphoid patches of the intestines, was common among the radiation casualties in Japan.

BONE MARROW

11.58   Since most of the constituents of the blood, other than the lymphocytes, are manufactured in the bone marrow, the fact that this is very radiosensitive is of great significance. Under normal circumstances, the mature blood cells leave the marrow and make their way into the blood stream; here they remain for variable periods before being destroyed by natural processes. In general, the shorter the life of a particular type of blood cell, the more quickly will it reveal evidence of radiation injury by a reduction in the number of such cells circulating in the blood. This reduction is indicative of the inability of the affected lymph glands and bone marrow to manufacture more cells. The lymphocytes, with the shortest lives, are reduced first; then the granulocytes and the platelets (or thrombocytes), the latter being important in connection with the clotting of blood (cf. Fig. 11.44a). The number of the former may be increased at first, but later it decreases. The red blood cells, which have the longest lives, are the last to show a reduction in number after exposure to radiation.

11.59   Bone marrow exhibits striking changes very soon after exposure. The tissue forming the blood cells ceases to function and in some severe cases it was observed that tissue which normally produced granulocytes was forming plasma-like cells. Extreme atrophy of the bone marrow was characteristic of many of those dying from radiation sickness up to 3 or 4 months after exposure, although there was some evidence of attempts at repair and regeneration. In some instances a gelatinous deposit had replaced the normal marrow tissue.

REPRODUCTIVE ORGANS

11.60   Almost every postmortem examination of males dying from radiation sickness revealed profound changes in the testes. Even as early as the fourteenth day after exposure, when gross changes were not apparent, microscopic observation showed remarkable alteration in the layers of epithelium from which the spermatozoa develop. Many of the cells were degenerated, and evidence of healthy cell division was lacking. Some of the blood vessels of the testes presented the most marked radiation changes of any vessels in the body.

11.61 Changes in the ovaries were less striking than in the testes. Except for hemorrhages, as part of the general tendency to bleed, no gross changes were observed, neither were there any striking microscopic changes. In many instances, the ova were not developing normally after exposure, and this induced alterations in the menstrual cycle. Cessation of menstruation occurred, but it was transient. There was also an increased incidence of miscarriages and premature births, and an increased death rate among expectant mothers. In general, these manifestations varied in severity according to the proximity of the individual to the explosion.

11.62 In connection with changes in the reproductive organs, it may be noted that the total body dose of radiation required to sterilize a man is believed to be from 400 to 600 r, which would be lethal in most cases. Temporary sterility can occur with smaller doses, however, as happened among Japanese men and women, and the vast majority of these have since returned to normal. It cannot be stated that all have recovered because it is not known how many were sterile from other causes, such as disease and malnutrition, before the bombings, but many afflicted with radiation sickness have since produced normal children.

Skin and Hair

11.63 Because of the great penetrating power of the high-energy gamma rays, evidence of the effects of radiation on the skin of the Japanese casualties was not definite. Epilation, i. e., loss of hair, was common, mainly on the scalp, among those who survived for more than two weeks after the explosion. The time of onset of epilation reached a sharp peak, for both males and females, between the thirteenth and fourteenth day. The hair suddenly began to fall out in bunches upon combing or general plucking, and much fell out spontaneously; this continued for 1 or 2 weeks and then ceased.

11.64 In most instances the distribution was that of ordinary baldness, involving first the front, then the top and back of the head. The hair of the eyebrows and particularly the eyelashes and beard came out much less easily. In a small group, which may or may not have been typical, 69 percent had lost hair from the scalp, 12 percent from the armpits, 10 percent from pubic areas, 6 percent from the eyebrows, and 3 percent from the beard. Even in severe cases, hair began to return within a few months; in no instance was the epilation permanent.

Gastro-Intestinal Tract

11.65   The mucous linings of the gastro-intestinal tract were among the first tissues to show gross changes. Even before hemorrhages and associated phenomena were noticed, there was swelling, greenish and yellowish-gray discoloration, and thickening of the mucous membranes of the cecum and large intestine. Patches of lymphoid tissue were especially involved. At times, a diphtheria-like membrane covered the mucous lining, and sometimes the tissues underneath were swollen and water-logged. Subsequently, hemorrhages occurred into and under the linings of the stomach and intestine, initiating a series of changes similar to those occurring in the initial stages. There was first, swelling, then ulceration, of the most superficial layers of the mucous membranes lining the tract, proceeding to deeper ulceration and a membrane-like covering of the ulcer, suggesting, but not entirely simulating, that seen in bacillary dysentery.

11.66   In the third and fourth weeks, inflammation of the intestines, and occasionally of the stomach, was a common postmortem observation. In the small intestine, the early changes were often seen in the crypts of the folds of the mucous membrane, when the membranes appeared blanched; later they became greenish or yellowish-gray in color. In the later stages of this cycle, in those individuals who survived for longer periods of time, the large intestine had a more widespread involvement of everything from the lower end of the small intestine to the rectum. Thickening of the intestinal wall was a common feature. All these changes, including the tendency to produce false membranes, resembled those of acute bacillary dysentery. The effects depended on the devitalization of tissues as a primary result of radiation, lowered local resistance, and lowered efficiency of the defense mechanisms ordinarily supplied in the circulating blood. Under the microscope, the notable changes were the swelling of cells and the absence of infiltration of the white blood cells.

Other Pathological Phenomena

11.67   The reticulo-endothelial system comprises a group of extremely radiosensitive cells that are concerned with a variety of functions, including the formation of certain blood cells, the storing of fatty material of the body, the destruction of red blood cells, and the conversion of hemoglobin from the blood into bile pigments. These cells are found especially in the normal spleen, the lymph glands, the liver, bone marrow and certain connective tissues, and together they form a complicated system whose vital functions are damaged or lost entirely under exposure to radiation. Injury to the cells of the reticulo-endothelial system appears to account for a considerable share of the complex phenomena characterizing radiation sickness.

11.68 Certain parts of the urinary tract, the muscles, and all soft tissues of the body may show subsurface hemorrhages varying in size from a pinpoint to several inches or larger. These changes are significant, for they present clinical evidence of the nature and severity of the radiation sickness. If the hemorrhages occur in important centers of the body, e. g., heart, lungs or brain, the resulting effects may be disastrous, the severity of the damage depending on the location of the large hemorrhagic lesions in relation to the tissues of the particular vital organs involved. Some hemorrhages present external signs, or may be observed on special examination, such as those into the linings of the mouth, nose and throat, behind the retina of the eye, or into the urinary tract. Large hemorrhagic lesions may occur in the drainage tracts of the kidney, in the small tubes leading from the kidney to the bladder, and in the urinary bladder.

11.69 Hemorrhages breaking through a surface layer of epithelium laden with bacteria may give rise to other effects. The tissues may become so devitalized and so lacking in resistance to bacterial infection that they make an ideal place for even weakly invasive bacteria or for those that are rarely dangerous under ordinary circumstances. This bacterial invasion may lead to serious local tissue destruction and perhaps blood poisoning and systemic infection. The normally harmless bacteria ordinarily found within the digestive tract and on the skin may actually gain access to the blood stream and cause blood poisoning and fatal infection. Boils and abscesses may occur in any part of the body through a similar cause, but are characterized by a more localized series of events.

11.70 When this form of tissue change occurs in the throat, the medical findings may resemble a condition found after certain chemical intoxications that injure the bone marrow and the reticulo-endothelial system; or they may resemble those that occur in certain of the blood diseases characterized by an absence of granulocytes in the circulating blood (agranulocytosis). In radiation sickness, ulcers may extend to the tongue, the gums, the inner linings of the mouth, the lips, and even the outer part of the skin of the face. These ulcerations may occur independently of any associated local hemorrhagic change. Throughout the entire gastro-intestinal tract, similar changes occur and appear to become established on the same basis. Within the lungs, a form of pneumonia may develop, different from most pneumonias in the almost complete absence of infiltrating leukocytes.

Atomic Bomb Cataracts

11.71 Because of the discovery of cataracts in a number of cyclotron workers about 3 years or so after exposure to excessive amounts of radiation, probably neutrons, the Atomic Bomb Casualty Commission (§11.28, footnote) has made a detailed study of the incidence of cataracts among the survivors of the bombings of Hiroshima and Nagasaki. By early 1950, 45 cases of cataracts had been identified in persons who were within 3,300 feet from ground zero at the times of the respective explosions. The cataracts are similar to those which have been previously associated with overexposure to X-rays or gamma rays, and hence they are probably due to the initial radiation from the atomic bombs. Whether these were gamma rays or neutrons it is impossible to state, but the high biological effectiveness of the latter suggests that they were, at least, a contributory factor.

11.72 Most persons in the same zone, with respect to the center of the explosion, died either from thermal or mechanical injuries or from radiation sickness. All the survivors who developed cataracts must have been exposed to considerable intensities of radiation, as is evidenced by the complete (transient) epilation in all cases and the development of symptoms of radiation sickness in several of them. There is little doubt that were it not for fortuitous shielding, the persons under consideration would have succumbed to this sickness soon after the atomic explosions.

E. RESIDUAL RADIATION HAZARDS

Introduction

11.73 In an atomic explosion, the radiation sickness discussed in the preceding sections would be almost exclusively the result of the initial nuclear radiations, particularly the gamma rays, described in Chapter VII. The possible biological effects of the radioactive contamination, e. g., fission products and plutonium or uranium, which is responsible for the residual radiations (Chapter VIII), will now be considered.

11.74 It should be emphasized at the outset that a radiological hazard due to these radiations is likely to arise in special circumstances only. In the case of a high or moderately high air burst, the danger will be essentially nonexistent. There was no evidence after the atomic explosions in Japan that any radiation injury or sickness resulted from the fission products or the bomb material. However, an underground burst or an underwater burst accompanied by a base surge could lead to contamination of inhabited areas, in which case the hazard due to residual radiations might be significant. A similar situation could arise if a radioactive material were used as a radiological warfare weapon (§8.107 *et seq.*). In general, contaminated areas would be rapidly evacuated by the inhabitants before the effects of the radiation were appreciable, although this might not be possible for those responsible for the measurement of radioactivity (§12.62 *et seq.*) and for carrying out decontamination procedures.

11.75 Although the residual radiation hazard following an atomic explosion is thus not likely to be serious except in special cases, the subject will be considered here for the sake of completeness. In this connection it is convenient to distinguish between (a) external radiation, and (b) internal radiation. The former applies to instances where the source of radiation lies outside the body, and the latter refers to cases in which the source is taken into the body by ingestion, inhalation, or through breaks in the skin.

External Radiation

11.76 If the radiation from an external source is to have any effect on the body it must pass through the skin in order to reach the underlying tissue. Because of their short range in air (§8.46), and even shorter range (about 0.05 mm.) in tissue, alpha particles are unable to penetrate the outer layer of the skin. Consequently, these particles are of no importance as an external radiation hazard.

11.77 The total range of a beta particle may be some meters in air (§8.40), but it is only a few millimeters in tissue. As a result, beta particles from external sources do not penetrate to the bone marrow or to other vital parts of the body. Nevertheless, these particles have a deleterious effect on the skin and if present in sufficient amounts they may represent a significant radiation hazard.

11.78 The reactions following contact with beta emitters represent a form of radiation injury. They may vary from temporary redness to complete destruction of the skin, depending on the dose absorbed. Even mild doses may result in delayed degenerative changes of the skin. When the hands have been exposed to large amounts of beta radiation, they become swollen within a few days and this is followed by reddening of the skin. Hemorrhages develop in the superficial tissue of the exposed region, the appearance being similar to a bruise. Subsequently, large blisters form, become confluent, and finally turn into a slough, several weeks being required for the damage to reach a maximum. Unless the exposure of the body to beta particles has been extensive, no generalized illness, i. e., radiation sickness, is associated with the skin injuries.

11.79   Gamma rays are, as seen earlier, much more penetrating than beta particles, for they are, in fact, identical with X-rays of short wave lengths. These rays thus constitute the most important type of external radiation. The extent to which gamma rays can penetrate the body depends on the energy of the photon. It will be recalled, in this connection, that the mean energy of the gamma ray photons from the initial nuclear radiations, is about 3 Mev (§ 7.44), compared with about 0.7 Mev for the residual nuclear radiations (§ 8.11); the former are thus highly penetrating. It is of interest to note that in Japan, where the radiation injuries and radiation sickness were 'due entirely to the initial radiations, the serious damage was mainly of a deep-seated character. For reasons already given, it is unlikely that many individuals will remain in a contaminated area long enough, following an atomic explosion, to accumulate a dangerous dose of external radiation due to residual gamma rays.

11.80   Too little is known of the cumulative effects of moderate but continued, i. e., chronic, doses of radiation, such as would be absorbed in a contaminated area, to permit an approximate estimate to be made of safe levels. All that can be said is that persons who have received up to 0.1 r daily for years have shown no ill effects. Larger doses may have to be taken in cases of emergency, but it would be inadvisable to do so at frequent intervals. In general, the clinical symptoms and pathological changes due to chronic doses of radiation over the whole or a large part of the body, may be expected to be similar to those for acute doses, the degree of severity depending on the dosage rates and the total accumulated dose.

Internal Radiation

11.81   The chances of radioactive material entering the system following an atomic explosion are believed to be extremely small.

Thus, no form of illness or injury due to internal radiation has been reported following the high air bursts at Hiroshima and Nagasaki. Even when there is considerable contamination of the ground, due to fission products, plutonium or uranium, it would be a matter of great difficulty for an appreciable quantity to enter the blood stream. Although the amounts of fission products, for example, that must be fixed within the body to produce injurious effects are minute, in comparison with the quantities necessary to cause damage by external beta or gamma radiation, it is believed that, following an atomic explosion, the internal hazard will be significant only while the external hazard exists. In other words, if in a given area the dosage due to external radiation is down to a safe level, there will, in general, be little, if any, danger of enough radioactive material being fixed in the system for it to constitute an internal hazard. In view of these circumstances, brief reference only need be made to the subject of internal radiation associated with an atomic explosion.

11.82 The chemical characteristics of the radioactive material which enters the body are important, for these will determine where a particular species will be deposited. Radioactive isotopes will follow the same metabolic processes as the naturally occurring inactive isotopes of the same elements, but an element not otherwise found in the body will tend to follow the metabolic pattern of one with similar chemical properties that is normally present. Thus barium, strontium, and radium, which are analogous chemically to calcium, will be deposited in the bone.

11.83 The hazard represented by a particular ingested radioactive substance will depend on its solubility, chemical properties, physical state, etc., for these will determine how much will be absorbed from the gastro-intestinal tract. It should be noted that in order to constitute an internal radiation hazard, the active materials must gain access to the circulating blood, from which they can be deposited in the bones, liver, spleen, etc. Thus, for all practical purposes, while the radioactive substances are in the stomach and intestines, they are essentially a source of external, rather than internal, radiation.

11.84 The extent of absorption is dependent on the chemical form of an element, and it is fortunate that most of the fission products, which are mainly present as oxides after an atomic explosion (§ 2.23), are almost insoluble in the body fluids. The same would be true for the oxides of the uranium or plutonium which had escaped fission in the bomb. The oxides of cesium and barium are, of course, soluble in water, and such iodine as might be present would also be largely in a soluble form.

11.85 Entry of radioactive material into the system through wounds or abrasions can be a serious internal radiation hazard. Soluble substances introduced into the blood stream in this manner are deposited in the body in a very short time. For this reason, care of wounds, where radioactive contamination is possible, becomes particularly important. The treatment should be the same as for any other wound contaminated with potentially harmful material, such as bacteria, toxic substances, etc. Good surgical care locally is all that is necessary.

11.86 The danger associated with the inhalation of radioactive dusts, such as might be present after an atomic explosion, especially an underground burst, depends both on the chemical nature and the size of the particles. The nose will filter out almost all particles over 10 microns, i. e., 10^{-3} cm., in diameter, and about 95 percent of all particles exceeding 5 microns. The optimum particle size for passage from the alveolar space of the lungs to the blood stream is under 5 microns, and insoluble particles from 1 to 5 microns in diameter may reach the lymphatic system. These facts are important in connection with the design of air filters and respirators for reducing the extent of inhalation of radioactive dusts (§ 12.56).

Biological Half-Life

11.87 From the point of view of biological effectiveness, one of the prime considerations is whether a particular radioactive element tends to concentrate in certain portions of the body from which it is eliminated slowly. In order to describe this behavior, a quantity called the *biological half-life* has been introduced. This is defined as the period of time during which the amount of a particular radioisotope deposited in the body is reduced to half its initial value. The biological half-life of a given species thus depends on its ordinary radioactive half-life, which determines the natural rate of decay, and also on the rate of its excretion from the body.

11.88 · An isotope with a very short radioactive half-life will inevitably have a short biological half-life, but for substances with moderate or long radioactive half-lives, the biological half-life may be long or short, depending on whether the particular isotope tends to be concentrated in the body or not. In general, a substance with a fairly long biological half-life is to be regarded as an internal hazard. The biological half-life of plutonium in man, for example, is very long. This indicates that once plutonium has been fixed in the body, it is eliminated at an extremely slow rate, the loss being due almost entirely to the natural radioactive decay. On the other hand, the biological half-life of cesium 137 is about 15 days, compared with a radioactive half-life of 37 years. This element is evidently easily eliminated from the system.

11.89 In addition to the biological half-life, the injury caused by a given radioisotope in the system will depend on the region where it tends to concentrate, and also on the particular radiation it emits. One reason why plutonium is such a danger is that in addition to having a long biological half-life, it expels alpha particles, which have a high biological effectiveness and so are capable of causing severe local damage, even though their short range prevents them from penetrating very far.

SOURCES AND EFFECTS OF INTERNAL RADIATION

11.90 It may be mentioned that in the rare event of sufficient fission products entering the blood stream as to become a source of danger, strontium and barium, which resemble calcium chemically, will tend to concentrate in parts of the bone (cf. Fig. 11.90). Lan-

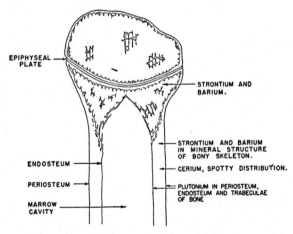

Figure 11.90. Deposition of elements in growing bone of rodents.

thanum and cerium would be deposited in the liver, and to a much smaller extent in the spleen. Plutonium, strontium, and barium, on the other hand, have been found in both liver and spleen. With very few exceptions, however, most radioactive substances are readily eliminated from the liver. Despite large amounts of material that pass through or accumulate in the kidney, this organ seems to be exceptionally resistant to the action of radiation.

11.91   The lymphocytes of the blood have been found to be sensitive to internal radiation, as also are the early red cells (erythroblasts). Almost invariably, the deposition of any radioelement in bone results in damage to the blood-forming tissue, with a consequent reduction in the constituent cells of the blood.   The most sensitive indication of acute or near-acute effects of a fission product, irrespective of whether it is localized in bone or generally distributed, is the reduction in the number of lymphocytes.

11.92   One of the earliest systemic effects of a relatively large dose of internal radiation would be a reduction in the number of white and red blood cells.   This would be associated with extreme weakness and anemia.   Malignant growths may subsequently develop in those regions where the radioactive material has concentrated.   It may be mentioned that no form of internal radiation illness has been observed as a result of an atomic explosion; the effects described above have been derived from animal experiments.

11.93   Plutonium compounds tend to concentrate in the liver and spleen, and also on certain surfaces of bone, particularly the periosteum, the endosteum, and the coverings of the trabeculae of the bones (Fig. 11.90).   In spite of their short range, the continued action of the alpha particles, due to the long biological half-life of plutonium, causes severe damage to tissues, such as the marrow and the spleen, where various blood cells are formed.

11.94   For normal peacetime working conditions, the permissible quantity of plutonium which may be fixed in the body is taken to be the extremely small amount of 0.5 microgram, i. e., five ten-millionths of a gram, for an average adult.   This figure undoubtedly represents a very conservative estimate and involves a large factor of safety. As a result of long experience with radium, which is an alpha emitter, the maximum weight of this element that can be safely held in the body is well known and, purely on the basis of the rate of energy absorption from the alpha particles, the corresponding quantity of plutonium would be 5 micrograms.   The presence of 40 micrograms in the body would be dangerous, and 100 micrograms might be fatal. However, as has been stated earlier in this book, it is only under certain unexpected conditions that plutonium is likely to constitute an important hazard following an atomic bomb explosion.   In most cases, the danger due to this element can be ignored, compared with that due to fission products, for a period of at least two months, in any event. By this time, it may be presumed that an inhabited locality will have been largely decontaminated.

11.95 Uranium 235 has a much longer half life than plutonium (§ 1.18), and so a given weight of the former expels alpha particles at a much slower rate than an equal weight of the latter. For this reason, and also because it does not tend to concentrate in the body, uranium does not need to be considered a radiological hazard. Although uranium is also a chemical poison, it is highly improbable that sufficient amounts could be absorbed in the body following an atomic explosion to have any toxic effects.

F. GENETIC EFFECTS OF RADIATION

RADIATION AND GENETIC MUTATIONS

11.96 Because of the possible importance of the subject for the future of the human race, no discussion of radiation injury would be complete without consideration of the genetic effects. These effects differ from most other changes produced by radiation in that they appear to be cumulative and, within limits, independent of the dosage rate of the energy of the radiation.

11.97 The mechanism of heredity is essentially similar in all sexually reproducing plants and animals including man. The material responsible for inheritance is organized into discrete structures, the chromosomes, which are visible microscopically in the nuclei of dividing cells. The chromosomes are considered to be fine threads of nucleoprotein which are differentiated along their length into thousands of distinctive but submicroscopic units, the genes. The development of inherited characteristics is controlled by the action of the genes. Chromosomes, and hence the genes, occur in pairs in the nuclei of the cells of individuals, one member of each pair being contributed by each parent through the sperm or egg.

11.98 Mutations, defined as changes in inherited characteristics, may be classified roughly into two categories. Microscopically detectable changes in chromosome structure are called *chromosomal mutations* or *aberrations*. They may be responsible for visible changes in inherited characteristics, may cause reduced fertility, and frequently may be lethal, preventing development of the embryos. The second category, *gene mutations*, includes those cases in which sudden changes in inherited characteristics are not the result of demonstrable changes in chromosome

---

[10] Hemophilia and color blindness are examples of characters associated with sex-linked genes carried by the female.

structure but rather are believed to be due to changes in the chemical composition of the normal genes. The possibility remains, however, that many so-called gene mutations may actually be ultra-microscopic changes in chromosome structure.

11.99 Mutated genes are commonly classified as dominant over the normal genes, in which case an individual will show the particular characteristic if he receives the mutated gene from either parent, or recessive, in which case an individual must receive the mutated gene from both parents before exhibiting the characteristic. Mutations of genes in the sex chromosome are partial exceptions to this rule since the male offspring receive sex-linked genes only from their female parent and, hence, exhibit even recessive sex-linked genes. While most gene mutations appear to be recessive, recent evidence indicates that many so-called recessives are partially dominant.

11.100 Gene mutations produce a wide spectrum of effects ranging from visible changes with no apparent effects on viability and fertility to lethal mutations which kill the individuals in which they are expressed. However, almost all mutations are deleterious, the occurrence of beneficial mutations being very rare.

11.101 The normal or spontaneous frequency of chromosomal aberrations and gene mutations is low. The rate of both can be increased by higher than normal temperatures, certain chemicals and radiation. The same kinds and about the same relative frequencies of the various kinds of gene mutations are observed following radiation as occur spontaneously. The frequency of radiation induced genetic changes increases with increasing dose.

RADIATION AND HUMAN GENETICS

11.102 Any study of human genetics is complicated by the long life-span of man, the small number of off-spring and the difficulty of making long-term observations. Radiation genetic studies in man encounter a further difficulty in the fact that, although dominant mutations express themselves in the next generation, recessives may lie hidden for many generations. Enough work has been done with mice to show that mutations are produced in them by radiation, but quantitative estimates of the genetic hazards of radiation to man have had to be based largely on the fruit fly and other organisms that are not closely related to man or even to mammals. However, radiation-induced gene mutation rates have been shown to be about the same magnitude over a wide range of organisms. It is, therefore, reasonable to assume that a similar rate would be found in man.

11.103 On the basis of this rate and of estimates of the rate of naturally occurring mutations in man, published estimates of the dose that might be expected to double the gene mutation rate in man range from as low as 3 r to as high as 300 r and it is conceivable that the true value lies outside these limits. Since there is so much uncertainty about such a basic factor as this, not to mention the many other factors that would enter into an evaluation of the total effects of a given increase in mutation rate, it is apparent that at present, as one investigator has said, "no judgments of the genetic consequences of radiation in man can be taken very seriously."

11.104 In the face of the large number of gaps in our knowledge, it is hard to arrive at meaningful practical recommendations. Some guidance may be derived from an important point which has emerged from experimental work. There is a large body of data which indicates that any dose of radiation, no matter how small, increases the probability of genetic changes. Until recently the risk would have been thought to apply mainly to distant descendants. New information on the frequency of partial domenants (see paragraph 11.99) indicates that the risk may not be negligible even to the first generation.

11.105 Incomplete experimental work as reported thus far has shown that the rate of induction of at least certain types of chromosomal aberrations is much greater in mice than it is in the fruit fly. However, if the mice are not bred until some time after the exposure to radiation, the frequency of such chromosomal aberrations is greatly reduced. The important practical conclusion can, therefore, be drawn that the probability of passing on chromosome aberrations to the next generation will be greatly reduced if individuals exposed to doses of radiation refrain from begetting offspring for a period of two or three months following exposure. It should, however, be stressed that, according to the evidence available from experimental work, this practice would cause little or no reduction in the risk of transmitting gene mutations.

11.106 It may be stated, therefore, that many of the basic data necessary for a reliable estimate of the genetic effects of radiation in human populations have not yet been obtained. We are not yet able to calculate the exact magnitude of the risk. The specific practical recommendations have had to be limited to those which we know will reduce the risk. The extent to which these measures will reduce it, and the level to which it should be reduced, cannot be determined at the present time. It is obvious, therefore, that until more basic knowledge is available, exposure of personnel should be kept to a minimum.

11.107 Laboratories of the Atomic Energy Commission and of cooperating universities are vigorously pursuing research designed to supply some of the basic data required. The Atomic Bomb Casualty Commission is carrying out an extensive, long term, genetic study of survivors of the blasts at Hiroshima and Nagasaki. Large scale mouse genetics programs will supply reliable data on radiation-induced mutation rates and the frequency of semisterility due to chromosome aberrations following irradiation. Extensive genetic studies of Drosophila populations following acute and chronic exposure to radiation will supply information concerning the accumulation of lethal mutations in populations. Mutation rates and cytological effects of various types of radiation are being studied in several different species in an effort to gain better estimates of the genetic effects of radiation and to determine the mechanism by which the genetic effects are produced. As results of these and similar studies become available, more refined estimates of the human genetic risks may be made, but accurate estimates will not be possible until many more basic human genetics data are available.

CHAPTER XII[1]

PROTECTION OF PERSONNEL

A. INTRODUCTION

TYPES OF DAMAGE

12.1   In the preceding chapters of this book the destructive effects of an atomic bomb have been described and discussed.   These effects include damage due to air blast, ground and water shock, thermal radiation, initial nuclear radiations, and residual nuclear radiations. In addition, extensive fires, due to various secondary causes, will follow the atomic explosion.   Fortunately, the situation as regards protection from these hazards, although by no means simple, is not as complex as the existence of so many danger factors would imply. In general, it appears that proper protection against blast, shock and fire damage, could also minimize the danger to personnel from thermal radiation and the initial nuclear radiations.

12.2   As far as burning caused by thermal radiation is concerned, the essential points are protection from direct exposure for human beings and the avoidance of easily combustible materials, especially near windows.   The only known defense against the gamma rays and neutrons constituting the initial nuclear radiation is the interposition of a sufficient mass of material between the individual and the atomic bomb, including the rising ball of fire.   The use of concrete as a construction material, which is necessary to reduce air-blast and ground-shock damage, will, to a great extent, decrease the initial radiation hazard.

12.3   From the standpoint of physical damage, the problems of construction and protection from atomic bombs are not fundamentally different from those associated with bombs of the conventional type. It should not be forgotten, however, that the former are enormously more powerful, and the damage will cover an extensive area, probably several square miles (Fig. 12.3).   These facts are important in connection with planning for control of fire-fighting and rescue operations.

12.4   An attempt to indicate the magnitude of the consequences of the explosion of a nominal atomic bomb is illustrated in Figs. 12.4a,

1 Material contributed by E. A. Bemis, S. Glasstone, J. O. Hirschfelder, G. M. Lyon, S. B. Smith, W. E. Strope, D. W. Sweeney, T. N. White.

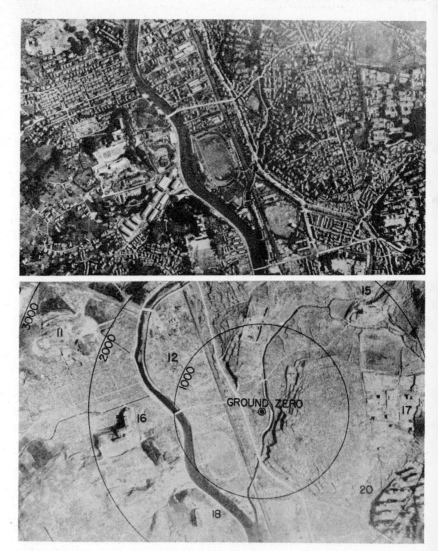

Figure 12.3.   Ground zero at Nagasaki before and after the atomic bomb
explosion; 1,000 feet circles are shown.

b, c, d, and e. These show a plan of a hypothetical city having
a water front, the areas over which various effects could be expected
being indicated.   In Fig. 12.4a, there are depicted the approximate
areas over which different degrees of damage might result from an air
burst of a bomb exploded at a height of 2,000 feet above the point,
near the center of the river, marked with a cross.   The hazards due

to the initial nuclear radiation and to thermal radiation of unprotected personnel, from the same burst, are represented in Figs. 12.4b and c, respectively.[2]   In the case of a detonation in the air at a fair

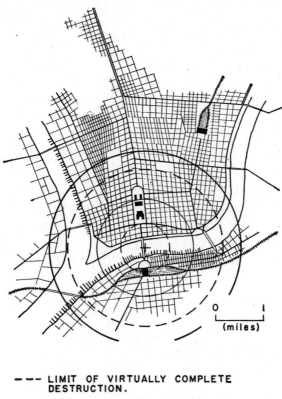

   O   I
    (miles)

— — LIMIT OF VIRTUALLY COMPLETE
      DESTRUCTION.
———— LIMIT OF SEVERE DAMAGE.
— — — LIMIT OF MODERATE DAMAGE.
———— LIMIT OF PARTIAL DAMAGE.

Figure 12.4a.   Hypothetical city showing approximate limits of damage due to
blast from an air burst.

height above the ground or water, the effect of the residual nuclear radiation, i. e., due to fission products or plutonium, will probably be completely negligible.

    12.5   In Figs. 12.4d and e are given the expected consequences of an underwater burst occurring in the water below the point indicated

---

[2] In Fig. 12.4c, the energies required to produce incendiary action and moderate skin burns are assumed
to be 10 and 3 cal. per sq. cm., respectively (§ 6.50); the distances apply to a clear day (Fig. 6.31).

by a cross. The former shows the areas of damage by air blast; these are seen to be much less than in Fig. 12.4a for an air burst, since only about one-fourth of the blast energy of the bomb exploded underwater is transmitted through the air. Damage to underwater structures, such as piers and ships will, of course, be more severe in the latter case. The effects of thermal and initial nuclear radiations can be ignored, but the fall-out and base surge will introduce a con-

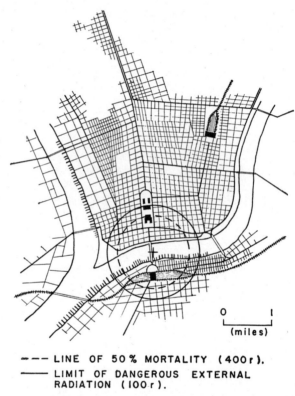

--- LINE OF 50% MORTALITY (400r).
—— LIMIT OF DANGEROUS EXTERNAL
RADIATION (100r).

Figure 12.4b. Hypothetical city showing approximate limits of initial nuclear radiation dosages due to an air burst.

siderable hazard, due to radioactive contamination, as indicated in Fig. 12.4e. In this case it is assumed that a wind of 5 miles per hour is blowing in the direction shown, so that the activity extends some distance downwind. For winds of higher velocity, the contamination would be carried still further.

12.6 It must be clearly understood, of course, that the diagrams merely represent an attempt to estimate a rough average, for the

actual effects of an atomic bomb will depend on many factors.   Among
these may be mentioned the height of burst and energy yield of the
bomb, the topography of the region, e. g., presence of rivers and hills,
and meteorological conditions.   All these may produce marked local
variations and will considerably distort the areas of damage.   Further,
it should be remembered that the results apply to the detonation of a

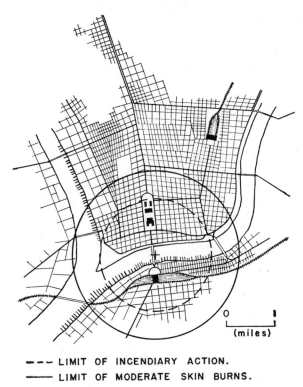

━ ━ ━ LIMIT OF INCENDIARY ACTION.

━━━ LIMIT OF MODERATE SKIN BURNS.

Figure 12.4c.   Hypothetical city showing approximate limits of effects of thermal
radiation from an air burst.

nominal atomic bomb of 20 kilotons TNT energy equivalent.   In
the event of a bomb of different energy being used the results would,
of course, be different.   Some idea of the changes can be obtained
by means of the various scaling laws which are summarized below in
Fig. 12.13.

RADIOLOGICAL EFFECTS

12.7   Protection from the effects of radioactive contamination
presents a problem that has not previously been encountered.   The

results of blast and fire are visible and can generally be controlled in a relatively short period following an explosion. But nuclear radiation cannot be detected by the senses, without the use of instru-

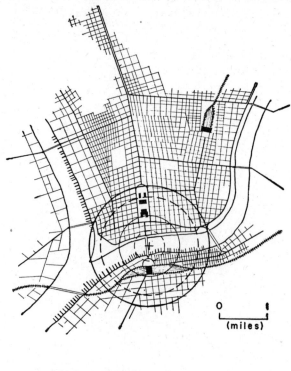

- - - LIMIT OF VIRTUALLY COMPLETE DESTRUCTION.
———— LIMIT OF SEVERE DAMAGE.
- - - LIMIT OF MODERATE DAMAGE.
———— LIMIT OF PARTIAL DAMAGE.

Figure 12.4d.   Hypothetical city showing approximate limits of damage due to air blast from an underwater burst.

ments, and, unless the contamination is removed, the deleterious effects may continue for weeks, months, or longer.

12.8   Even though the dangers from radioactivity following an atomic explosion are uncertain and perhaps exaggerated, nevertheless some consideration must be given to possible contamination of areas, structures, and equipment. Monitoring of regions close to, and especially downwind from, the explosion should be undertaken soon after the detonation for the guidance of fire fighters and rescue teams.

Subsequently, more detailed monitoring may be required to find which areas are safe for occupation. Some of the essential aspects of the decontamination problem were described in Chapter X, and it was mentioned that in some cases a preliminary washing-down treatment might be advisable. In this respect, fire and radioactive contamination may be combated simultaneously, although the fate of

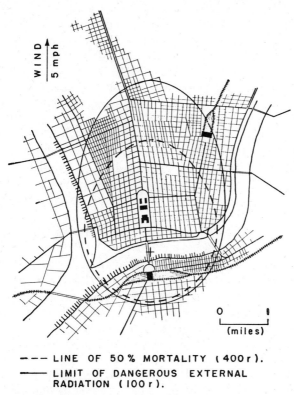

--- LINE OF 50% MORTALITY (400r).
——— LIMIT OF DANGEROUS EXTERNAL RADIATION (100r).

Figure 12.4e.   Hypothetical city showing approximate limits of residual radiation dosages from an underwater burst.

the water which runs away is important in the latter case. It should be emphasized that in the event of a high air burst, the radioactive contamination would be negligible (§ 11.2) and little or no risk would be involved in ignoring it completely.

General Considerations

12.9   Consideration of the more drastic measures which might be taken to minimize damage from atomic weapons, such as dispersion and underground construction, is beyond the scope of this book, but mention may be made of a number of steps which can be taken to reduce both the personal casualties and the physical damage effects of an atomic explosion. The essential purpose is to provide the basic data for the planning of protective and control measures, and many important factors, other than the direct effect of atomic weapons, are involved.

12.10 The planning of new construction affords the best opportunity for the inclusion of protective measures at minimum cost. But existing structures can in many cases, be strengthened so as to make them more resistant to blast, fire, and radiation, thus increasing the protection afforded to personnel and equipment. For example, blast damage can be reduced by strengthening structures, particularly against lateral and downward forces. It is desirable to keep to a minimum fixtures, ornamental plaster, or other interior treatments that might be dislodged when the buildings are subjected to violent forces. The fire hazard may be decreased by avoidance of exposed inflammable material; and general protection against gamma radiation can be achieved by a sufficient thickness of structural material.

12.11 In later sections of the present chapter various suggestions will be made in connection with the design of new structures and the improvement of those already in existence. Before proceeding with this discussion, however, a provisional answer, at least, must be given to an important question. In taking protective measures, how far away may it be supposed that the atomic explosion will occur? Of course, it is impossible to supply a definite answer, but a decision must be made as to the distance from the explosion at which protection becomes practical. Steps can then be taken to provide protection appropriate to this distance.

12.12 Obviously, a calculated risk is involved, for the bomb might explode in closer proximity, in which case the protection would be inadequate. The alternative would seem to be to make the structure so strong that it could withstand any atomic explosion directly overhead. Such an alternative imposes extreme requirements, including the elimination of glass in the construction, full dependence on artificial lighting and air-conditioning, and provision of independent power supply and many other disaster-proof facilities and services. Even if these requirements were met in one structure, they might be largely ineffective unless all surrounding structures were of the same type.

12.13 In making a decision concerning what might be termed the practical distance for protection from an atomic explosion, Fig. 12.13

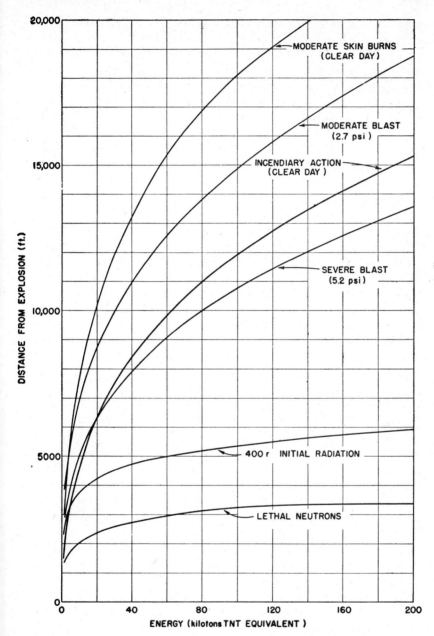

Figure 12.13.   Distances from explosion at which various effects are produced as function of bomb energy.

may be helpful. This shows the limiting distances [3] from the explosion at which atomic bombs of various TNT energy equivalents produce the indicated effects with respect to blast, initial gamma radiation, thermal radiation, and neutrons, respectively. In deriving these curves the various scaling laws given throughout the book have been used. It is seen that, as the energy of the bomb increases, the lethal ranges increase, at first, quite rapidly and then more slowly, in each case. The most economical scheme would perhaps be to try to develop protection that will be effective at the distance where the increased energy of the bomb results in a relatively small gain in the lethal range.

12.14 Taking various factors into consideration it seems that a distance of about half a mile from ground zero would be a reasonable compromise for the planning of general protective measures. The assumption is made that the bomb is exploded in the air at such a height as will provide maximum physical damage. It must be admitted that the choice of distance involves an element of risk, for there may be accidental or deliberate bursts of several bombs in close proximity at the same time. Further, there is a possibility that these bombs may have different energies and be detonated at different heights. Entirely different conditions would be produced in all these circumstances, and the problems of protection would not be the same. The combination of an atomic bomb with a radiological warfare weapon would, of course, add a further complication.

12.15 There is some justification for the choice of half a mile from ground zero, from a nominal atomic bomb, as the point from which protection should be considered. In the first place, the evidence from the Japanese bombings indicated that within this distance the chances of survival, due to one cause or another, were very poor. The percentage mortality as a function of distance from ground zero is shown in Fig. 12.15; [4] it is seen that it is only beyond 3,000 feet or so, that the proportion of persons killed begins to fall off at an appreciable rate. Suitable protective measures would result in an even sharper drop than that shown. Further, protection against blast, initial radiation, and thermal radiation becomes practical at a half mile from ground zero, while at closer distances it would not generally be feasible. In certain cases, however, stronger construction may be desirable on the grounds of the essential nature of the operations carried out in a particular building.

[3] The distances given as the ordinates are the actual distances from the exploding bomb; distances from ground zero will be somewhat less, depending on the height of burst. The curves for moderate skin burns and incendiary action are for energies of 3 and 10 cal. per sq. cm., respectively (§ 6.50).

[4] Adapted from "The Atomic Bombings of Hiroshima and Nagasaki," Manhattan Engineer District, 1946, p. 19.

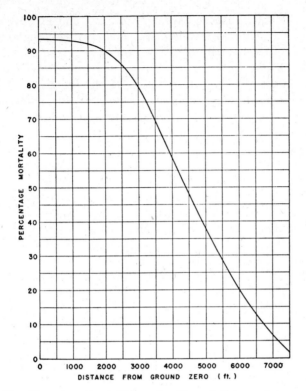

Figure 12.15.   Percentage mortality as function of distance from ground zero.

B.   PROTECTION AGAINST DAMAGE

DESIGN OF NEW CONSTRUCTION

12.16   If buildings must be constructed in possible target areas [5] for an atomic bomb attack, they should be designed so as to increase the safety of occupants and offer the greatest practical resistance to collapse and damage.   Any building to be constructed within three miles of a vital target should be considered as being within the target area, although the degree of protection aimed at in the design would be governed by the location of the building in the area.   In addition, consideration may be given to the importance, in the event of an emergency, of the industry or activity carried on in the building.

12.17   In order to provide a basis for design of a building, it may be assumed for the purposes of this discussion that the bomb will

[5] For a general consideration of target areas, see "National Security Factors in Industrial Location," National Security Resources Board.

explode over the probable target at an altitude of approximately 2,000 feet. The·distance, direction, and vertical angle from the proposed building site can then be determined. From the information in Chapter V the time-pressure curve may be developed for any reasonable shape, size, and orientation of the building. A study of the transient loads on proposed structures with different shapes should permit the selection of a design that will result in the minimum blast load on the structure consistent with other requirements connected with its use.

12.18   Given the time-pressure curves, it is necessary to consider how to design the structure and its component parts. It is possible to compute so-called equivalent static loads corresponding to the dynamic loads. These are the static loads that would produce the same elastic deflections or deformations as the dynamic loads being considered. Such equivalence is only valid, however, within an elastic limit. A structure designed to resist the blast pressures within the elastic limit, at about half a mile from the explosion of a nominal atomic bomb, is very much stronger than Japanese experience indicated to be necessary. There were no reinforced-concrete buildings of earthquake-resistant design in Nagasaki that suffered serious damage to the frame at distances of 2,000 feet or more from ground zero (Table 5.45). An approach to the problem of design might be to apply an experience factor based on observed damage to comparable buildings in Japan.

12.19   If it is assumed that some distortion of the building frame and elements is permissible for the time that it may be exposed to atomic blast, then plastic design offers another solution. First, the criteria must be established as to the amount of distortion of the frame and deflection of panels that may be accepted. The probability is that very little distortion of the frame is safe, but the dishing of panels would be permissible. The breakage of windows and destruction of light portions of structures must be accepted.

12.20   Having established limits, it will then be possible to analyze the building using the time-pressure curves to obtain the variation of the applied force with respect to time. Resisting such a force will be the mass of the building and its yield strength during the period of acceleration. When the applied force has dropped to the value of the yield strength there will be no further acceleration. Momentum will continue the motion until the building is brought to rest by the resisting force. The assumption here is that the building has one degree of freedom and that the elastic limit is exceeded in a very short time, so that elastic behavior plays little part in the distortion.

12.21   The great difficulty is that the yield strength of buildings subjected to dynamic loads in the plastic range is not known.   In view of this, there is little that can be done practically in the use of plastic design at present.   Considerable study is being given to the problem of resistance to large transient forces, but a great deal remains to be done before satisfactory design procedures can be established.

Tentative Design Suggestions

12.22   Until further information is forthcoming, some tentative design suggestions can be made; these are given below for structures of various types.   Before proceeding with the discussion, one point of general applicability should be emphasized.   The extensive use of bricks and other loose facings, or large amounts of glass would supply dangerous missiles to be thrown about by the blast and debris to block the streets at a critical time.

(a)   *Multistory Reinforced-Concrete or Steel-Frame Buildings.*[6]—The recommendations are based on the experience in Japan with buildings of this type, limited to 100 feet in height.   They may be open to question for various reasons but they are justifiable, at least, on the grounds that no better information is available. Wind load is believed to be the best basis for design to resist blast.   The design should allow for a horizontal wind component of 90 pounds per square foot, with a vertical component of 70 pounds per square foot, to provide protection against structural collapse at a distance of a half mile from an atomic burst.   The proposed horizontal wind component compares roughly with an earthquake-resistant design for a lateral force equal to 10 percent of the weight.   Since earthquake-resistant buildings in Nagasaki suffered no damage to the frame at distances of 2,000 feet, and beyond, from ground zero, this conclusion appears reasonable. The details and methods employed in wind- and earthquake-resistant design should be adopted for the building and its component parts, with allowable stresses increased by one-third to one-half.   For greater distances than half a mile from a probable target, the design pressures may be reduced in proportion to the expected reduction in peak pressure of the shock wave, allowing for the increased distance and the change in the vertical angle.

---

[6] Although concrete is an excellent structural material from several points of view, it should be remembered (cf. Chapter X) that porous concrete would be very difficult to decontaminate if it absorbed radioactivity from rain or mist (base surge).

(b) *Smaller Reinforced-Concrete Buildings.*—These should be designed for the pressures prescribed for multistory buildings as monolithic structures, employing principles of earthquake-resistant design.

(c) *Steel-Mill Buildings.*—The design specifications should be for a horizontal component of wind pressure of 90 pounds per square foot and vertical component of 70 pounds per square foot for resistance of the frame at a distance of one-half mile from the expected target. This assumes that failure of corrugated metal or asbestos-cement siding and roofing will reduce the load on the frame, thus compensating for the lighter weight. Use of a material such as asbestos cement, which will break up more readily than corrugated metal, will contribute to reduction in load on frames and reduce injuries and damage from pieces of siding or roofing striking occupants and equipment.

(d) *Bridges.*—Since most of the bridges exposed in Japan were small in size there is little indication as to what would happen to larger bridges of varying types that are found in the United States. It is recommended that large bridges be analyzed dynamically. For chord members or suspension cables drag force would receive primary consideration. The vertical component of blast on the deck could be serious, but bridges are designed for vertical load. Stressing of cross bracing beyond the elastic limit by the lateral component of the blast force would probably not be critical.

RIGIDITY, REDUNDANCY, AND DUCTILITY

12.23   It was shown in Chapter V that rigidity, redundancy, and ductility are factors which can affect the resistance of buildings to blast damage. It is now opportune to suggest how these may be incorporated into design methods so as to serve the required purpose. Stability is also a contributory factor, but in the usual case it will be less important than those mentioned above. However, the stresses produced by an overturning effect should be considered in all cases.

12.24   With regard to rigidity, it is believed that the general solution of the problem of design of a building to resist high lateral and downward pressures lies in the provision of additional resisting elements such as transverse shear walls, lateral beams and deep lateral trusses, and in the design of concrete floors and roofs to transmit the lateral forces to vertical shear walls. In bending due to frame action, the conventional use of columns as the resisting elements is unsatisfactory for high lateral forces. The establishment of design requirements for a static wind load is largely arbitrary, but is useful in providing a criterion to which design may be directed. It will be beneficial to include any design feature that will provide greater strength where cost is not materially increased. It will also be found that limiting the height of buildings is desirable in order to avoid high lateral stresses.

12.25 In the sense adopted here, redundancy is that quality of the structure that resists damage when certain members fail, by bringing into play other structural elements. Suppose, for example, that first-story columns were damaged by shearing action but that there were reinforced-concrete walls that would help support the load from above. The walls would be damaged too, but any contribution they made to the support of the second floor would help. In a Manila public building several columns in a row in the first story were destroyed by artillery fire; the second floor sagged slightly, but the damaged portion was bridged by the undamaged structure above. In general, reinforced concrete has this quality. No absolute guide can be laid down for design, but a study of probable points of failure, and possible support that might be afforded by adjacent portions of the building, will indicate to the designer what can be done in this respect.

12.26 Within the elastic limit, a ductile material would usually deform to a greater extent, under the same load, than one that is less ductile. In this sense the requirement for ductility is not consistent with rigidity; nevertheless, it is an important consideration in resisting collapse. When the elastic limit of a material such as steel is exceeded, considerable yield results before failure occurs. On the other hand, a brittle material such as concrete would yield to only a limited extent before failing.

12.27 Tests have shown that in this respect a structural or intermediate-grade steel is much better for reinforcement than a hard-grade steel. When a reinforced-concrete structure is subjected to heavy blast forces and damage occurs, the softer steel may elongate or deform without failure where the hard-grade steel snaps. More energy is absorbed in the plastic range by the structural or intermediate-grade steel. In the usual case such a selection will have little effect on rigidity.

ESSENTIAL INSTALLATIONS

12.28 Certain structures, which are concerned with essential industrial production or are used for important military purposes, will demand special treatment. Each of these installations may require individual consideration, with particular evaluation of strategic, tactical and logistic factors. In such cases, maximum protection may be required, regardless of the nearness of the burst, making complete underground placement desirable. However, this discussion is not intended to cover such situations.

12.29 There are apparently no fundamental difficulties in constructing and operating underground various types of important facilities. Such facilities may be placed in a suitable existing mine or a site may be excavated for the purpose.. The terrain should permit horizontal drift accesss with adequate protective cover, depending upon the importance of the facility and the expected type of attack.

HEAVY CONCRETE CONSTRUCTION

12.30 Military requirements may call for heavy concrete structures that will afford protection against direct hits of high-explosive bombs, and which will provide protection against the atomic bomb except at extremely close range. Such structures would be of little avail in an area where large-scale fires might occur which would render them untenable, or where they might become isolated by surrounding damage to communications. There seems to be little justification for such construction in a city, but it may be demanded for vital above-ground facilities in vulnerable areas.

REDUCING BLAST HAZARD IN EXISTING BUILDINGS

12.31 Aside from the question of the design of new construction considered above, there is the matter of making changes in existing buildings so as to reduce the hazard due to blast damage. This is a much more difficult problem than that of incorporating appropriate measures in new design. The most serious danger to persons and equipment in a building is from total collapse. It is necessary, therefore, to analyze the structure in order to find the weak points, and then to determine the best methods for strengthening them. It is believed that adding bracing and shoring or new transverse reinforced-concrete walls will, in general, be more feasible than strengthening the frame.

12.32 From an over-all point of view, an important consideration would appear to be to reduce the hazard to persons in buildings, which are able to resist collapse but which would probably be damaged to some extent. A well-attached, reinforced-concrete shell on a frame of either steel or reinforced concrete will provide a high degree of protection to persons both inside and outside the building. A lightly attached wall of concrete blocks or of bricks, on the other hand, would provide almost no protection inside the building and would supply missiles, both inside and outside the building.

12.33 In all circumstances, avoidance of danger from flying glass, displaced equipment, falling fixtures, false ceilings, etc., is· important. The great hazard due to glass should be considered in design, and glass areas should be provided only to the extent essential for the use of the building. Measures used in protection against flying glass caused by the explosion of conventional bombs, such as muslin glued or pasted over the surface of the glass and frame, would have little value, because the long duration of the blast from an atomic bomb would cause the glass to be blown out, in any event. Tentatively, wire glass plus half-inch-mesh wire screening securely nailed to the frame is suggested as a partial measure of protection. This would not cut off light appreciably and would stop the larger, more dangerous, pieces of flying glass. Another possible solution would be the use of plastic substitutes for glass.

12.34 Consideration should be given to the possible hazard from fixtures and heavier ornamental plaster or other interior treatment that might be thrown down by the blast or by the wracking action of the building. The safest procedure would be to remove any hazardous item. If this is not fully practicable, such partial safeguards should be provided as may be feasible. Overhanging cornices, finials, etc., on the outside of a building will be a hazard to passers-by, and their removal should be considered. The flying-missile hazard, however, is not peculiar to atomic weapons and the steps taken to reduce it are also of importance in case of conventional bombing.

12.35 Blast walls of the type provided to localize damage from ordinary bombs will be helpful in reducing injury from flying missiles and will afford some protection against atomic blast (Fig. 12.35a). Similarly, walls around essential equipment, such as transformers, will be effective in reducing damage (Fig. 12.35b). These walls should be of reinforced concrete 12 inches thick and should be made resistant to overturning.[7] This may be accomplished by use of counterforts, providing a wide base or, better, by use of steel beams incorporated into the wall and extending into the ground.

[7] Both concrete and earth-filled, wooden walls (Fig. 12.35c) were used in Japan for protection against blast. The former were more effective, but the latter, even though badly damaged by the atomic bomb explosions, did prevent serious damage to equipment.

Figure 12.35a. Precast, prismatic reinforced-concrete blast walls, 4,500 feet from ground zero.

Figure 12.35b. Reinforced-concrete blast walls protecting transformers, 5,400 feet from ground zero.

Figure 12.35c.   Earth-filled, wooden blast walls used to protect machinery, 4,600
feet from ground zero.

UNDERGROUND EXPLOSION

12.36   Should an atomic bomb be employed so as to produce an underground explosion, there would be almost complete destruction within the crater area.   Beyond that area, there would be earth-shock effects that are roughly comparable to those of an earthquake (see Chapters IV and V).   It appears, therefore, based on present information, that design for earthquake resistance is a requirement in probable target areas.   Such design should provide for a lateral loading of one-tenth the vertical load, which would be comparable with the wind load suggested in §12.22 for a multistory building to be resistant against air blast.   In this connection, while there would be some air blast in an underground explosion, it is not believed necessary to design for both earth shock and air blast as occurring simultaneously. Structures should be designed for the condition that is likely to cause most damage.

12.37   Houses should, in general, be reasonably resistant to earth shock from an underground explosion beyond the crater area, as these structures are relatively light.   Shifting of the house on its foundations would be likely, with overturning of piers in some cases.   Here also, the same design as for earthquake resistance should be considered if within 3 miles of any probable target.

12.38   The primary cause of damage to underground utility lines is differential earth displacement.   Sewers, especially those made of brick, large gas mains, and other shallow piping of low strength may also be damaged by the pressure from the explosion.   Primary consideration must be given to localizing damage by cut-out valves, loop systems, and protection against damage at points where differential displacement is likely to occur.

12.39   Tunnels and subways in earth would be seriously damaged by underground explosions if they are just outside the crater area, but might be quite resistant at greater distances, since they are generally designed to withstand heavy pressures.   An analysis of the time-pressure curves of the structures (see Chapter V) is recommended. Where below the water table, provision of mobile pumps to drain flooded sections might be indicated.   Consideration of means of limiting flooding by emergency gates would also be important where applicable.

UNDERWATER EXPLOSION

12.40   In the event of an underwater atomic explosion taking place close to the shore, the actual harbor works are expected to suffer some damage (§ 5.114).   The blast effect on shore installations, warehouses, etc., must, of course, be taken into consideration, but the problems are essentially the same as those for an air burst.

12.41   A special case would arise in the event of an underwater explosion which succeeded in breaching a hydraulic dam.   Apart from the associated damage to penstocks and valves, the large-scale flooding might cause great damage to industrial facilities downstream.   In designing a dam or assessing probable damage to an existing dam, the theoretical calculations in Chapter IV, although not exact, may act as a guide.

FIRE PROTECTION

12.42   As noted in Chapter VI, fires due to an atomic explosion are started by radiant heat (thermal radiation) and by secondary effects, such as overturning stoves and furnaces, rupture of gas pipes, etc. Fire-resistive construction and avoidance of fabrics and other light materials of inflammable character are essential to reduce fire damage. The methods of fire-resistive design of buildings and of city planning are well known and there is no need to repeat such information here.[8] A special requirement is the reduction of the chance of ignition by thermal radiation of combustible, especially black, material that might be exposed at windows and other openings. It has been recommended, in this connection, that all such openings be shielded from rays from all directions. Vital above-ground plants with combustible contents should be housed in structures without openings.

12.43 To judge from Japanese experience, it would appear that steel columns and other steel members should be protected from fire, for the distortion by heat of exposed structural steel frames was evident. Further, narrow firebreaks were found to be of little value, so that it should be borne in mind that such firebreaks as may be provided in city planning or by demolition must be adequate for a major conflagration. A minimum width of 100 feet has been suggested.

12.44 One of the most important lessons learned from the atomic bomb attacks on Japan is the necessity for the provision of an adequate water supply for the control of fires. In Nagasaki the water pressure was only 30 pounds per square inch at the time of the explosion and because of breaks in mains and house service lines it soon dropped to 10 pounds per square inch; on the following day the pressure was almost zero. This drop in the water pressure contributed greatly to the extensive destruction caused by fire. The experience at Hiroshima was quite similar.

12.45 A large proportion of the fire devastation in Japan after the atomic bomb attacks was due to the fact that the fire-fighting services were incapacitated (Fig. 12.45). It would seem to be advisable that fire departments of strategic cities and industrial plants should be housed in structures capable of withstanding the blast at about half a mile from the explosion. Underground construction or concrete walls 2 feet thick would provide this degree of blast protection.

C. ESSENTIAL DISASTER FACILITIES

CONTROL AND FIRST AID CENTERS

12.46 Facilities for the direction of disaster-relief activities and provision of first-aid in a city, require a protected area on one of the

---

[8] For a discussion of this and related matters, see "Fire and the Air War," edited by H. Bond, National Fire Protection Association, Boston, Mass., 1946.

lower floors of a well-constructed, fireproof, reinforced-concrete or steel-frame building. To avoid the hazard of a general conflagration, the building should not be situated among others that are not fireproof. The protection provided should be such as to assure reasonable safety against blast and radiation injury at a distance of roughly half a mile from an atomic explosion. A total thickness of about 2 feet

Figure 12.45. Fire station wrecked and its equipment rendered useless, 4,000 feet from ground zero.

of concrete would be required for this purpose as stated above, and in a concrete building this could probably be achieved by enclosing an area with a 12-inch reinforced-concrete wall anchored to the floor to prevent displacement, and braced or secured at the top to avoid overturning.

12.47 In order to satisfy the requirements of a control and first-aid room in an industrial plant, special construction may be necessary. In a steel-mill type of factory building, for example, where there is little external protection, the room should be of reinforced concrete 2 feet in thickness. Consideration in design should be given to possible debris load, blast pressure, and wracking action. In framed structures, the roof of the room should be designed for a static load of 500 pounds per square foot, although locations should be avoided where heavy debris loads might be encountered. The walls of the room should be designed for a similar load to protect against blast. Fillets at the corners, with diagonal bars to resist wracking action, are recommended. There should be no windows; and exit doors, of which there must be at least two, should be designed for the same pressure as the walls. Proper attention should be paid to ventilation requirements and to the necessity for emergency lighting in the event of a power failure.

12.48　Facilities required for rescue and damage control operations, in addition to the measures found necessary on the basis of World War II experience with conventional explosives, must be given special treatment in view of some of the novel effects of atomic weapons. The problem of radiological hazard control requires more elaborate facilities, and this hazard as well as the magnitude of the mechanical damage effects requires that careful consideration be given to the communications networks, probable need for duplicate facilities, special storage requirements, emergency medical services, evacuation procedures, and immediate debris clearance.

Shelters Inside Buildings

12.49　The problem of providing shelters inside buildings is a complex problem, but it is essentially the same for atomic as for TNT bombs. In brief, it may be stated that such shelters should be located in fireproof, reinforced-concrete or steel-frame buildings that are resistant to collapse. The areas chosen should be on the lower floors and in halls, or in the interior portions of the buildings, since these seem to offer the most reasonable possibilities for protection. Secondary hazards, such as those from falling plaster or fixtures, or from fire should, of course, be avoided.

12.50　With regard to details of protection, the data in Table 5.45 will indicate the shock pressures to be expected in the open at various distances from an atomic burst. The reduction in pressure that might occur inside a building must be largely an estimate, based on such factors as the amount of glass, which would be broken, and the strength of intervening partitions. A 12-inch reinforced-concrete wall, well tied into the structure would, especially in a concrete building, provide adequate protection against blast (§ 12.35) and nuclear radiation at distances over half a mile from ground zero.

12.51　In the case of a surface or sub-surface burst, dustborne radioactively contaminated particles might be widely dispersed by wind, and steps should be taken to reduce to a minimum the inhalation of dust. This would require shutting down the ventilating system and closing all windows and doors in case of an emergency. At distances beyond 12,000 feet from ground zero, many windows would not be broken in an atomic burst, and occupants could remain in buildings with reasonable safety until directed to leave. Provided there were no leakage from outside, air-conditioning systems could remain in operation with advantage.

Outside Shelters

12.52 Shelters outside of larger structures should, in general, be designed to resist the effects of blast and radiation from an atomic bomb at a reasonable distance, say one-half mile. They should be located well clear of buildings to avoid hazard from debris and fire. A buried or semiburied shelter will usually be the best choice for protection from an air burst, as the earth cover will act as a protection against radiation (Figs. 12.52a and b). In addition, blast effects will

Figure 12.52a.   Tunnel shelters in hillside, very close to ground zero in Nagasaki, protected the occupants from blast and from thermal and nuclear radiations.

be less than on a surface shelter. Such buried shelters would, of course, be useless in the event of a nearby underground detonation of an atomic bomb.

Figure 12.52b. Simple earth and pole shelter, undamaged by fire or blast at 5,000 feet from ground zero, although surrounding buildings were destroyed. (The debris was cleared from the roadway before the photograph was taken.)

12.53   The general aim in structural design of a shelter is to provide strength to resist blast and with sufficient cover to protect against the initial radiations from an atomic bomb.   Reinforced concrete is a good constructional material and can be made strong enough to resist the pressures involved.   Alternatively, corrugated sheet iron of the type used in culverts has strength and is capable of a high degree of distortion without failure.   Wood is also a suitable structural material, but it is less permanent.   In each case an adequate layer of soil or of sandbags would be necessary to make a total thickness equivalent to about 2 feet of concrete.

12.54   Tentatively, shelters may be designed for a static load of 500 pounds per square foot, with usual design stresses to provide an adequate factor of safety.   Additional allowance should be made for the dead load due to the earth cover, etc., and adequate drainage should be provided.   The survival of persons in shelters near ground zero in Japan shows that doors are not needed if a baffle or turn in the entrance shields from the direct heat rays of the bomb.   A ramp entrance is preferable to steps, and two means of exit are essential.

12.55   Although there would be little danger from airborne particles contaminated with radioactivity after a high burst, it might be advisable to construct shelters so that they would provide protection in case of surface or subsurface bursts, in which the spread of radiation through the air might be a hazard. Hence, special consideration should be given to the problem of insuring suitable ventilation for shelters.

12.56 The most effective method for providing adequate ventilation is to use a pressurized installation in which the air is forced through special air filters which will remove radioactively contaminated particles.[9] The practicability of such extreme measures, however, is open to question. Air-conditioning and cooling systems where provided can be left in operation for cooling and otherwise improving inside air conditions. The length of time that any structure under these conditions can be occupied without addition of fresh air will depend upon many factors, including the number of people inside, heat transmission through walls, removal of carbon dioxide, etc.

HOME SHELTERS

12.57 Basements of homes, especially if they extended beyond the main structure of the house, would offer reasonable protection against blast damage, provided they are not too near the center of the explosion. However, care must be taken to provide escapes to be used in case the house catches fire or collapses. A shallow rampart of soil or of sand bags outside the house would probably be advantageous. Semiburied shelters for individual families, of the type used in Europe during World War II, for protection against conventional bombs would also provide worthwhile protection against atomic explosions.

EMERGENCY SHELTER

12.58 The discussion of shelters, given above, has been based on the tacit assumption that there is sufficient warning of air attack to permit people to take shelter. In the event of a surprise atomic explosion, immediate action could mean the difference between life and death. The first indication of an unexpected atomic burst would be a sudden increase of the general illumination. It would then be imperative to avoid the instinctive tendency to look at the source of this light, but rather to do everything possible to cover all exposed parts of the body.

---

[9] The Chemical Warfare Service No. 6 Filter is satisfactory for handling large volumes of air.

12.59 If a person is in the open when the sudden illumination is apparent, then the best plan is instantaneously to drop to the ground, while curling up so as to shade the bare arms and hands, neck, and face with the clothed body. Although this will not protect against gamma rays, it may help in reducing flash burns (§ 6.53). This is important since disabling burns can be suffered well beyond the lethal range for gamma rays (Fig. 12.13). The curled-up position should be held for at least 10 seconds; the immediate danger is then over, and it is permissible to stand up and look around to see what action appears advisable.

12.60 If in the street, and some sort of protection, such as a doorway, a corner or a tree is within a step or two, then shelter may be taken there with the back to the light, and in a crouched position to provide maximum protection, as described above. No attempt should be made to reach a shelter if it is several steps off; the best plan then is to crouch on the ground, as if completely in the open. After 10 seconds, at least, a standing position may be resumed, but it is strongly advisable to press the body tightly against the side of a building to avoid breaking glass or falling missiles, as far as possible.

12.61 A person who is inside a building or home when a sudden atomic bomb attack occurs should drop to the floor, with the back to the window, or crawl behind or beneath a table, desk, counter, etc.; this will also provide a shield against splintered glass due to the blast wave. The latter may reach the building some time after the danger from radiation has passed, and so windows should be avoided for about a minute, since the shock wave continues for some time after the explosion. The safest places inside a building are the interior partitions, and it is desirable to keep as close to these as possible.

D. PROTECTION FROM RESIDUAL RADIATIONS

Introduction

12.62 As stated earlier, protection of large numbers of people from the effects of the residual nuclear radiations, that might follow the explosion of an atomic bomb, represents an entirely new problem concerning which there has been no previous experience. After the attacks on Japan the fission products were so widely dispersed as not to be an appreciable danger; at least, there is no evidence that such a hazard existed. In special circumstances, however, for example, an underwater burst close to the shore or an underground or surface burst, or in the event of the use of radiological warfare weapons, precautions would have to be taken against the residual radiations.   In the present section an outline will be given of the general lines of procedure that might be followed for radiological defense; in view of the lack of experience, these may be regarded as tentative and subject to improvement.

12.63   Since the possibility of combating radioactive contamination is bound up with the extent of the associated physical damage, it is desirable to make a rough classification of the possible combinations that might arise.   Three general types may be distinguished:

(a) *Heavy Physical Damage and Heavy Contamination.*—Such a condition might be due to a combination of an air-burst atomic bomb followed, or accompanied, by the use of a radiological weapon.   In view of the wasteful nature of such action, it may be regarded as not too probable, although it cannot be ignored. An underwater burst in a harbor of a large city, close to the shore, might cause both heavy damage and contamination over a limited area.   In this event, radiological safety measures might be delayed by the necessity of clearing away debris, establishing communications, etc.

(b) *Heavy Physical Damage and Light Contamination.*—This would arise from an atomic explosion of the type experienced at Hiroshima and Nagasaki.   The problem of protection against radioactivity would not be serious in this case.   It would be necessary for monitoring teams to follow the radioactive cloud downwind in case there were a marked fall-out in any particular area.   It is of almost equal importance to know definitely that there is no hazard.

(c) *Moderate or Little Physical Damage and Moderate to Heavy Contamination.*—Such circumstances could arise from a radiological warfare attack, from dry or wet fall-out, from base surge on a ship or on shore at some distance from an underwater explosion, or from an ineffective ("fizzle") explosion of an atomic bomb. The radioactive protection would be of the greatest significance, and to meet these conditions the radiological defense system must be especially prepared.

STAGES OF DISASTER

12.64   In considering the practical problems of a radiological hazard it may be supposed that there will be three stages, the duration and severity of which will depend on circumstances described above. These are as follows:

(a) *Complete Disorganization.*—In the event of heavy and widespread physical damage, it may be presumed that roads will be blocked for some distance from the explosion, and that all normal communication systems will be out of commission. Emergency transportation and communication, except perhaps for self-contained radio equipment, will not be immediately in effect.

(b) *Emergency Control Stage.*—This phase will begin as soon as margin roads have been cleared, and transportation and communication has been reestablished, at least on an emergency scale, so that information can be transmitted to a control room. In the case of moderate physical disaster (§ 12.63 (c)), the emergency control phase would start immediately, and might last a week or more.

(c) *Recovery Stage.*—The final phase would be reached when most people were out of immediate danger of injury, and there is time to start more thorough decontamination operations where necessary (Chapter X).

12.65   In the emergency control phase, an important factor in the operation of radiological defense is the rapid gathering of data regarding contamination. The radiations which may be encountered are gamma rays and beta particles from fission products, neutron-induced activity or other radioactive material, and alpha particles from plutonium or uranium. Of these, the gamma radiation can be measured most readily; this is perhaps the greatest immediate hazard because of its considerable penetrating power. Beta particles as such are not a serious menace unless the source enters the system or remains on the skin for some time.

12.66   Monitoring of suspected contaminated areas for gamma radiation should be carried out at the earliest possible moment after an atomic explosion in which such contamination is likely to have been produced. Initially, this might even be done by means of low-flying aircraft; from the gamma radiation dosage measured at a known height above the ground it will be possible to obtain an approximate indication of the area and intensity of contamination (see Fig. 8.35). However, ground monitoring for gamma radiation, with portable instruments, will be necessary at the first opportunity. The monitoring for beta radiation will, in general, be an auxiliary measurement, made in the later stages after the immediate emergency has passed.

12.67   It was pointed out in Chapter XI that while the danger
from external beta and gamma radiation might exist, the hazard due
to alpha particles, from plutonium or uranium, can be ignored.   This
is fortunate, for measurement of alpha contamination is a laborious
and time-consuming process.   The detection of surface contamination
by a source of alpha particles requires that the instrument be held
very close to the suspected surface on account of the short range of the
particles.   In any event, the measurement would be extremely
difficult, with portable instruments, in the presence of high concentrations of beta and gamma activity.

12.68   Because the specific danger from alpha particles will not
arise for some weeks, search for alpha emitters is probably best
carried out by taking samples to a laboratory for testing.   The amount
of alpha active material suspended in the air can be estimated re-
liably only by collecting the active material from a large sample of
air, using a suitable filtering device (Fig. 9.24b) and then measuring
the activity of the deposit on the filter.

PERMISSIBLE RADIATION LEVELS

12.69   The question of the amount of exposure to the residual
nuclear radiation that is permissible for control and rescue personnel
is one which is very difficult to answer exactly, for a good deal will
depend on circumstances and the risks which must inevitably be taken.
In the initial disorganization phase, when the radioactivity is also
most intense, it will be important for emergency personnel to avoid
overexposure to radiation except where it is necessary to carry out
missions of the greatest importance.

12.70   It may be noted in this connection, however, that because of
the rapid initial decay of the fission products, a person who is exposed
to the radiation from this mixture for the first hour following an
explosion will not suffer any further appreciable injury by staying for
several hours more.   A situation of this kind might arise due to the
immediate fall-out from an underground or an underwater burst.

12.71   During the emergency control phase the radiological
defense system should be fully operable.   As indicated above, estimates of contamination will be based largely on measurement of
gamma activity.   Every effort should be made to minimize the dose
received by the general population.   If contamination is due to
fission products, the actual value will be somewhat higher at the
beginning and lower at the end of the period.

12.72 In the recovery stage, the main objective would be to achieve as effective decontamination as possible so as to reduce the general contamination level to that permitted for routine workers with radioactive material, e. g., 0.3 r per week (§ 8.4). Although there is not complete agreement on the subject, because of the lack of adequate knowledge, the information given in Table 12.72 may

TABLE 12.72

PERMISSIBLE CONTAMINATION

Contaminated material	Fission product	Alpha-emitter
Air	2×10^{-10} microeurie/cc	2.5×10^{-11} microgram/cc.
Water	4×10^{-6} microcurie/cc	2×10^{-5} microgram/cc.

be taken as indicating a few approximate permissible contamination levels for continued exposure. It is assumed that plutonium is the alpha emitter, since this is probably the most dangerous of those likely to be encountered.

12.73 It should be noted that the figures given in the table refer to permissible levels for personnel exposed to radiation every day, as a result of their peacetime occupation.

12.74 With regard to the internal radiation hazard, it is not possible to make any sound estimate of the amount of material which is likely to be ingested in various circumstances. A person working under normal indoor conditions, for example, would absorb much less than one engaged in an occupation in which there was much dust. Children, because of their habits and closeness to the ground, would be expected to ingest more than adults. These factors would greatly complicate a rehabilitation program, and make it almost impossible to attempt to assess universal permissible contamination levels.

MONITORING EQUIPMENT

12.75 All emergency workers, no matter what their duties, who are sent into areas contaminated with beta or gamma radiation, should be provided with, or closely accompanied by, instruments for personnel monitoring (see Chapter IX). During the disorganization phase and for part, at least, of the emergency control phase, these would have to be of the self-reading, pocket dosimeter type. Instruments of various total ranges, in roentgens, are available, and it would be necessary to use the particular range appropriate to the work to be undertaken. Provision must be made for recharging the dosimeters after each period of use, for otherwise they would be valueless.

12.76   Because of the high cost of the self-reading instruments, their number would presumably be limited, so that only one might have to be supplied to a group operating in close proximity.   With improving transportation, communication, and control, the pocket chambers, which require to be read by an electrometer device, could be used. The combined charger and reader could be available on a rescue truck or other similar vehicle.   The film badge is the simplest and cheapest of personnel-monitoring devices, but its disadvantage lies, as stated in Chapter IX, in the fact that time is required to collect, develop, and interpret the films.   This handicap might be overcome by the use of a transportable photographic laboratory with relatively simple equipment.

12.77   Some indication of the time which emergency workers could spend in a particular location in a contaminated area can be obtained from Fig. 12.77,[10] which gives the total accumulated dosage for various times spent in a contaminated area, divided by the dosage rate at the time of entry.   By taking a reading of the dosage rate in roentgens per hour at the time of entering a contaminated area, the total dosage acquired during any subsequent interval can be determined.   For example, if a person enters the area at 1.5 hour after the explosion and the dosage rate is found to be 15 r per hour, then if he stays for 2 hours the total dosage will be the ordinate, corresponding to the abscissa of 1.5 hour and the parameter 2 hours, multiplied by 15, i. e., $1.2 \times 15 = 18$ r.

12.78   Survey instruments (see Chapter IX) carried by teams operating during the first two phases should be of the area survey type for gamma radiation.   They should be able to measure at least 5 r per hour, and a certain number should be capable of responding to beta, as well as to gamma, radiation, as they will be required at a later stage.   Alpha-beta-gamma survey meters, reading up to 25 r per hour, will be useful in the emergency control stage if there are insufficient beta-gamma survey meters available.   However, as stated previously, it is important that no time should be wasted in a search for alpha radiation in the early stages.   This work should be left until considerably later, and is best carried out in the laboratory.   Where aerial monitoring is undertaken and measurements are made at some distance above the earth's surface, sensitive gamma-ray meters would be required.

---

[10] The difference between Fig. 12.77 and Figs. 10.21a and b lies in the fact that the former requires a measurement of the dosage rate to be made at the time operation in an area is started; for the latter, the measurement can be made at any time.

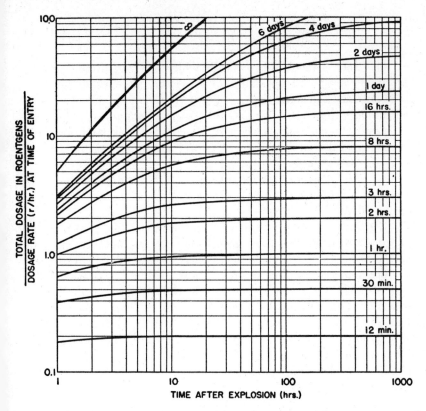

Figure 12.77. Determination of total radiation dosage received in a contaminated area.

Protective Clothing

12.79 Personnel entering a contaminated area, whether to perform monitoring or other emergency work, should wear protective clothing of some kind. Actually ordinary clothing is adequate protection against alpha and beta radiation, but since it is likely to become contaminated it would have to be destroyed. It is preferable, therefore, to make use of relatively cheap coveralls, worn over the clothing. These could be washed if not too badly contaminated, or discarded altogether. Smocks, made of fabric or plastic, which protect a large part of the clothing, while not so effective as coveralls, will have some value. As a general rule, rubber suits will not be necessary for work in a contaminated area. But if there is any chance of the clothing becoming wet, either in a washing-down operation or in any other way, such suits, which cover the whole body, should be provided (see Fig. 10.39). They can be cleaned with a stream of water and used several times.

12.80   Booties made of canvas and which slip over the shoes, should always be worn in a contaminated area; the bottoms of the trouser legs should be tied over the outside of the booties. Gloves of some kind should also be provided. Ordinary cotton gloves will afford good protection in most cases, although surgeons' gloves, made of rubber, may be preferable in some cases. Hard leather gloves should be used when rough handling is involved as, for example, when digging in rubble. Some sort of tight-fitting cap, preferably of the type used by surgeons, covering the hair as completely as possible, should be worn at all times.

12.81   Soon after an atomic explosion there is likely to be a large amount of dust in the air, especially in the regions of appreciable destruction. As stated in § 12.55, there is practically no danger in this dust being contaminated after a high air burst. However, other types of deliveries could spread radioactivity on the ground. Consequently, all members of emergency teams entering a contaminated area should wear respirators. Masks covering the nose and mouth, of the type developed as a protection against chemical warfare agents, have been found to be satisfactory in preventing the inhalation of dust particles. Where the amount of dust is very large, it might be necessary to use a respirator hood to give complete protection of the head.

E.   CONCLUSION

12.82   It will be evident from the material presented in this chapter that adequate protection against the effects of an atomic bomb attack will require very comprehensive and detailed planning. Such planning will be necessary to avoid panic, for mass hysteria could convert a minor incident into a major disaster. It has been the purpose of this book to provide the essential scientific and technical information that will permit the necessary plans to be made for dealing with the new and unusual situations that would arise as the result of the explosion of an atomic bomb. The organization, preparation, and techniques designed to deal with these situations involve considerations beyond the scope of this book. Their precise nature depends upon many factors which must be evaluated nationally, and their application will vary with the patterns of regional and community development.

APPENDIX A[1]

AN APPROXIMATE METHOD OF COMPUTING THE DEFORMATION OF A STRUCTURE BY A BLAST WAVE

A.1   The method to be described is applicable in the case where the magnitude of the forces exerted by the blast is large in relation to the static strength of the structure.   Assume that an analysis of the diffraction of the blast wave by the structure has been made according to the approximate methods given in Chapter V and that the resulting force on the structure as a whole divided by the area of the front face can be represented by an equivalent pressure-time curve as in Fig. A.1a.   The resistance of an actual structure of simple form to such a

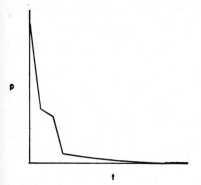

Figure A.1a.   Pressure-time curve
for force on structure

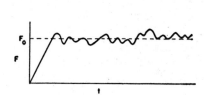

Figure A.1b.   Failure of structure
beyond elastic limit.

pressure-time curve will first increase until the elastic limit is passed, after which progressive failure will occur in a manner that is not well established but may be somewhat as represented in Fig. A.1b.   If it is assumed that the absorption of energy and the deflection during the elastic loading phase is small compared to the deflection and energy absorption during the plastic phase, then the average resistance during the deformation can be assumed to be essentially ·constant and equal to F_0, which is the total lateral force just causing failure.

[1] By C. W. Lampson and S. B. Smith,

A.2   If the structure under consideration is of the simple single-story type, such as may be encountered in a powerhouse or similar building, then as a first approximation its behavior as a whole, neglecting detailed failures, may be represented by a model consisting of a single concentrated mass supported on a plastic spring as in Fig. A.2.   If the

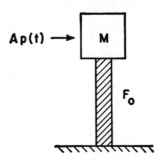

Figure A.2.   Mass supported on plastic spring equivalent to single-story structure.

plastic spring has a resisting force independent of deflection and rate of loading, the equation of motion of the structure may be written as

$$M\frac{d^2x}{dt^2}+F_0=Ap(t),\qquad\qquad\text{(A.2.1)}$$

where M is the mass of the structure, i. e., w/g, F_0 is the resisting force of the structure, x is the deformation of the center of mass, A is the area of the front face, and $p(t)$ is the effective blast pressure acting on the structure as a function of time.

A.3   The first integral of the equation may be written as

$$v=\frac{1}{M}\int_0^t [Ap(t)-F_0]dt.\qquad\qquad\text{(A.3.1)}$$

This equation, which gives the velocity v as a function of time, can be integrated graphically if the constant resisting force F_0 is superimposed on the force-time curve shown in Fig. A.3.   The structure receives an impulse during the time (0 to t_1) which it then dissipates during the time (t_1 to t_2) so that at the time (t_2) the structure is brought to rest. The shaded area above the line F_0, between 0 and t_1, is equal to the area below the line between t_1 and t_2, so that the positive and negative impulses are made equal.

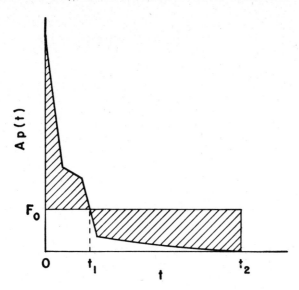

Figure A.3.   Force on structure as function of time.

A.4   The velocity at time t_1 is then equal to

$$v_1 = \frac{1}{M} \int_0^{t_1} [Ap(t) - F_0]dt, \qquad \text{(A.4.1)}$$

which is proportional to the area under the curve between 0 and t_1. The velocity at a time subsequent to t_1 will be

$$v = v_1 - \frac{1}{M} \int_{t_1}^t [F_0 - Ap(t)]dt. \qquad \text{(A.4.2)}$$

A graphical integration of the quantity of $\frac{1}{M}[Ap(t) - F_0]$ as a function of time will result in a graph of velocity as a function of time similar to Fig. A.4.

A.5   A graphical integration of the velocity as a function of time will give the displacement of the center of mass of the structure as in Fig. A.5.   The maximum value of the displacement x_m will be the quantity of interest indicative of the deformation and, consequently, of the degree of damage suffered by the structure.

A.6   This general method is applied to a building of the exterior dimensions discussed in Chapter V but at a slightly increased distance

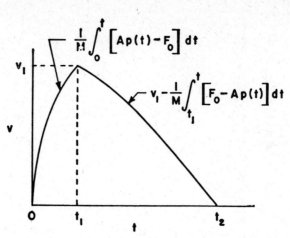

Figure A.4. Velocity of structure as function of time.

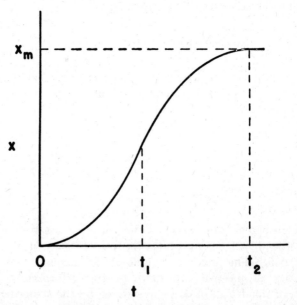

Figure A.5. Displacement of center of mass as function of time.

so that the pressure-time curve is as shown in Fig. A.6.   The characteristics of the building are as follows:

Dimensions_____ 75 ft.×75 ft.
Height_____ 38 ft.
Frame_____ Reinforced concrete.
Design_____ Earthquake resistant for 10 percent vertical
                       load.
Weight_____ 2,100,000 pounds.

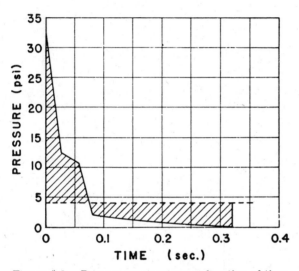

Figure A.6.   Pressure on structure as function of time.

The resisting force of such a structure is assumed to be constant and is estimated by a tentative rough calculation to have a value of 1,640,000 pounds, which is approximately 4 pounds per square inch of frontal area.

A.7   The assumed constant resisting force is shown in Fig. A.6 at the proper level, and a graphical integration gives the momentum of the structure per unit frontal area.   These values of momentum are divided by the mass of the structure per unit frontal area, i. e., 0.16 slug per square inch, giving the velocity of the center of mass of the structure in feet per second as plotted in Fig. A.7.

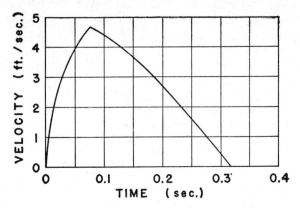

Figure A.7. Velocity of center of mass as function of time.

A.8 A graphical integration of the velocities in Fig. A.7 will give the displacement of the center of gravity of the structure, since

$$x_m = \int_0^{t_2} v\,dt. \qquad\qquad (A.8.1)$$

The maximum value of the displacement x_m of the center of gravity of the building is found to be 0.88 foot (Fig. A.8). If the center of

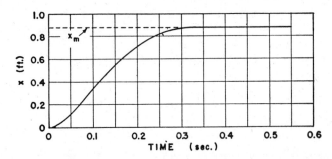

Figure A.8. Displacement of center of mass as function of time.

gravity were at the center of the building then the displacement at the top would be approximately 1.76 feet. This rough calculation is of limited practical value but is illustrative of the methods involved in the analysis of a model involving plastic flow.

A.9 A more precise procedure applicable to a complex structure, such as a multistory building, would be to consider the dynamic loads as applied at floor levels and the masses to be concentrated at the same points. The forces resisting shear in each story would be calculated in terms of relative displacements of the floor above and below. The structure then is represented by a model as in Fig. A.9, where

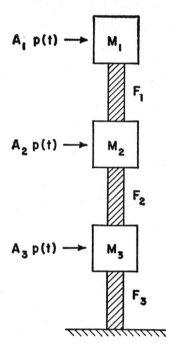

Figure A.9. Masses supported on plastic springs equivalent to multistory structure.

M_1, M_2, and M_3 are the concentrated masses of each floor while F_1, F_2, and F_3 are the constant plastic resisting forces acting between each floor. $A_1p(t)$, $A_2p(t)$, and $A_3p(t)$ are the proportioned blast loading forces applied to each story.

A.10 Such a model requires a more complex set of coupling coefficients as is evident from an inspection of Fig. A.9, since the motion of mass M_2, for example, is affected by the motion of masses M_1 and M_3, as well as by the resistance forces F_1 and F_2, and by the value of $A_2p(t)$, which is the direct force acting on the mass M_2. The forces resisting shear in each story could be calculated in terms of the relative displacement of the floor above and below. If such resisting forces could be considered as plastic yielding resistances of constant value for a first approximation, it would then be possible to calculate roughly the behavior of each floor. In each case the floor above would tend to be displaced at a faster or slower rate than the one immediately below it, and would accelerate or retard the motions of the lower floor, and vice versa. Thus, it will be seen that the behavior of each independently considered portion of the structure would be affected by the behavior of that above and below it. After a first approximation the general behavior would be evident. In a well-designed building it is probable that the relative displacement of each floor might be of the same order.

A.11   The constancy of the resisting forces is, of course, only a first approximation to the actual force which may be a complicated function of displacement as shown in Fig. A.11. In this case the solution

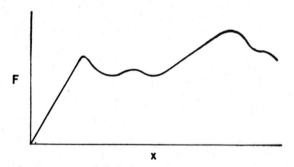

Figure A.11.   Force on multistory structure as function of displacement.

of the problem of the single mass and resisting force is more complicated, since the equation to be solved now becomes

$$M \frac{d^2x}{dt^2} + F(x) = F(t). \tag{A.11.1}$$

An equation of this sort may be solved by straightforward but laborious methods of numerical integration which give the deflection as a function of time; alternatively, a solution can be attempted by taking the value of $F(x)$ to be constant and obtaining by graphical means the deflection as a function of time. This solution can be applied to $F(x)$ to give a first approximation to a value of $F(t)$. This procedure can be repeated to give a better solution provided the functions are of such form as to render the process convergent.

A.12   The solution can be carried out in the same manner as indicated above, except that F is no longer a constant but might be something similar to Fig. A.12a. In this case the superposition of the $Ap(t)$ curve as a function of time (Fig. A.12b) would allow a graphical integration of the differences between the functions; this would give the momentum as a function of time and so would allow the maximum deflection to be computed in the same manner as before.

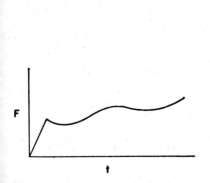

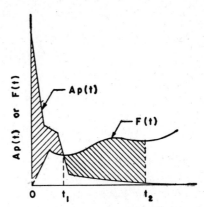

Figure A.12a.   Force as function of time.

Figure A.12b.   Pressure and force as functions of time.

APPENDIX B [1]

UNDERGROUND EXPLOSIONS

PROPAGATION OF THE PRESSURE WAVE FROM AN EXPLOSION

B.1   In the vicinity of the high-pressure gas bubble (§ 4.86), earth acts as a nonlinear plastic medium; this means that Hooke's law of proportionality between stress and strain is not obeyed and that the strains are related in some more complex way to the stresses.   This characteristic of earth as a medium for the transmission of pressure waves is illustrated in Fig. B.1 which shows an experimentally ob-

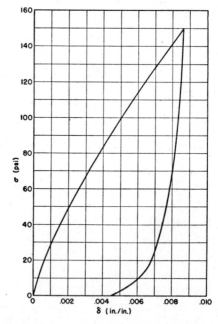

Figure B.1.   Experimental dynamic stress-strain curves for free earth (clay silt).

tained dynamic stress-strain curve for a certain variety of silty-clay soil found in Oklahoma.

---

[1] By C. W. Lampson.

410

B.2   The net effect of the plastic behavior of the medium is to cause a pronounced distortion of the pressure wave as it is propagated away from the explosion (see Fig. B.2).   From the theory of wave

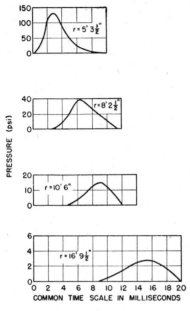

Figure B.2.   Pressure-time curves at various distances from 64 pound **TNT** charge in earth.

propagation in solids, it is known that the velocity of an incremental pressure difference is proportional to the square root of the slope of the position it would occupy on the stress-strain curve.   Hence, it can be readily seen, by inspection of Fig. B.1, that the velocity of the peak of the wave will be less than that of the initial part of the wave. The greater slope of the unloading portions of the stress-strain curve, except at very low pressures, indicates that the rear of the wave has a higher velocity than the front.

B.3   The effect of these properties of the stress-strain curve is that the wave suffers a continual change of shape in the rear as well as in front.   The peak is simultaneously retarded with respect to the front of the wave and eaten away by the more rapid rarefaction part following it.   The low speed of the tail of the wave results in an over-all spreading out of the wave in space and time in addition to these other changes.

B.4   When the radial pressure waves from a buried charge meet the surface of the earth, they are reflected with a reversal of phase. In practice, the wave is so spread out in time and space that the reflection is progressive, and the reflected part subtracts from the compression wave below it to produce an increase of attenuation of the pressure with distance near the surface, rather than a clean-cut incident and reflected wave.   The boundary conditions at the surface require the existence of an auxiliary set of surface waves of which the Rayleigh waves are a special case.   These waves travel at a lower speed and with less attenuation than the direct compressional waves and are responsible for the majority of surface effects at remote distances from the explosion.   The magnitude of these effects from explosives of normal sizes is small enough, so that their behavior is only of theoretical interest from a damage viewpoint, but this is no longer true when explosions of the magnitude of the atomic bomb are considered.

Effect of Soil Characteristics

B.5   The magnitude of the transmitted pressure wave from an explosive charge is profoundly influenced by the properties of the soil through which it passes.   Certain soils, such as wet clay, are very good transmitters of pressure, while other soils, such as silty loam and loess, are very poor in this respect.   The ratio of transmissibilities between the two extremes may be as large as 100 to 1.   This large ratio does not mean that the radii of damage from explosive charges in soil are in these ratios but, as will be shown later, these radii will have a maximum ratio of approximately 2 or 3 to 1.   The transmissibility of a soil is expressed quantitatively by a number, called the soil constant k, which is correlated roughly with the initial slope of the stress-strain curve; this is ordinarily called the initial modulus of elasticity, although the material is plastic rather than elastic.   The magnitudes of other phenomena in the medium, such as particle velocity, acceleration, transient motion, and impulse, are found to be proportional to some function of this soil constant, which thus turns out to be the quantity that is most descriptive of the propagation qualities of the soil.

B.6   Referring to Fig. B.1, which is the stress-strain curve for a typical soil, two facts, readily verified by experiment, can be deduced. These are: (1) the finite area enclosed by the stress-strain loop implies that considerable energy is dissipated per unit volume of material so that the waves must be rather rapidly attenuated, and (2) the displacement of the point of intersection of the unloading curve with the abscissa of the graph implies that the medium is left with a permanent strain or displacement after the passage of the wave. If the material were elastic, the peak pressure would decrease as the inverse distance; experimentally it is found that in earth, near the charge, the permanent displacement and the peak pressure decrease in magnitude approximately as the inverse cube of the distance from the charge, indicating that the rate of energy dissipation in earth is very large.

B.7   The magnitudes of pressure, acceleration, and transient displacement near the crater may be very large. For example, in a typical silty-clay soil and for an atomic bomb, the peak pressure near the edge of the crater may be 1,000 pounds per square inch, while the acceleration is about 60 times the acceleration of gravity and the transient displacement may be nearly 100 feet. No information exists as to the magnitudes of these quantities in the crater region since normally everything is destroyed, including all measuring equipment that may be placed there.

VARIATION OF PEAK PRESSURE IN FREE EARTH

B.8   The pressure in earth resulting from the detonation of an explosive charge on or below the surface, is propagated as a wave that is characterized by a continuous change of shape, amplitude, and length with distance from the source. This change of amplitude and shape is a consequence of the spherical divergence of the wave and of the character of the stress-strain relation of the medium which causes the higher pressure levels to be propagated more slowly than the low-pressure levels. The magnitude of the peak pressure of the wave is determined essentially by five factors: (1) the distance from the charge; (2) the character of the soil; (3) the coupling of the explosive energy to the soil, i. e., depth of burial of charge; (4) the amount and kind of explosive; and (5) the depth of measurement.

B.9   The general equation that is found to fit all the results obtained in the range of distances $2 \leq \lambda \leq 15$ is

$$p = FEk\lambda^{-n},$$

(B. 9.1)

where p is the peak pressure in pounds per square inch, λ is equal to $r/W^{\frac{1}{3}}$, i. e., the distance in feet divided by the cube root of the weight of explosive charge in pounds, k is the constant characteristic of the soil, F is a coupling factor related to the depth of burial of the charge,

E is an energy factor which depends on the type of explosive, and n is an exponent whose value is determined by the depth of charge or gauge.

B.10   The normal value of the exponent n is 3, except for depths of charge or gauge less than a critical value of approximately $\frac{3}{2} W^{1/3}$ feet. At depths less than this, the exponent approaches the value 4. The cause of the apparent increased attenuation near the surface is not very well understood, but it may be due to surface yielding or to a reflection of the pressure wave from the surface in the opposite phase with a consequent reduction of the pressure level as the distance from the charge increases. The value of 3 for n at depths greater than critical is well established by several series of tests in different types of soil.

B.11   The explosive factor E varies over a range of 1 to 1.4 for ordinary explosive. It is taken as unity for the present discussion. The coupling factor F is a function of the depth of burial of the charge and is shown in Fig. B.11 with the abscissa in units of depth (ft.)/$W^{1/3}$

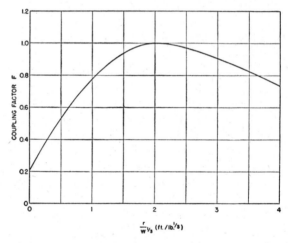

Figure B.11.   Coupling factor as function of charge depth/(charge weight)$^{1/3}$.

(lb.). This experimentally determined curve has a maximum value at a depth of burial corresponding to $r/W^{1/3}=2$, and falls off rather rapidly at smaller depths and rather slowly at greater depths. The reason for the lower value at the more shallow depths is due apparently to the escape of gases before the material of the medium near the explosion has reached the limit of its outward expansion. The fall off at the greater depths of burial is thought to be due to a reflection from the surface which probably would not be evident were the pressure also to be measured at greater depths. The most striking feature is the nearly linear rate of decrease at depths less than the critical depth of $\frac{3}{4}\ W^{\frac{1}{3}}$ feet and the relative constancy at greater depths.

B.12   For charges of TNT buried at depths of approximately $2\ W^{\frac{1}{3}}$ feet and with pressure gauges at a depth greater than $\frac{3}{2}\ W^{\frac{1}{3}}$ feet, the equation for pressure as a function of distance reduces to

$$p = k\lambda^{-3}. \qquad\qquad\qquad\text{(B.12.1)}$$

This simple form of the empirical equation for variation of pressure with distance allows the transmission characteristics of the soil to be expressed by a single parameter k, i. e., the soil constant. If λ is taken as a dimensionless variable, then k has the dimensions of a modulus of elasticity whose range of values represents the variation in the soil if the same energy per pound of explosive is released at every shot. The constancy of energy release is verified by other explosive tests. A systematic variation of k with the weight of explosive charge would be evidence of a scale effect.   No such variation is detected in any of the data.

B.13   The soil constant may vary by a factor of more than 100 depending on the type and condition of the soil, whereas the coupling factor does not show a range of variation exceeding about 7 to 1. This indicates that the type of soil is the most important single variable governing the transmission of pressure.   Table B.13 shows the range

TABLE B.13

SOIL CONSTANTS FOR PRESSURE AS A FUNCTION OF SOIL TYPE AND LOCATION

Soil type	Location	k (min.)	k (max.)	k (av.)
Loess	Natchez, Miss	400	1, 700	800
Clay silt (loam)	Princeton, N. J	1, 300	2, 500	2, 000
Silty clay	Camp Gruber, Okla	1, 300	9, 000	5, 100
Clay, unsaturated	Houston, Tex	10, 000	20, 000	15, 000
Clay, saturated	do	50, 000	150, 000	100, 000

of values of k encountered in different types of soil.   The general variability to be expected in soils can be seen from the range of the maximum and minimum values of k given in the table for each soil type.   This range is due largely to differences in the moisture content which varies in a somewhat unpredictable manner.   In some localities, the soil constant varies rapidly with depth, a situation which seems to accompany a shallow water-table.

B.14   A rough correlation exists between the soil constant k and the velocity of propagation of low amplitude seismic waves in the material.   The velocity of the low amplitude waves is associated with the initial slope of the stress-strain curve and is to be distinguished from the velocity of the peak of a finite wave.   Such measurements are made by shallow refraction shooting with very small charges using a modification of the techniques of geophysical prospectors in the search for oil.   The equation connecting these two quantities, which has an accuracy of approximately ± 25 percent, is

$$=\frac{1}{25}\,\rho v^2, \tag{B.14.1}$$

where k is the soil constant in pounds per square inch, ρ is the density of the soil in pounds per cubic inch divided by 384 inches per second ^{2}, and v is the velocity of the seismic wave in inches per second (384 inches per second ^{2} is the acceleration due to gravity).

B.15   Tests in the field have shown that the peak pressure exerted against a massive wall due to reflection will be about twice the pressure that would exist in free earth if the wall were not present.

Variation of Impulse per Unit Area in Free Earth

B.16   The positive impulse per unit area of a pressure wave in earth is the forward momentum carried by a unit cross-section of the wave and is given by the time integral of the pressure up to the time t_0 at which the pressure falls to zero in the tail of the wave, i. e.,

$$I=\int_0^{t_0} p\,dt. \tag{B.16.1}$$

Experimental determinations of the impulse from charges in free earth have shown that it obeys an empirical equation of the form

$$I=E'F'k'W^{1/3}\lambda^{-1/2}, \tag{B.16.2}$$

where I is the impulse per unit area in psi-sec., E', F' and k' are the explosive and coupling factors, and a soil constant for impulse, respectively, and W and λ have the same significance as in § B.9.

B.17   The explosive factor E' does not have the same value for impulse as for peak pressures, but it has been so normalized that its value is 1.00 for TNT as it is for peak pressure. The coupling factor F' is the same as F for peak pressure and is shown as a function of charge depth in Fig. B.11.

B.18 As in the case of peak pressure, if the explosive is TNT and the depth of the burial is of the order of 2 $W^{\frac{1}{3}}$ feet the impulse per unit area can be expressed by the simple empirical equation

$$I = k' W^{\frac{1}{3}} \lambda^{-\frac{5}{4}}. \qquad (B.18.1)$$

In this equation, only one arbitrary parameter is present which may be associated with the transmissibility of the soil. The impulse constant k' has a much smaller range of variation with soil type than does the soil constant k. Its measured values for several different soil types are given in Table B.18. This constant has been also

TABLE B.18

IMPULSE SOIL CONSTANTS FOR VARIOUS SOILS

Soil type	Location	k'(av.)
Loess	Natchez, Miss	1. 60
Clay silt (loam)	Princeton, N. J	4. 77
Silty clay	Camp Gruber, Okla	5. 44
Clay	Houston, Tex	6. 64

roughly correlated with the seismic velocity with, however, somewhat greater dispersion than for the peak pressure but still good enough to afford a rough guide to expected values. The equation is

$$k' = 1.15 \; \rho \; v = 5.75 \; \rho^{\frac{1}{2}} k^{\frac{1}{2}}, \qquad (B.18.2)$$

where k' and k are the soil constants for impulse and pressure, respectively, ρ is the soil density in the same units as in § B.14, and v is the velocity of seismic wave propagation in inches per second.

B.19 The impulse experienced by a massive target would be expected to be approximately twice the impulse of the incident wave but experimentally, this ratio is found to be larger. This results from the fact that the earth against the target may be left with a more or less permanent deformation which may exert a residual pressure of long duration. The residual pressure in the tail of the wave is included in an integration of the pressure time curve, with a consequent increase of impulse. The ratio of reflected to incident impulse is found experimentally to approach a value of 3 to 1, but is subject to considerable fluctuation since a relatively slight deflection of the target will relieve this residual pressure to an appreciable degree.

Variation of Particle Acceleration and Displacement in Free Earth

B.20   An extensive series of measurements of particle acceleration near the surface resulting from the detonation of buried charges of TNT gave results that could be expressed by the empirical equation

$$A_g = F \frac{k}{\rho W^{\frac{1}{3}}} (120\lambda^{-4} + 0.3\lambda^{-2} + 0.04\lambda^{-1}) \times 10^{-5}, \qquad \text{(B.20.1)}$$

where A_g is horizontal or vertical acceleration in units of gravity (384 inches per second^2); ρ is the soil density in the same units as in § B.14, and F, k, W, and λ have the same meaning as before. From these experiments it can be inferred that the variation of acceleration with depth of burial of the charge is the same as the variation in peak pressure, so that the coupling factor derived from the pressure experiments may be applied to particle accelerations as well.

B.21   The acceleration is, of course, a vector quantity that must be specified in direction or by components along a set of axes. Experimentally, it was found that at the charge depths used in these tests, the horizontal and vertical components of acceleration were approximately equal to each other at every distance (Fig. B.21). The angle of emergence of the acceleration vector was consequently at 45° to the surface.

B.22   The displacement of the particles in the medium due to the passage of a compression wave can be found by integrating the strain in each spherical shell over which the wave extends at the moment of maximum displacement. A first approximation is the assumption that the maximum displacement of each particle occurs before appreciable negative velocity is attained by the particles. If this assumption is made, the displacement D at any radius r is

$$D = \int_r^\infty \delta \, dr, \qquad \text{(B.22.1)}$$

where δ is the strain in the material. If the empirical pressure-distance and stress-strain curves for these soils are used, it is possible to derive an expression of the following form for the maximum displacement when the explosive charge is at a depth of $2 \, W^{\frac{1}{3}}$; thus,

$$\frac{D}{W^{\frac{1}{3}}} = \frac{k^{\frac{1}{3}}\lambda^{-3}}{8}, \qquad \text{(B.22.2)}$$

where D is the displacement in feet. This displacement is presumably in a radial direction at depths below the surface.

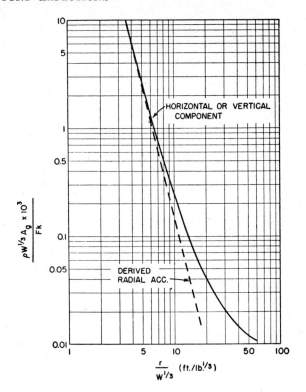

Figure B.21. Components of maximum acceleration as function of distance from charge.

B.23 The experimental values of the transient displacement at charge depths $2\ W^{\frac{1}{3}}$ can be expressed by the following empirical equations:

$$D\ \text{(horizontal)} = W^{\frac{1}{3}}\ (3.94\ \lambda^{-3} + .0018\ \lambda^{-1})\ \text{ft.} \qquad (B.23.1)$$

$$D\ \text{(vertical)} = W^{\frac{1}{3}}\ (1.05\ \lambda^{-3} + .0027\ \lambda^{-1})\ \text{ft.} \qquad (B.23.2)$$

The maximum horizontal and vertical displacements at the surface are not necessarily attained simultaneously but, except at the greater distances, are approximately in phase. Then approximately at the nearer distances, the total transient displacement D_r is found to be

$$D_r = 4\ W^{\frac{1}{3}}\ \lambda^{-3}\ \text{ft.} \qquad (B.23.3)$$

B.24 The value obtained from the derived formula, taking the average value of k as 5100, turns out to be

$$D_r = 2.15 \ W^{\frac{1}{4}} \ \lambda^{-3} \ \text{ft}. \tag{B.24.1}$$

The ratio between these values could easily be accounted for by the surface reflection effect which would tend to enhance the amplitude of the motion at the surface as indicated by the experimental results. The derived result allows estimates to be made of the displacements in other types of soil than those in which the experiments were made.

B.25 The foregoing equations do not take into account the effect of depth of the charge since the data on which they are based is taken as a single depth of explosive. However, it is reasonable, as a first approximation, to introduce the coupling factor F into the equation for other depths of burial. It is probable that somewhat different ratios between horizontal and vertical displacement may occur at different depths of charge but insufficient evidence exists to treat the subject quantitatively.

B.26 Experiment shows that the permanent horizontal displacement is approximately one-third the maximum transient displacement given by the equation above. This is slightly less than would be indicated by the stress-strain curve, but again the effect of the surface introduces a modifying factor so that direct predictions from the stress-strain curve would be in error.

B.27 Accepting the dependence of displacement on the numerical value of $k^{\frac{1}{4}}$ allows a plot of λ against $(D/W^{\frac{1}{4}})$ $(1/k^{\frac{1}{4}})$ to be made which facilitates the estimation of the displacements in soils having different values of the soil constant k.

The Cratering Effect of a Buried Explosive Charge

B.28 The size of the crater produced by a buried charge has been shown experimentally to be much less sensitive to type of soil and kind of explosive than to the depth of burial of the charge. The exact mechanism of crater formation is not understood well enough to allow any theoretical predictions to be made concerning the factors governing the size, but it has been shown that the model law is obeyed and that predictions of size based on empirical data are reasonably reliable.

B.29 Analysis of the available data has indicated that the crater size can be represented empirically by the product of an explosive factor E, of a depth factor C, of a soil factor, equal to 1.3 $k^{\frac{1}{12}}$, and of the cube root of the charge weight, i. e., $W^{\frac{1}{3}}$. The radius of the crater is then

$$R \text{ (ft.)} = 1.3 C E k^{\frac{1}{12}} W^{\frac{1}{3}} \qquad \text{(B.29.1)}$$

The explosive factor E is taken as unity for TNT, consistent with previous practices. The depth factor (Fig. B.29) varies over a wider

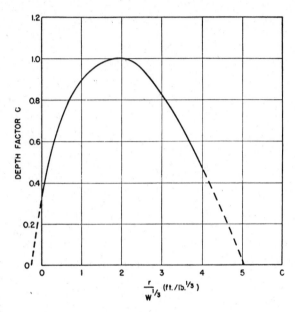

Figure B.29. Depth factor for crater size as function of charge depth/(charge weight)$^{1/3}$.

range than do the others, displaying a maximum value at a charge depth of 2 $W^{\frac{1}{3}}$ ft. and descending quite sharply toward zero as the charge depth approaches zero. The decline with increasing charge depth beyond the maximum is slower, but an extrapolation of the measured part of the curve indicates that at about 5 $W^{\frac{1}{3}}$ ft. the crater radius approaches zero with the formation of a camouflet.

B.30   In Figs. B.30a, b, and c are given samples of experimental data on pressures, impulses, and accelerations in order that an idea of the spread of the experimental data can be formed. The empirical equations were derived from many such measurements and represent the results to be expected in an average case. Fig. B.30d is a plot of the empirical and derived equations for ground displacement which is valid at charge depths of 2 $W^{\frac{1}{3}}$. The displacements expected from smaller depths of burial of the charge can be found to a first approximation by a simple multiplication by the coupling factor F.

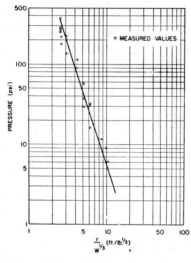

Figure B.30a.   Pressure in free earth as function of charge depth/(charge weight)$^{1/3}$.

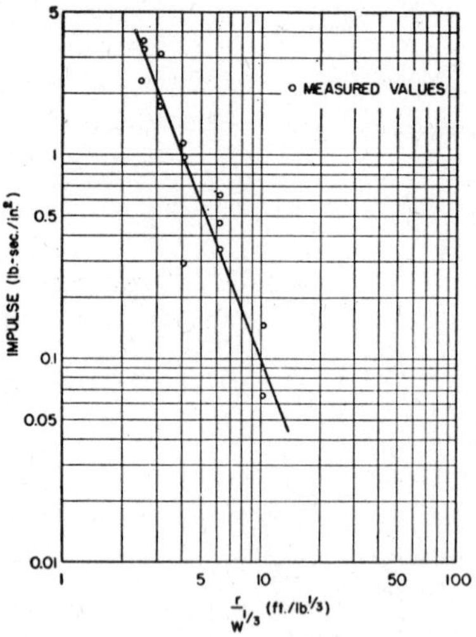

Figure B.30b.   Impulse in free earth as function of charge depth/(charge weight)$^{1/3}$.

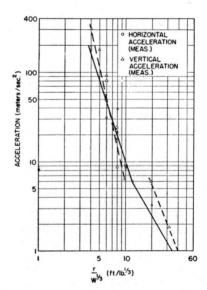

Figure B.30c.   Acceleration as function of charge depth/(charge weight)$^{1/3}$.

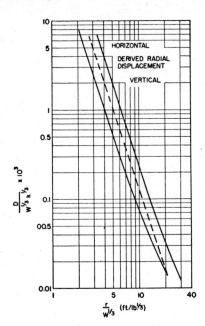

Figure B.30d. Transient earth displacement at surface as function of charge depth/(charge weight)$^{1/3}$.

APPENDIX C[1]

MEASUREMENT OF X AND GAMMA RAYS IN ROENTGENS

SIGNIFICANCE OF THE ROENTGEN

C.1 The energy absorbed by tissue is related to the ionization produced in air by X or gamma rays to an extent, and over an energy range, generally suitable for most biological purposes. The unit of dose is called the roentgen (r) and is defined as the "quantity of X or gamma radiation such that the associated corpuscular emission per 0.001293 gram of air produces, in air, ions carrying 1 electrostatic unit (esu) of quantity of electricity of either sign." (The value of 0.001293 gram represents the mass of 1 cc. of dry air at 0° C. and 76 centimeters mercury pressure.)

C.2 For X and gamma rays of moderate penetrating power, practically all of the ionization in air is caused by the secondary electrons that are ejected from the air atoms by the radiation. The average kinetic energy lost by one of these electrons in producing a pair of ions in air is about 33 electron-volts (ev), independent of the kinetic energy of the electron over a wide range, viz., several thousand to several million electron-volts. It follows therefore that the total number of ion pairs produced by an electron is a good measure of the initial kinetic energy of the secondary electron, provided its initial energy is within the range mentioned above. One esu of electric charge corresponds to 2.083 x 10^9 electronic charges, hence to $2.083 \times 10^9 \times 33 = 6.8 \times 10^{10}$ ev, or to 0.11 erg. This is therefore a measure of the total initial kinetic energy of all of the electrons ejected by 1 roentgen of radiation from 0.001293 gram of air. To the extent that energy is removed from the beam only by transfer to kinetic energy of electrons the roentgen is therefore a measure of radiant energy absorbed in air. One roentgen corresponds to the absorption of 84 ergs per gram of air by this means.

C.3 For a rather wide range of radiations, there is a nearly constant difference between the energy absorbed per gram of air and the energy absorbed per gram of tissue, which is mostly water. Throughout this region, 1 r of radiation gives an energy absorption of about 93 ergs per gram of water. With photon energies so low that photo-

---

[1] Material supplied by F. R. Shonka, L. S. Taylor, T. N. White.

electric absorption becomes important in tissue elements, the roentgen loses much of its usefulness as a measure of radiation exposure. This is because the relation between the energy absorption in air and in tissue becomes difficult to estimate. This difficulty increases rapidly as the photon energy drops below 50 Kev. There must also be an upper limit to the usefulness of the roentgen. Since the chief point here is the energy absorbed in tissue, it is clear that the exact amount of energy lost by a photon at one point in the tissue is not of much interest if most of this energy is carried to distant parts of the tissue by the secondary electron to which this energy is transferred. The significance of a measurement in roentgens begins to be doubtful when the radiation is capable of producing electrons with a range of more than 1 cm. in tissue. These difficulties become important when the photon energy rises above a few Mev.

C.4   For those accustomed to think of X and gamma radiation in terms of number of photons per cm.², it is useful to remember that the true absorption coefficient of air remains constant within 12 percent for a range of photon energies from 0.08 to nearly 2.5 Mev. Within these limits, 1 r corresponds to $(2 \times 10^9)/E$ incident photons per cm.², where E is the photon energy in Mev.

C.5   One feature of the roentgen should always be kept in mind: it provides a measure of energy absorbed *per unit mass of tissue*. A beam of radiation so confined as to deliver 1,000 r of radiation to only a carbuncle may cure the carbuncle; 1,000 r delivered to the whole body will be fatal.

MEASUREMENT OF THE ROENTGEN

C.6   From the definition of the roentgen it is apparent that one must measure all of the ions produced along the paths of the secondary electrons created by the primary photons in a definite mass or volume of air. In general, the ranges of the secondary electrons are much greater than the dimensions of the defined volume and hence the volume has to be surrounded by a larger free air volume, so as to contain essentially the full paths of the secondaries. Under such circumstances the loss of ions along the paths originating within, but going outside of, the definite volume may be exactly compensated by other ions produced within this volume by secondaries originating in the surrounding air space.

C.7   To examine the conditions of exact compensation, consider a body of air of standard density traversed by a beam of radiation (Fig. C.7). Within this body of air we define a volume A (1 cc.),

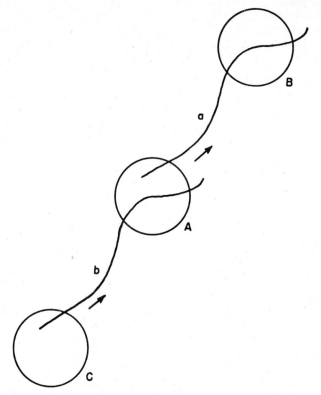

Figure C.7.   Beam of radiation traversing air.

and consider the path a of an ionizing electron ejected from within the volume A.   To determine in roentgens the radiation at A, it is necessary to measure all the ionization along the path a.   Consider now, the ionization that occurs within a volume B (1 cc.), as illustrated. If the ionization in A is measured, that in B is missed.   If, however, there is some volume C that bears to A exactly the same phenomenological relation as A bears to B, then there will be exact compensation, within A, for the ionization occurring in B.   If this requirement is extended to cover other parts of path a, and all other possible paths originating within A, it follows that:

(a) Every volume of the type C, from which electrons can be shot into volume A, must be traversed by radiation of the same intensity and direction as that which traverses volume A.

(b) There must be no ionization in volume A other than that due to electrons originating within A, and that due to the compensating influence of volumes of the type C.

C.8   Even if the ionization in 1 cc. of free air could be measured without introducing disturbing influences, it would still be difficult to meet the above conditions in practice, especially with radiations that eject electrons to distances of several meters in air.   It is possible, however, to achieve the same result by measuring the ionization within a cavity surrounded by solid walls of a material having an atomic number not too different from that of air.   To visualize this, suppose volume A is retained as before, but all of the surrounding air is compressed, by a factor of 1,000, to include the most distant volume of type C.   The maximum distance of any volume C would be simply the range in air of the most energetic electron ejected by the radiation. The volume A would then be surrounded by a shell of dense air, in which all of the electron paths from volumes C up to volume A would be reproduced on a 1,000-fold smaller scale.   The ionization in the volume A would be just the same under the two conditions since it would be traversed by the same secondary electrons from the compressed as from the free air.

C.9   The ionization per unit volume in this cavity would be a measure of the radiation in roentgens.   This condition is essentially met within what is known as a thimble chamber, having walls of "air equivalent" material.   Except for very low energy radiation (below about 100 kv X-rays with 1 mm. Al filtration) a wall of plastic material (lucite, bakelite, etc.) and of thickness equal to the range of the most energetic secondary electrons produced by the radiation, may be considered as "air equivalent."   Such chambers, with a volume of about 1 cc., are used as secondary standards for measuring radiation in roentgens.

C.10   Since the roentgen is defined in terms of the ionization produced in a known mass (or volume) of unrestricted air it is neces· sary to have a suitable device for performing this unequivocally.   This device is known as a free-air ionization chamber and one type is illustrated diagrammatically in Fig. C.10.   This is essentially a parallel plate ionization chamber having guard plates of such width that the electric field is uniform in the region of the collecting electrode.   Any ions produced within the region of width L will then be drawn to the collector-electrode C and measured in the form of a current.

C.11   Except in the case of a true point source of radiation, the precise determination of an irradiated air volume within the width L is difficult on account of the presence of a penumbral region.   The same radiation flux passes through the diaphragm at A and through the region L, except for a small difference due to absorption which can be

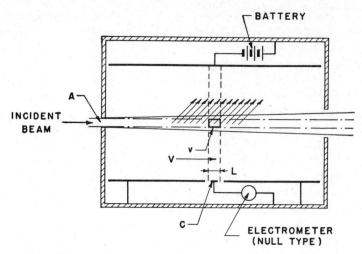

Figure C.10.   Free-air ionization chamber (diagrammatic).

corrected if necessary.   It is therefore customary to consider the irradiated air volume V as a cylinder of length L and cross-sectional area equal to that of the diaphragm, and the radiation dose is considered as measured at the diaphragm.

C.12   To see whether or not exact compensation can exist, it will simplify matters to assume that the paths of all secondary electrons are straight, in the same direction, and that ionization is uniform along the paths.   The paths are represented by arrows in Fig. C.10. Under these conditions, the definition of the roentgen makes it necessary to measure the ionization within a parallelogram with a base of width L, and sides formed by the arrows from the ends of this base.   The ionization, being proportional to the area of the parallelogram, is obviously equal to the ionization that occurs within the rectangular region of the experimental measurement, which has the same base and the same height.   It can be shown that exact compensation will also occur with real secondary electrons, with curved paths, nonuniform ionization, and different directions, provided that attention is centered on a set of paths with identical properties at any stage of the argument.   The experimental conditions that must be met in order to assure exact compensation are easily inferred, viz., (1) the volume V is as far from A as the maximum range of secondary electrons in the direction of the beam, (2) the spacing between electrodes and the central radiation beam is as great as the maximum lateral range of the secondary electrons from the beam,

(3) the attenuation of the beam between A and L is negligible, (4) a method of electrical measurement of the ions reaching the collector-electrode, C, be employed such that there be negligible electric field distortion at the collector-electrode edges.

C.13 The distances stipulated in (1) above, range from about 5 centimeters for 50 kilovolts to 15 centimeters for 200 kilovolts X-rays, and up to 10 meters for gamma rays from radium. Similar values for total plate separations are required for compliance with specification (2). Attenuation between A and L can usually be neglected within 2 percent for radiations having components no less than about 100 kilovolts, but must be considered for softer components. For ordinary practical considerations, it is not feasible to construct free-air standard ionization chambers operating at atmospheric pressure for measurements above about 250 kilovolts, although they have been developed for use up to about 2 million volts by operating at higher air pressures.

C.14 To calibrate a secondary instrument (thimble chamber, survey meter, etc.) a radiation beam is calibrated at a particular point, P, by means of a free air standard with the limiting diaphragm A placed at point P. The standard is then removed and the secondary chamber calibrated at the same point, P, in the beam. Such calibrations are particularly important for radiations having components of less than about 150 kilovolts since in the lower energy region most secondary instruments are critically energy-dependent. For example, a thimble chamber, which is essentially energy-independent for filtered radiations above 100 to 150 kilovolts, may easily be in error by 30 percent for 50 kilovolts by unfiltered radiation. It is essential that all instruments be calibrated in this region since there will often be such soft components in atomic energy events.

C.15 Secondary chambers made of organic materials are less critical with regard to energy above about 150 kilovolts where the photoelectric effect becomes negligible. In this region it is most important to assure that the chamber wall thickness is at least as great as the range of the most energetic secondary electrons associated with the radiation to be measured. This requirement is contradictory to that for the measurement of radiation having very soft components where radiation absorption in the chamber walls may introduce substantial errors. In fact if it is required to measure radiation covering a wide energy band it is desirable to use two chambers—one with thick walls for the higher energies and one with thin walls for the lower.

C.16 Chambers which closely approximate thimble chambers in size may be used for survey measurements when the total dose is required. However, if used as dose rate meters approximating permissible radiation levels, they are generally too insensitive because of the small volume within which the ions are produced. Under such circumstances larger chambers (100 to 1000 cc.) are required. Such large chambers, however, may not be suitable for measuring very soft radiation components (below 100 kv) unless carefully calibrated therefor.

APPENDIX D [1]

SPECIAL PROBLEMS IN GAMMA RAY TRANSMISSION

CIRCULAR AREA OF RADIOACTIVE CONTAMINATION ON THE GROUND

D.1 The special case considered here is the evaluation of the ionization produced in the air as a function of distance h above a circular area on the ground uniformly contaminated with radioactive material. This situation might arise from the deposition on the ground of fission products after the explosion of an atomic bomb. Let $j(\alpha_0)$ be the number of gamma rays of energy α_0 (Mev) emitted per second and per cm.² from the contaminated area. The present interest is in distances h, which are so small compared with the mean free path of the photons in air that only the unscattered contribution to the radiation received need be considered. Further, the dosage rate will be calculated at a point h above the center of the area. At this location, for given h, the maximum dosage rate is obtained; and, if the radius R of the contaminated area is much greater than h, it may be shown that the dosage rate will be essentially constant at the height h over all the area except near the boundary.

D.2 The unscattered gamma ray energy intensity in units of Mev per cm.² per second received at h from the element of area $2\pi\rho d\rho$ (cf. Fig. D.2a) is given by the equation

$$dE(h) = \frac{2\pi\rho d\rho j(\alpha_0)\alpha_0 \exp\left[-\mu_c(\alpha_0)(\rho^2+h^2)\right]^{\frac{1}{2}}}{4\pi(\rho^2+h^2)}$$

$$dE(h) = \frac{j(\alpha_0)\alpha_0}{2} \frac{\exp\left[-\mu_c(\alpha_0)(\rho^2+h^2)\right]^{\frac{1}{2}}}{(\rho^2+h^2)} \rho d\rho, \qquad \text{(D.2.1)}$$

where μ_c is the Compton scattering coefficient. The integrated energy intensity coming from the entire contaminated area is

$$E(h)_R = \frac{j(\alpha_0)\alpha_0}{2} \left[Ei(-\mu_c\sqrt{h^2+R^2})-Ei(-\mu_c h)\right] \frac{\text{Mev}}{\text{cm}^2}. \qquad \text{(D.2.2)}$$

The dosage rate in roentgens/sec. is $1.45 \times 10^{-5}\mu_A(\alpha_0)E(h)$. Here μ_A is the Klein-Nishina coefficient for energy absorption in air at

[1] By S. T. Cohen and M. S. Plesset.

431

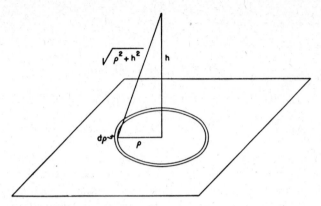

Figure D.2a.   Uniformly contaminated circular area.

standard conditions as given in Fig. D.2b.   For R very large, there
is a special case of equation (D.2.2), namely,

$$E(h)_\infty = \frac{j(\alpha_0)\,\alpha_0}{2}\,[-Ei(-\mu_c h)], \qquad (D.2.3)$$

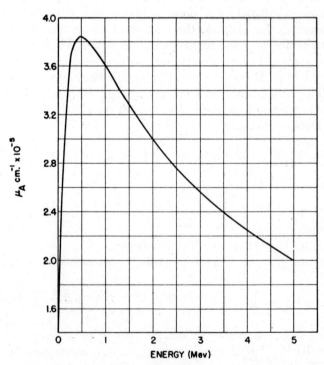

Figure D.2b.   Klein-Nishina absorption coefficient for air.

so that equation (D.2.3) corresponds to an infinite contaminated sheet. In Fig. D.2c, the ratio $E(h)_R/E(h)_\infty$ is shown, for various values of h, as a function of R. These curves apply to the case where the emitted gamma radiation has the energy 1 Mev. In Fig. D.2d, the ratio of the dosage rate, $E_\infty(h)$, at a height, h, in meters above an infinite contaminated area on the ground to the dosage rate, $E_\infty(1)$, at a height of one meter above the infinite contaminated area is

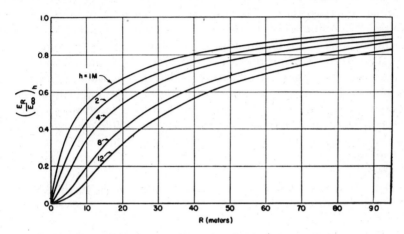

Figure D.2c.   Relative dosage rate at various heights above a finite contaminated slab as function of the radius, for 1-Mev gamma radiation.

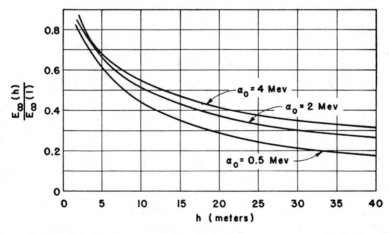

Figure D.2d.   Relative dosage rate for various gamma-ray energies as function of the height above an infinite contaminated slab.

shown as a function of h for three values of the emitted gamma ray energy.

SEMI-INFINITE CONTAMINATED SLAB

D.3   This case could correspond to a large body of water contaminated from the surface to a depth large compared with the mean free path of the gamma rays in water.   The energy intensity of the emitted gamma radiation will be determined at a height h in air above the water.   The number of gamma rays of energy α_0 emitted per cc. per second will be taken as constant over the contaminated volume and equal to $i(\alpha_0)$.   If the gamma ray flux emerging from the water surface, as reduced by self-attenuation, is determined, this problem then becomes similar to the case discussed above.   The important contribution to the gamma ray flux emerging at the surface comes from the layer of water near the surface which is only a few mean free paths thick.   A slight underestimate of this emerging flux will be made by calculating it on the basis that only unscattered radiation makes an appreciable contribution.

D.4   With this approximation, the energy intensity (in Mev/sec. cm.²) at the water surface is (cf. Fig. D.4)

$$d^2 E_S = \alpha_0 i(\alpha_0)\,\frac{2\pi\rho^2\,\sin\,\theta d\theta d\rho e^{-\mu_c(\alpha_0)\rho}}{4\pi\rho^2},\qquad \text{(D.4.1)}$$

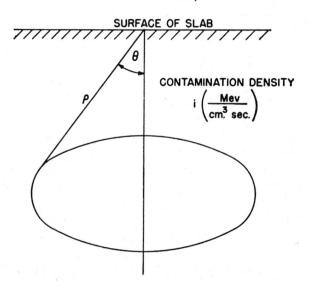

Figure D.4.   Semi-infinite contaminated slab.

where μ_c is the Compton scattering coefficient for water.   The equivalent isotropic energy intensity at the water surface is given by integration as

$$E_S = \frac{\alpha_0 i(\alpha_0)}{2\mu_c(\alpha_0)}. \tag{D.4.2}$$

If this value for E_S is now used for $\alpha_0 j(\alpha_0)$ in equation (D.2.3), the value for the energy intensity in air at a distance h above the water surface is found to be

$$E(h) = \frac{\alpha_0 i(\alpha_0)}{4\mu_c(\alpha_0)} [-Ei(-\mu_c h)], \tag{D.4.3}$$

where μ_c is the Compton scattering coefficient for air for the photon energy α_0.   The dosage rate (roentgens per second) is again $1.45 \times 10^{-5} \mu_A(\alpha_0) E(h)_\infty$.

D.5   The dosage rate inside a volume of radioactively contaminated water, large compared with the mean free path in water, is given by

$$1.45 \times 10^{-5} \mu_A(\alpha_0) i(\alpha_0) \alpha_0 \int_0^\infty e^{-\mu_c(\alpha_0) l} B(\alpha_0, l) dl.$$

APPENDIX E[1]

CALCULATION OF HAZARD FROM WORLD-WIDE CONTAMINATION

I. PLUTONIUM

Assume:

1. A 20 kiloton TNT energy equivalent bomb leaves 100 pounds of plutonium.
2. The surface of the earth is 5.1×10^{18} square centimeters.
3. The contamination is distributed uniformly over the surface of the earth.
4. Hazard to humans is from agricultural areas, in which contamination is uniformly mixed with the top 1 centimeter of soil.
5. Concentration of plutonium in the ash of food eaten is the same as in the soil. This assumption overrates the danger, as plants are known to select against plutonium.
6. A man eats 1,000 pounds of food per year, of which 1 percent is ash.
7. Of plutonium ingested, 0.007 percent is fixed in the body (J. G. Hamilton, *Rev. Mod. Phys.*, *20*, 718, 1948).
8. The safe rate of fixation of plutonium in the body is 0.07 micrograms per year.

From these assumptions it is readily calculated that: From one bomb there is 2.5×10^{-6} microgram of plutonium in 1 pound of soil. From a man's yearly ration he absorbs 1.8×10^{-10} microgram of plutonium from each bomb which has exploded up to that time; hence the number of bombs to endanger is 0.07 divided by 1.8×10^{-10}, or 4×10^8.

To calculate the hazard from respiration of plutonium, the following additional assumptions are required:

9. That, on the average, an individual retains 5 grams of dust per year in his lungs.
10. That all plutonium entrapped as dust in the lungs becomes fixed in the body.

From these assumptions it follows that the yearly rate of absorption is 10^{-9} microgram, and the number of bombs to endanger is 0.07 divided by 10^{-9}, or 7×10^7.

---

[1] Material supplied by E. S. Gilfillan, H. Scoville, Jr.

436

II. Fission Products

Assume:

1. All fission products have settled uniformly over the surface of the earth and there remains no fission product activity in the air.
2. The surface of the earth is 5.1×10^{18} square centimeters.
3. The fission product activity is 6×10^9 curies at 1 hour after detonation of a nominal atomic bomb and the fission products decay according to the $t^{-1.2}$ law.
4. All bombs are exploded at the same time and the time after detonation for which these calculations are made is 6 months.
5. The level of activity is 0.1 r per 24 hours.
6. One thousand curies per square mile will produce an exposure of 0.1 r per 24 hours.
7. There is no shielding.

Curies at end of 6 months (4,320 hr.)

$$= 6 \times 10 \times \frac{1}{(4,320)^{1.2}}$$

$$= \frac{6 \times 10^9}{23,040} = 2.6 \times 10^5 \text{ curies per bomb at 6 months after detonation}$$

Curies per square centimeter per bomb at 6 months

$$= \frac{2.6 \times 10^5}{5.1 \times 10^{18}} = 5.1 \times 10^{-14} \text{ c/cm}^2 \text{ bomb}$$

Curies per square centimeter for 0.1r/24 hours exposure

$$= \frac{1,000}{2.6 \times 10^{10}} = 3.85 \times 10^{-8} \text{ c/cm}^2 \text{ (1 square mile} = 2.6 \times 10^{10} \text{ cm}^2)$$

Number of bombs needed for 0.1r/24 hours

$$= \frac{3.85 \times 10^{-8}}{5.1 \times 10^{-14}}$$

$$= 7.55 \times 10^5 = 755,000 \text{ bombs for 0.1r/24 hours at 6 months after}$$
detonation.

APPENDIX F[1]

METEOROLOGICAL TRAJECTORY ANALYSIS

The fall-out trail can be estimated in the following manner if the wind velocities are known at a series of heights: $h_1 < h_2 < h_3 < . . . < h_n$. Let $V_x (h_i; \tau)$ be the component of wind velocity at the height h_i at the time τ from the north direction (a negative value of V_x corresponds to a southerly component); $V_y (h_i; \tau)$ be the component of wind velocity from the east; x is the distance north of ground zero; y is the distance east of ground zero. Consider a particle which is located at a height h_j at a point (x_0, y_0) at a time $t=0$ and require the time t to reach the ground. This particle will land at a point (x, y) given by the equations

$$x = x_0 - \frac{t}{h_j} \sum_{i=1}^{i=j} (h_i - h_{i-1}) V_x \left(h_i; \tau = t \left(\frac{h_i - h_{i-1}}{h_j} \right) \right)$$

$$y = y_0 - \frac{t}{h_j} \sum_{i=1}^{i=j} (h_i - h_{i-1}) V_y \left(h_i; \tau = t \left(\frac{h_i - h_{i-1}}{h_j} \right) \right)$$

If a rough initial distribution of the active material is assumed at a time $t=0$, these equations suffice to map out the trail. For example, it might be assumed that initially all of the active material is located in a cylinder 1 or 2 miles in radius extending up to the base of the stratosphere. Calculations for a series of points on the surface of the cylinder and a series of assumed times of fall, t, will suffice to rough out the fall-out trail and the time of arrival of the activity. This type of analysis has been used successfully at Alamogordo and Bikini in connection with the experimental bomb tests.

---

[1] By J. O. Hirschfelder.

INDEX

○